Celtic Art in Ancient Europe
Five Protohistoric Centuries

L'Art Celtique en Europe protohistorique:
débuts, développements, styles,
techniques

Celtic Art in Ancient Europe Five Protohistoric Centuries

Proceedings of the Colloquy held in 1972 at the Oxford Maison Française

L'Art Celtique en Europe protohistorique: débuts, développements, styles, techniques

edited by: Paul-Marie Duval *and* Christopher Hawkes

1976

Seminar Press

London · New York · San Francisco

A Subsidiary of Harcourt Brace Jovanovich, Publishers

SEMINAR PRESS INC. (LONDON) LTD.
24/28 Oval Road,
London NW1

United States Edition published by
SEMINAR PRESS INC.
111 Fifth Avenue
New York, New York 10003

Library of Congress Catalog Card Number: 73-9
ISBN: 0-12-823850-7

PRINTED IN GREAT BRITAIN BY
W & J Mackay Limited, Chatham

Contents

Préface

Le Directeur de la Maison Française d'Oxford est particulièrement heureux d'avoir été associé à l'organisation du colloque sur l'Art Celtique qui a eu lieu en juillet 1972 dans cet établissement sous la présidence des Professeurs Hawkes et Duval. L'une des vocations principales de la Maison Française est en effet de favoriser autant qu'elle le peut les contacts entre les universitaires français et britanniques et je suis reconnaissant à mes amis Paul-Marie Duval et Christopher Hawkes de m'avoir donné l'occasion de jouer ce rôle. Le projet de colloque que nous avons formé ensemble en janvier 1972 a pu se concrétiser grâce à la bonne volonté de chacun des participants, et à l'aide du Ministère français des Affaires Etrangères et de l'Université d'Oxford. Le colloque lui-même s'ést déroulé, à ce qu'il me semble, à la satisfaction générale, et la Maison Française a été honorée de compter alors parmi ses hôtes tant d'érudits qualifiés.

Nous ne voulions cependant pas en rester là et pensions que ces communications et débats méritaient d'être connus de tous les intéressés; c'est pourquoi nous avons attaché tant d'importance à la publication de ce volume et sommes vivement reconnaissants à la "Seminar Press" d'avoir pris ce travail en charge; il convient ici de rappeler le nom de Mr John Cruise, malheureusement disparu, qui, au nom de cette maison d'édition, fut le premier à négocier avec nous à ce sujet et manifesta le plus vif intérêt pour nos efforts.

A ma connaissance, c'est la première fois qu'un colloque tenu à la Maison Française fait l'objet d'une publication scientifique; je serais heureux que nous ayons par là créé un précédent.

Jean Lequiller

Maison Française,
Oxford, Mars 1973.

Neuf mois après de nous donner ces lignes, et encore à Oxford, une atteinte subite nous a enlevé Jean Lequiller. Nous laissons ses mots, et ceux qui vont suivre en langue anglaise, sans changement. L'un de nous, rédacteurs du volume, fut son ami depuis la jeunesse, l'autre pour trop peu de temps, et à Oxford seulement. Mais nous nous unissons, en nos souvenirs d'un tel esprit, à ceux qui l'ont aimé, et à lui-même en souhaitant que ce livre, né d'un colloque, pourrait créer peut-être un précédent à servir nos pays par d'autres ententes, fondées sur l'érudition mais de large portée.

Preface

It was a great pleasure for me, as Director of the Maison Française at Oxford, to be able to join in the organization of the Colloquy on Celtic Art which was held there in early July 1972, with Professors Hawkes and Duval together presiding. One of the principal commitments of my post is in fact to promote, as far as is possible, contacts between French academics and British, and I am grateful to my friends Paul-Marie Duval and Christopher Hawkes for affording me this opportunity of doing so. The project, formed between us in January that year, was realized through aid from the Ministry of Foreign Affairs in Paris and from Oxford University (Sir John Rhys Memorial Fund), and through the goodwill shown by the scholars taking part. Everyone in the Maison felt honoured to be entertaining them, and the sessions seemed to me to have pleased them all.

So much so indeed that we immediately went further, convinced that the whole proceedings should be brought to a wider public; hence the importance to all our minds of the publication of this book, and our gratitude to Seminar Press for undertaking it. Mr John Cruise, who took the matter in hand on the side of the firm, showed an eager interest in it; he attended some of the sessions, and gave us generous advice. We regretted his untimely death.

I believe it is the first time that a conference held at the Maison Française has attained publication in such a form. If we were found to have created a precedent, I should be very much delighted.

Jean Lequiller

Maison Française, Oxford,
March 1973.

Nine months from his writing for us the preface above translated, Jean Lequiller died very suddenly, at home in Oxford. His words have been left unchanged; likewise my own which appear below. Friendship with him, for me so short, for my colleague Duval had been long; but we join with all who loved him in our memories of his spirit, and with himself in his thought that our book, born from a conference, might be a precedent, for bringing scholarship further to spread goodwill between our nations.

As the Englishman invited to join in preparing the Colloquy and this book, I am happy first to thank my French colleagues for their support: Jean Lequiller for his management and much other collaboration, and Paul-Marie Duval with whom I shared the Colloquy's chairmanship, and have shared the book's editorial preparation. We gratefully appreciate, with M. Lequiller, the welcome accorded to the book by the directors of Seminar Press and the patience and skill of all their staff in preparing it for printing. The work has been equally Franco-British and Anglo-French; and the contributions taking part have made it more widely international.

Of the nations represented among them, four are Continental: France with Professor Duval himself, Czechoslovakia with Dr Kruta (resident in Paris too, at present, and contributing in French), Denmark with Professor Klindt-Jensen, and the

German Federal Republic with Professor Frey and Dr Schwappach. The contributions of these last three, given at the Colloquy in English, are rendered in French translations which all have studied and approved. Their countries have long and proud traditions in Celtic archaeology: Denmark from study of its wealth of Celtic influences and imports (above all, the Gundestrup cauldron with its religious figurations), and the rest as having been wholly or partly Celtic lands themselves. Italy, Switzerland and Belgium, too, and the Danube countries eastward, have Celtic material variously exemplified in these pages, since Celtic Europe (all except its Hispanic Peninsular provinces) had everywhere the Celts' distinctive art of the five pre-Roman centuries, the art of the period and culture named La Tène.

From the insular Celtic lands come our remaining nine contributions, besides the summing-up of the whole by Professor Piggott. Mrs Champion's and Miss Sandars's subjects are each still on the mainland; Professor Jope and Dr Savory, Professor Duignan and Mr Allen, bring the mainland into the insular (as I have sought to do myself); Mr Lowery and Mr Savage have a theme peculiarly British. The Colloquy, for its sessions, was given a round-table arrangement. The named participants sat facing inwards across the circle; and on one side was a second row for various invited auditors (for example Mr Timothy Champion, Mr Roger Goodburn, Miss Ursula Slevogt, Miss Marion Wilson), among whom Dr Dennis Harding and Mrs Sonia Chadwick Hawkes contributed by speaking in discussions.

M. Jean Lequiller, whose son Dominique took the part of lantern operator, had the two days' proceedings given a continuous record on tape, by his secretaries Mme Gandrey and Miss Aldham, who afterwards typed it. It covered the set communications alike with the free discussions upon them; thus the editors here, from the transcript (with their personal notes and memories), can present an account of every discussion, as explained below on p. xxi. English is used to report the substance of everything uttered in French, French where required for its spoken authenticity. Where English was spoken (as mostly) abridgements have not diminished the content. Four of the discussions have been given an additional note, to clarify or enlarge some aspect which time had not sufficed for. As regards the communications, each has been given a balanced résumé, French where the text is English and vice versa. The captions of illustrations are understandable bi-lingually; notes and references to literature are of course the authors' own.

The index is divided into three, for names, objects and subjects. Abbreviations, on pp. xvii–xx, are also divided on a system, for ease in referring to documentation of works of Celtic art, whether in periodicals, monographs or other standard publications; such are the "Manuel d'archéologie celtique" of Joseph Déchelette (Epoque de La Tène, Paris 1914, and re-prints), the "Early Celtic Art" of Paul Jacobsthal (Oxford 1944, and re-print 1971), the "Art of the European Iron Age" of J. V. S. Megaw (Bath 1970), Professor Piggott's *Early Celtic Art* Exhibition Catalogue (Edinburgh 1970), and "Early Celtic Art in the British Isles" by E. M. Jope and (posthumously Jacobsthal), included through the kindness of Professor Jope and the Clarendon Press, in advance of its publication at Oxford.

Professor Jope helped the Colloquy also by exhibiting drawings, photographs and electrotypes, made for him in connection with that, of important Celtic metalwork. Professor Megaw (now Leicester), with also Professor T. G. E. Powell (Liverpool), was invited to take part but had to decline.

While the book was in final proof (Summer 1975), the news came of the deaths of Professor Powell and Mr Derek Allen, to the grief of all concerned and of every lover of Celtic archaeology.

CHRISTOPHER HAWKES

Foreword to the Introduction

The purpose, of the Colloquy and the book which thus records it, is set forth by Professor Duval in his Introduction. This, in his own French (inimitable in full translation), has its substance given in the following lines of foreword.

Celtic culture, through the last five centuries before Christ, widespread in Europe and carrying refined higher elements, was essentially non-literate, yet can speak to us through its art. Long neglected, in spite of its quality and its later Christian renaissance, this art, through its claims on congresses and display by exhibition, has been winning recognition for the modern growth of its fundamental literature, rising to a height in the "Early Celtic Art" of Paul Jacobsthal. To Oxford, where this was written and published, our meeting was thus appropriate. Its organizing, gratefully acknowledged above, at the Maison Française here, of course meant choosing themes: definition of styles and their sources, their static or dynamic forms; techniques, workshops, regions, art on pottery, art on the coinages; chronology, and provinces Continental, British, and Irish. Relations between the La Tène and the antecedent Hallstatt culture, models from Classical Greece, Italy, the Orient, Scythia too, converge on the nature of the Celts' originality. First: in transcending both older tradition and every outside influence, their art stands out—decorative, linear and plastic at once, exulting in curves, and rendering living forms by relish for fantasy. Second: through phases of early severity, of freedom, and of symmetry rendered afresh, it rivals contemporary civilized arts in its technical command, and in its libertarian face can yet disclose a passion for order, expressed by empirical even if not mathematical geometry. Thus where to-day we admire its refinements, we may to-morrow discover its rules. To aid its study, we need now detailed inventories of motifs, and an agreed terminology, internationally valid. Aesthetically and also conceptually, then, this book may incite to progress.

Christopher Hawkes

Foreword to the Introduction

Introduction

Les Celtes n'étaient pas des barbares incultes: ils ont développé dans une grande partie de l'Europe une culture très souvent raffinée, non dénuée de connaissances scientifiques et dont nous sont parvenues surtout les productions artistiques, puisque, n'utilisant pas l'écriture, ils ne nous ont pas laissé de littérature. L'histoire de l'art, avec ses procédés modernes d'analyse et d'investigation, est donc peut-être le seul moyen que nous ayons de connaître le degré de développement culturel des Celtes, la nature de leur sensibilité esthétique, leurs facultés d'imagination créatrice et l'évolution de leurs techniques d'art. Et cela n'est pas sans intérêt même pour l'histoire ultérieure de l'Europe, puisque des trois arts de l'Antiquité non classique nés sur ce continent, chez les Ibères, les Scythes et les Celtes, ce dernier seulement, qui a régné d'un bout à l'autre de l'Europe non méditerranéenne, a eu une postérité dans l'art médiéval, irlandais, britannique et continental.

Art de petits objets principalement, l'art celtique a été longtemps négligé par les archéologues, faute d'un large rassemblement des documents. Il n'a jamais eu sa part autonome dans les congrès scientifiques, même lorsque ceux-ci—trop rares—étaient consacrés exclusivement au monde celtique ancien. Toutefois, au IVe Congrès international d'études celtiques qui se tint à Rennes (France) en 1971, plusieurs communications traitèrent d'histoire de l'art de la Tène, et une importante exposition fut organisée sur ce sujet à Edimbourg puis à Londres en 1970. Il avait fallu, pour que cela fût possible, qu'aient paru sur l'art celtique quelques ouvrages ou mémoires fondamentaux, de Françoise Henry sur l'art irlandais et ses origines, de Sir Cyril Fox sur l'art celtique britannique, de Stuart Piggott sur quelques pièces majeures, de Jan Filip sur les Celtes en Europe centrale, de T. G. E. Powell sur les Celtes, de J. V. S. Megaw sur l'art de l'âge du fer en Europe et, surtout, le recueil fondamental de "notre maître à tous", Paul Jacobsthal, "Early Celtic Art" paru en 1944 à Oxford, où avait rayonné son enseignement.

C'est pourquoi il est heureux que ce premier colloque consacré à l'art celtique ancien ait eu lieu dans la ville même où l'oeuvre de Jacobsthal est née et où elle est pieusement continuée. L'initiative et l'hospitalité de la Maison Française si parfaitment dirigée par Jean Lequiller ont rendu possible cette rencontre, à laquelle l'Université d'Oxford a bien voulu prêter son aide: qu'elles en soient chaleureusement remerciées. Pour la premier fois, en effet, des savants de différentes générations et de plusieurs pays ont, deux jours durant, exposé leurs recherches et discuté à loisir sur ce sujet aussi nouveau que vaste. On ne pouvait, pour ce coup d'essai, embrasser l'ensemble des arts du second âge du fer. Nous avons préféré choisir certains secteurs déterminés et particulièrement ceux qui jusqu'ici avaient été peut-être les plus négligés: la définition des styles, la recherche des matériaux techniques (notamment l'usage des mesures mathématiques), les problèmes si ardus de la symétrie statique ou dynamique, l'intérêt artistique des monnaies, sans oublier cette question toujours sous-jacente à toutes les autres, la chronologie des oeuvres. C'est donc un choix de problèmes qu'on trouvera exposés ou esquissés, ou seulement même suggérés dans ce volume. Il s'agissait en quelque sorte de jeter les fondements d'une prospection raisonnée et d'une analyse renouvelée des matériaux de l'art celtique.

D'autres sujets, en attendant le moment où il sera possible de risquer une synthèse, pourraient retenir l'attention de colloques ultérieurs. Au cours des pages qui suivent, le lecteur remarquera que, d'une part, l'unité de l'art celtique s'affirme dans tous les domaines, d'un bout à l'autre de l'Europe, mais que, d'autre part, il existe des zones stylistiques qui commencent à se définir: l'Europe centrale et orientale se distingue ainsi de l'Occident et, à l'intérieur de ces vastes ensembles, des styles régionaux, des ateliers même peuvent être discernés. Parmi les catégories d'objets décorés, la céramique, incisée, peinte ou estampée, est assurément la moins étudiée. Or, production strictement locale, plus vulnérable au transport que toutes les autres sortes d'objets d'art, elle a des chances de nous éclairer le mieux possible sur les variétés locales et régionales du matériel artistique. La Gaule, l'Irlande, l'île de Bretagne, le Rhin Moyen, la Bohême, par exemple, apparaissent comme autant de provinces de l'art celtique général, où pourraient être définis des styles particuliers.

L'origine des motifs reçus et assimilés par l'art celtique est également un vaste sujet d'études, sur lequel les idées de Jacobsthal sont aujourd'hui précisées, ajustées ou discutées. Quel est le plus important, du *substratum* du premier âge du fer, de l'apport scytho-asiatique et de l'emprunt à l'Orient classique transmis par la Grèce et l'Italie? Ce dernier pays se signale aujourd'hui de plus en plus, selon une vue féconde de Jacobsthal, comme l'intermédiaire principal entre les matériaux orientaux ou orientalisants et le creuset celtique. Enfin, les études stylistiques devraient aider à éclairer le premier grand problème de l'histoire celtique: y a-t-il eu continuité ou rupture ethnographique ou culturelle entre la premier et le second âge du fer? à quelles circonstances est due l'apparition, qui peut sembler brutale, du style laténien? Autant de questions qui touchent à l'histoire générale de l'Europe.

Tel qu'il se présente actuellement, l'art celtique a maintenant ses lettres de noblesse parmi les arts de l'Europe antique. *Primo*, il s'est dégagé totalement des modèles méditerranéens qu'il a assimilés, pour s'affirmer comme un art décoratif, à la fois linéaire et plastique, épris de toutes les courbes, dont il joue avec une virtuosité et une liberté d'invention remarquables, mêlant à une interprétation schématique et même caricaturale des formes vivantes un penchant irrésistible à la métamorphose, un goût prononcé pour le fantastique, le monstrueux, le surnaturel. *Secundo*, dans ses trois phases successives de sevérité, de liberté et de retour à la symétrie, il manifeste une habileté technique digne des plus grandes civilisations contemporaines; et l'on commence d'entrevoir derrière les asymétries de ses créations les plus libres une ordonnance profonde et régulière à sa façon, peut-être cette sorte de symétrie dynamique qu'étudient les mathématiciens des "groupes" et des "ensembles", en tout cas des procédés empiriques, sinon des calculs, qui relèvent de la géométrie. Pourquoi les Celtes, qui connaissaient toutes les subtilités des problèmes de calendrier, n'auraient-ils pas eu, dans le domaine de l'art, leurs règles de composition? Tel est peut-être l'art finalement aussi rigoureux qu'il nous paraît déjà aujourd'hui raffiné, que révéleront les études de demain.

Deux derniers points ont été évoqués, concernant l'orientation de ces études. Tout d'abord la nécessité de faire maintenant des inventaires détaillés des motifs employés par les artistes celtiques, d'après les objets de toute nature qu'ils ont décorés et qu'il faudra comparer aux motifs connus par d'autres arts. En second lieu, l'urgence de mettre au point les questions de terminologie, pour s'entendre, d'une langue à l'autre, sur le nom exact d'un objet, d'un motif, d'une technique ou d'un style: fait pour les arts classiques, ce travail indispensable est encore à faire pour les arts laténiens.

Nous remercions de leur concours le Directeur de la Maison Française d'Oxford, M. Jean Lequiller, ses secrétaires et son fils Dominique; les membres du Colloque qui ont accepté de faire une communication; les auditeurs qui nous ont encouragé de leur présence; l'Institut d'archéologie d'Oxford, qui a mis à notre disposition des volumes de sa bibliothèque; nos collègues E. M. Jope, pour les galvanoplasties d'objets celtiques célèbres qu'il a exposées sous nos yeux, et Stuart Piggott, pour le bilan qu'il a bien voulu dresser de nos travaux. Nous avons regretté l'absence de nos collègues T. G. E. Powell, empêché au dernier moment de venir parmi nous et J. V. S. Megaw, que son séjour à l'étranger avait fait renoncer à accepter notre invitation.

Abbreviations

Our publishers' house style and all our authors' variations, personal and national, could not be reconciled fully, but allow of the following classified treatment.—*C.H.*

Common words in publication titles

Annual, Bulletin, Proceedings, Report, Anzeiger, Compte rendu, Obzor, Sbornik, Zprávy

Aarb.	Aarbøger
Ann. (litt.)	Annales (littéraires)
Ant., Antiq.	Antiquaries, Antiquaires, Antiquités
Arch., Archaeol.	Archaeology, Archéologie, Archäologie; -ical, -ique, -ische, -ická, -ický
Ber.	Bericht (-e), = Report (-s)
Bull.	Bulletin, Bullettino
Fundb.	Fundberichte, = Reports of discoveries
Jahrb.	Jahrbuch (-bücher)
Jahresh.	Jahresheft (-e)
J., Journ.	Journal
Medd.	Meddelanden
Mitt.	Mitteilungen
N.S., n.s.	new series
Prehist., Prähist.	Prehistoric, préhistorique, Praehistorische
Proc.	Proceedings
Rev.	Revue
Roy.; Nat.	Royal; National, = Národní
ser.	series
Zeitschr.	Zeitschrift

Miscellanies, Monographs, Reports or Acts of Congresses

Actes, Atti	Acts
Beih.	Beiheft (-e), = Supplement
Beitr.	Beitrag (-träge), = Contribution (-s)
Festschr. Mélanges	Festschrift Mélanges } = Complimentary volume for esteemed personage
Suppl.	Supplément

Common words in institution titles

Abt.	Abteilung, = Section
Acad.	Academy, Académie
Am.	American
Assoc.	Association
bern.	bernische, = of Bern (Switzerland)

Brit.	British
Celt.	Celtic, -ique
Class.	Classical
dt.	deutsche, = German
Ges.	Gesellschaft, = Society
hist.	historical, historique, historiska
hist. nat.	histoire naturelle
Inst.	Institute, Institut, Ústav
Ir.	Irish
Landesmus.	Landesmuseum
Mus.	Museum
Phil.	Philosophical
Prehist.	as above
preuss.	preussische, = Prussian
schweiz.	schweizerische, = Swiss
Soc., Spol.	Society, Société, Společnost
staatl.	staatliche, State, national
Univ.	University, -ité, -ität

Particular institution titles

Acad. (des) Inscr(ipt).	Académie des Inscriptions et Belles-Lettres, Paris
B.M.	British Museum
Čs.	Czechoslovak, tchécoslovaque
ČSAV	Čs. Academy of (Věd) Sciences
Mus. des Antiqs. Nats.	Musée des Antiquités Nationales, St. Germain-en-Laye
RGK, Röm.-Germ.Komm.	Römisch-Germanische Kommission des Deutschen Archäologischen Instituts, Frankfurt
RGZ-Mus. Mainz	Römisch-Germanische Zentral-Museum, Mainz
UISPP	Union Internationale des Sciences Préhistoriques et Protohistoriques

Periodicals, museum and monograph serials, congress publications

Aarb. f. nord. Oldk.	Aarbøger for nordisk Oldkyndighed, Copenhagen
Acta Arch. Acad. Sci. Hung.	Acta Archaeologica Academiae Scientiarum Hungaricae, Budapest
Antiq. Journ.	The Antiquaries Journal, London
Anz. f. Elsäss. Altertumsk.	Anzeiger für Elsässische Altertumskunde (to 1918), Strassburg
Arch. Austr.	Archaeologia Austriaca, Vienna (Wien)
Arch. Rozhled.	Archeologické Rozhledy, Prague
Bay. Vorgeschichtsbl.	Bayerische Vorgeschichtsblätter, Munich
Bonner Jahrb.	Bonner Jahrbücher, Bonn (Rheinisches Landesmus.)
Brit. Mus. Quart.	The British Museum Quarterly, London
B.S.P.F.	Bulletin de la Société Préhistorique Française, Paris
Bull. Palet. It.	Bullettino di Paletnologia Italiana, Rome
IV. Congr. Étud. Celt.	Actes du IVe Congrès International d'Études Celtiques, Rennes 1971 (Étud. Celt. XIII, 2), Paris 1972
VII Congrès UISPP 1966	Actes du VIIe Congrès International des Sciences Préhistoriques et Protohistoriques, 1966, Prague 1970
VI Congresso UISPP 1962	Atti del VI° Congresso Internazionale delle Scienze Preistoriche e Protostoriche, Roma 1962, Florence 1966
1° Congr. . . . Medit.	Atti del 1° Congresso Internazionale di Preistoria e Protostoria Mediterranea 1950, Florence 1952

Étud. Celt.	Études celtiques, Paris
Germ.	Germania, Anzeiger der Röm.-Germ. Komm. (Frankfurt), Berlin
Hamburger Beitr. z. Arch.	Hamburger Beiträge zur Archäologie, Hamburg (Univ. Seminar für Vor- und Frühgeschichte)
IPEK	Jahrbuch für Prähistorische und Ethnographische Kunst, Berlin
Istanbuler Mitt.	Istanbuler Mitteilungen, Istanbul (Deutsches Arch. Inst. Abt.)
Madrider Mitt.	Madrider Mitteilungen, Heidelberg (Deutsches Arch. Inst. Abt. Madrid)
M.A.G.W.	Mitteilungen der Anthropologischen Gesellschaft in Wien, Vienna
Památky arch.	Památky archeologické, Prague
Rev. arch.	Revue archéologique, Paris
Rev. arch. de l'Est	Revue archéologique de l'Est et du Centre-Est, Dijon
Rev. celt.	Revue celtique, Paris
Sovet. Archeol.	Sovetskaya Arkheologiya, Moscow
Trierer Zeitschr.	Trierer Zeitschrift, Trier (Rheinisches Landesmus.)
Wilts. Arch. Mag.	Wiltshire Archaeological and Natural History Magazine, Devizes

Books, articles, monographs, catalogues, museum guides

A Pedro Bosch Gimpera	(Title of vol. for his 70th birthday) Mexico 1963
BG	Caesar, De Bello Gallico
Bretz-Mahler 1970	Denise Bretz-Mahler, La civilisation de La Tène I en Champagne: le faciès marnien (XXII Suppl. à Gallia), Paris
B.M. (Iron Age) Guide	British Museum Guide to Antiquities of the Early Iron Age, London 1925
B.M. Guide Later Prehist. Antiqs.	Later Prehistoric Antiquities of the British Isles (British Museum Guide), London 1953
Civ. Prim. Ital.	Oscar Montelius, La civilisation primitive en Italie, Stockholm 1895–1904
Coll. Latomus	Collection Latomus (monograph series), Brussels
Coll. Millon	Joseph Déchelette, La Collection Millon, Paris 1913
Déchelette, Manuel II.2, 1913 (1970) = 1927 III; II.3, 1914 (1970) = 1927 IV	Joseph Déchelette, Manuel d'Archéologie préhistorique, celtique et gallo-romaine, Paris: Premier Age du Fer ou époque de Hallstatt, 1913, and Second Age du Fer ou époque de La Tène, 1914, were Parts 2 and 3 of his vol. II and were reprinted so 1970 (Gregg International); but the 1927 edition, Paris, re-numbered them as vols. III–IV, re-paged 1–1174 (instead of 495–1668), each with new index but both with the old fig.-numbers retained
Diss. Pann.	Dissertationes Pannonicae (monograph series), Budapest
ECA, ECABI	see Jacobsthal, Jope
European Community	The European Community in Later Prehistory: Studies in honour of C. F. C. Hawkes (edd. Boardman, Brown, Powell), London 1971
Filip, J. 1956, Keltové	Jan Filip, Keltové ve Střední Europě, Prague (with long German summary)
Fox, C., Pattern & Purpose	Sir Cyril Fox, Pattern and Purpose: A Survey of Early

	Celtic Art in Britain, Cardiff 1958 (National Museum of Wales)
Frere ed., Problems of the I.A.	S. S. Frere ed., Problems of the Iron Age in Southern Britain, London 1960 (Univ. Inst. of Arch.)
Hodson, Münsingen-Rain	F. R. Hodson, The La Tène Cemetery at Münsingen-Rain: Catalogue and relative chronology, Bern 1968
Hraže 1898/9	J. K. Hraže in Památky arch. 18
Jacobsthal, ECA	Paul Jacobsthal, Early Celtic Art, Oxford 1944, reprinted 1971; pieces may be cited by catalogue-number (no.)
Jope & Jacobsthal, ECABI	E. M. Jope and †Paul Jacobsthal, Early Celtic Art in the British Isles, Oxford forthcoming; pieces by catalogue-number (no.)
Keller 1965, Reinheim I	J. Keller, Das keltische Fürstengrab von Reinheim, Band I, Mainz
Kruta 1971	V. Kruta, Le Trésor de Duchcov dans les collections tchécoslovaques, Ústi nad Labem
Kruta 1973	V. Kruta in Études celtiques XIII, 2, 644–661
Libenice	see Rybová
Megaw 1970	J. V. S. Megaw, Art of the European Iron Age: a study of the elusive image, Bath; pieces may be cited by catalogue-number (no.)
Münchner Beitr.	Münchner Beiträge zur Vor- und Frühgeschichte (monograph series), Munich
Penninger 1972, Dürrnberg I	E. Penninger, Der Dürrnberg bei Hallein, Band I, Munich
Píč 1904/5	J. L. Píč in Památky arch. 21.
Proxima Thule	(Title of vol. ded. to King of Sweden), Stockholm 1962
Röm.-Germ. Forsch.	Römisch-Germanische Forschungen (monograph series RGK, Frankfurt), Berlin
Rybová & Soudský	A. Rybová and B. Soudský, Libenice: Sanctuaire celtique en Bohême centrale (monogr. ser. Monumenta Arch., X), Prague 1962
Schránil 1922	J. Schránil in Obzor praehistorický I, 15–24
Siblík 1906/8	J. Siblík in Památky arch. 22
Viollier 1916	D. Viollier, Sépultures du 2e Age du Fer sur le Plateau Suisse, Geneva
Wheeler, Maiden Castle	R. E. M. Wheeler, Maiden Castle, Dorset, London 1943 (Soc. of Antiquaries)
Woldřich 1886	J. N. Woldřich in M.A.G.W. 16

A Note on the Presentation of the Discussions

The discussions at the Colloquy, following each of the set contributions (except of course the final Summing-Up), were round-table discussions, using English and French indifferently (with an occasional word of German), and were all recorded on tape.

The transcripts typed from the tapes (with some notes taken by the editors) have formed the basis of the texts submitted for printing. Of course they required much editing.

Nine of the Discussions were such that for a clear and readable account, the form adopted had to be that of a *report*. (Hawkes, Champion, Sandars, Schwappach, Kruta, Jope, Savory, Klindt-Jensen and Duval).

The other four, however, were so coherent in the trend of the talking, that I judged it a pity to lose their freshness by reporting them like the rest. With comparatively little amendment of their conversational language—often none at all—I could reproduce them as *vivâ voce*. These were on the "Waldalgesheim" Celtic art-style (Frey); on the Turoe Stone (Duignan); on the British mirrors; and (Allen) on Celtic coins.

I believe this form, bringing out the liveliness, and the speakers' tone and character, is a genuine enhancement of the book's attractions. My choosing these four for it is a matter of personal judgment. Even in recording the others, I could use the actual words quite often. But these four stood out: I found the *vivâ voce* form was natural. For them, I find it a success, and am sure that readers will enjoy it.

Christopher Hawkes

1

Celts and Cultures: Wealth, Power, Art

CHRISTOPHER HAWKES
Oxford

Part I

THE COLLOQUY'S five centuries, from the VIth to the Ist B.C., in Europe outside the arc of the Alps around North Italy, can be called "protohistoric" after the usage of the French, giving the "ancient" of this book's English title a due precision. In French and the other Romance tongues, its use begins for the Bronze Age, when the eastern Mediterranean enters history's own domain, and particles of this begin to modify Europe's old prehistory. And when the transalpine First Iron Age, that known as the Hallstatt period, was attaining its maturity in the years around 600, the particles of history start to change the old scene further. Inhabitants known by names, extant mostly as rendered in Greek, make it appear more like the Italian scene, or the Balkan on the fringe of Greece itself; a scene where locations of names such as Ligurian or Iberian, Illyrian or Celt, confront the cultures of archaeology, which are entities drawn from recurring sorts of distinctive finds in the ground.

Hallstatt, an Austrian mining site with an early-discovered cemetery, where the finds defined the period through resemblances seen with Italy, had its site-name taken for an archaeological entity, the Hallstatt culture. But the extension given to this soon proved to be so enormous, down the Danube, down the Rhine, and across to the Atlantic, that further regional entities need distinguishing inside it. Only fractionally does the scheme of these cohere with the name of Celt, for a people known to western Greeks, away up-country from their city of Massalia, and given in our scanty record first not after about 500, a century from that city's foundation at Marseilles. Yet a mention sixty years later,[1] locating Celts at the sources of the Danube, muddled indeed though it is, may yet connect them with the inland region, in the hills of the Black Forest, where the Danube's sources are. And that, in Hallstatt times, was within an archaeological entity, included in the culture's major range but with well-marked features of its own, which was next, in the Vth century, followed by another in the next great culture. This, broadly continuous from that time till the Roman Empire, is the culture called La Tène. It belonged to the Celts of protohistory and ancient history, in the wider connotation which the advance of knowledge brought. And it gives us the Celtic art that is the subject of this book—through the Colloquy opened by Duval with the introduction above here printed, presenting the state of its studies and pointing onwards to their progress.

Yet the fractional correspondence of archaeological cultures with peoples, seen in Hallstatt protohistory, may continue into La Tène. Britain, as an island with ancient names and tongues pre-eminently Celtic, and Ireland too although with characters of its own, were formerly supposed to have been celticized decisively through invasions bringing La Tène culture in, fully formed. "The Coming of the Celts", like "the Coming of the Saxons", should be an event that archaeology could and surely would determine, as soon as sufficient finds had been dug from the ground. Since the days of that belief much has been dug, both here and in regions abroad (Fig. 1), where these invading La Tène Celts might be recognized in their homelands. But no fully-formed La Tène can be seen as sweeping over Britain throughout, in a manner to show that this was the culture that made the island Celtic. Still less can that be declared of La Tène in Ireland. For at least half a century it has been more and more apparent that La Tène culture here, as disclosed by our archaeology, not only varied regionally but appeared from the first in fragments, while older insular culture remained in the place of what failed to arrive.

Can we see factors determining what arrived and what failed to?[2] Who are the leaders expanding a culture? Are they leaders armed for battle, or are they commercial travellers, *MM. les voyageurs de commerce*? Either, in the case of an island, will need shipbuilders and skippers; goodwill, or their own control, on the coasts from which they will start. If they want these too on landing, the expedition must be prepared. And for southern Britain and the opposite lands, if we move back from La Tène, and back from the Final Hallstatt to the Early, with swords still bronze, and past it back through the Bronze Age, Late to Middle and Middle to Early, we shall always find in archaeology cultures in some way common to both the sides, if not in one part then in another, of the water that all must cross. What appears commercial or peaceful,

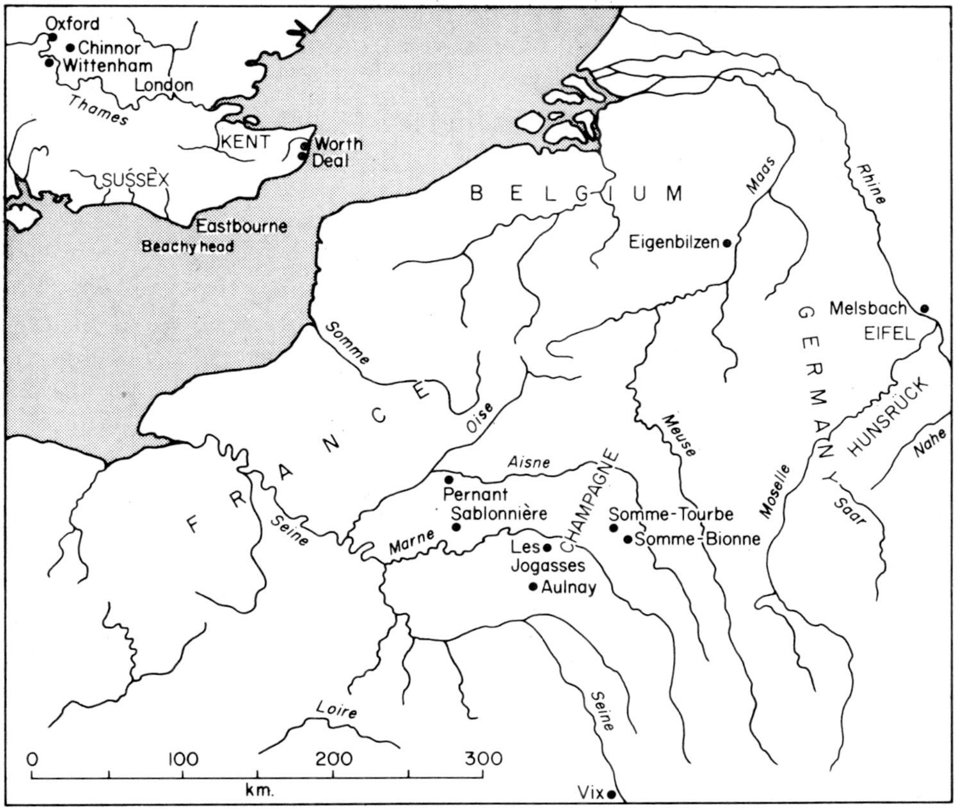

FIG. 1. Map, NW. Europe, with principal names used in the text.

too, may be cut by signs of the warlike; the Hallstatt sword of bronze,[3] though its features could influence older British, is itself never a weapon found in the hoards of the native bronze-smiths. Its time hereabouts, from the VIIth to middle or later VIth century, seems a phase when aggressive venturing—out of regions in modern Belgium—took advantage of older contacts, changed the scene, and prepared for more. As Hallstatt culture had iron-work now, our record in bronzes next fades out; but pottery on certain sites suggests, in our South and East, that the venturing led to settlement too: sometimes apart from, sometimes imposed on, the country's older inhabitants.[4] And all this while, as radiocarbon now is showing us, movements or reactions were being expressed in fortification: forecast of the forts, at last the *oppida*, of La Tène.[5] Are we to say that only with those, and with La Tène art on metal, comes the first sign of movements making Britain and Ireland Celtic?

Archaeology's cultures are not, in protohistory, the prisons of peoples. Insular Celts are not to be confined within La Tène; not even, I think, within Hallstatt. But with Final Hallstatt anyhow, and with Early La Tène supervening—with the later VIth and V[th] centuries—we are brought in southern Britain to ask what factors divide these phases. Canon Favret,[6] writing of the Marne, declared the transition there was *brusque*: "we only turn one page, but we change the chapter". What does his metaphor mean, in terms that are human?

Part II

Wealth, power, art: these achievements are all three human. Students of a culture's art may connect this readily enough with its wealth; but the middle term is power—a word less of archaeology than of history. Human societies, mirrored materially in cultures, have power to survive, or expand, or dominate others, through various factors. Wealth, if appropriately used, is one; poverty, where determining weakness, is another. Degrees of power, and of will to use it, vary with situations; but the will to use what these allow must be socially formed and led. Leadership issues from social structure; this was a class structure with the Celts, like most of the ancient Europeans, and power in the leading class varied with wealth and the means to gain it. A favourable situation could bring improvement in material, from buildings or transportation down to a more efficient fibula, in all of which La Tène culture came to improve on Hallstatt; but it also could arouse ambition to command more means to create display—display that would gratify the leaders and their women, while sharpening the pride in them felt by the led. And religion, which all were imbued with, had its claim on the same emotions. The display of Celtic art thus made for social exhilaration, reflected also in the craftsmen's technical skill and creative genius. That models for the expression of these were at hand from other cultures, as well as in their own traditions, contradicts this not at all; archaeology will trace the models, yet should admit the emotions too.

To wealth, and its gaining and showing and use, I mean to return below (Part III). I revert now to the question of the factors dividing Final Hallstatt, as extended to southern Britain, from ensuing Early La Tène. We have not to forget that British tradition inhibited furnished burial. Even cremation in a plain coarse pot is here a thing of extremest rarity, and anything like a cemetery of this age is quite unknown. What otherwise might have been grave-goods meet us as finds dredged from river-beds; Torbrügge's wide European study of river-bed deposition[7] shows it a strangely inveterate custom, which in these north-westerly parts of Europe can seem to exclude deposition in graves—though the bounds of the two may shift in different periods and cases. Hallstatt weapons from the Thames, till the middle or later VIth century,[8] have their Continental backgrounds centred farther east than France, and transmissions appearing likeliest through Belgium. But already within that century the background starts to move to France, and from near 500 B.C. provides dirks and daggers or their sheaths in a series, most

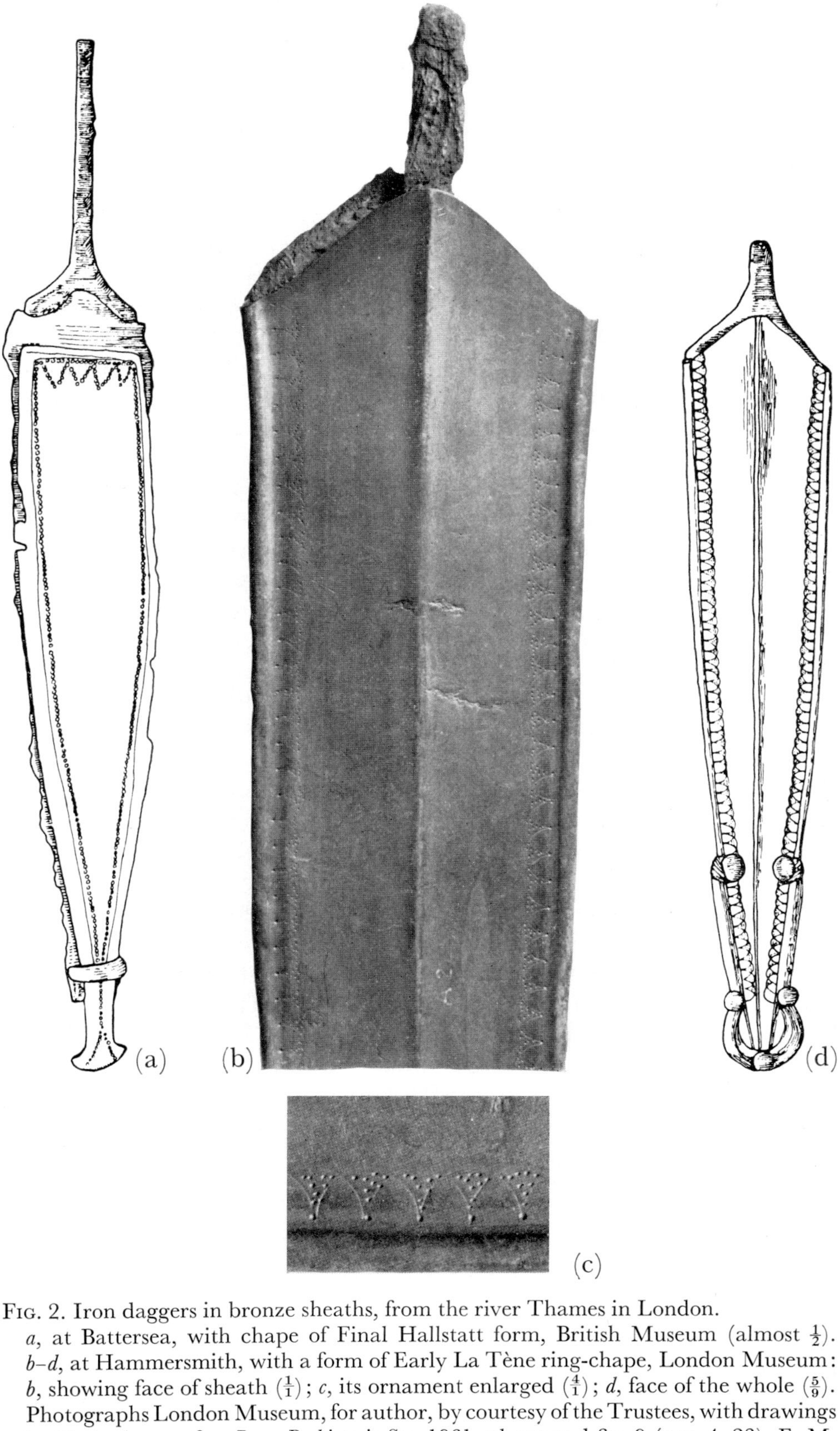

FIG. 2. Iron daggers in bronze sheaths, from the river Thames in London.
a, at Battersea, with chape of Final Hallstatt form, British Museum (almost $\frac{1}{2}$). *b–d*, at Hammersmith, with a form of Early La Tène ring-chape, London Museum: *b*, showing face of sheath ($\frac{1}{1}$); *c*, its ornament enlarged ($\frac{4}{1}$); *d*, face of the whole ($\frac{5}{9}$). Photographs London Museum, for author, by courtesy of the Trustees, with drawings by T. Ambrose after *Proc. Prehistoric Soc.* 1961, pl. xx and fig. 9 (nos. 4, 23), E. M. Jope.

with signs of being made in Britain, but from origins clearly in the Marne and Aisne basins. Fig. 2, *a* shows an example from the Thames at Battersea, London (no. 4, pl. xx, in the work just cited, n. 8); its "fish-tail" terminal chape shows its date to be still Hallstatt. The thin bronze face of the sheath is bordered by embossed simple pointillé, in a single line enhanced at the top by repetitive hanging triangles. The dates run into La Tène, in fact, from a start in Final Hallstatt, which in the Marne means the regional culture named there the Jogassian.[9]

These are weapons so fine in workmanship, where its features survive for study, that they bespeak a leading class, an aristocracy based round London.[10] Yet not only are there never any standard La Tène I swords, which are so frequent in the Marne (Fig. 3, k), but the British chape forms (Fig. 3, a) diverge from the Marne's, and the art of the decoration on the sheaths remains repetitive: mostly of fine-worked bordering, as in Continental Early Style, but excluding still that style's advances into comprehensive design. From Jope's demonstration of this, a dozen years ago, see the sheaths from the Thames at Hammersmith, London (Fig. 2, b–d and fig. 3, a).[11] The compass-drawn arcading on the one, and the twin rows of intersecting arcs on the other, emphasized respectively with pointillé and with hatching, are as far as it gets while still in the Early manner of the Continent. In the Marne, where the vase from Sogny grave 16 (Fig. 3, j) shows arcs used for 4-petalled flowers, forming friezes, this itself seems exceptional among the repetitive patterns on pottery.[12] Though Fig. 4, the sheath from the Minster Ditch (a channel of the Thames at Oxford), shows a composition of its own, with on its reverse a curious serpentine, yet its chape form marks it as British—although the serpentine, compass-drawn, may be influenced from IVth-century Gaul.[13] So perhaps may the chape of the well-known dagger from the Thames at Wandsworth, London, in the S-linked circlets of its openwork.[14] Of La Tène I fibula forms,[15] even those of Ia in Britain may already be distinguishably British (Fig. 5, a); further developments, local (b, c), show a knowledge of Ib, yet with these the IVth century appears more insular than the Vth.[16] The British could still use pins, making an insular ring-headed form which improved the Hallstatt swan-neck (Fig. 3, c from d).[17] As in costume-accessories, and weapons, so in decorative art: our regions of easy access got some parts of Early La Tène, but escaped the reach of fully-composed employments of Greek motifs, and of masks and animal forms, till after the Early Style was outrun. Nor have we torcs till after that, nor bracelets unless quite rarely.

Yet the pottery along the Thames can have as much from Early La Tène as the weapons—though it needs distinguishing, first, from some on the coast by the Straits of Dover (Fig. 1). The early-looking La Tène Ia fibula Fig. 3, b, comes from an excavated site at Worth, near the sea between Sandwich and Deal (Kent).[18] Along with this, and all beneath

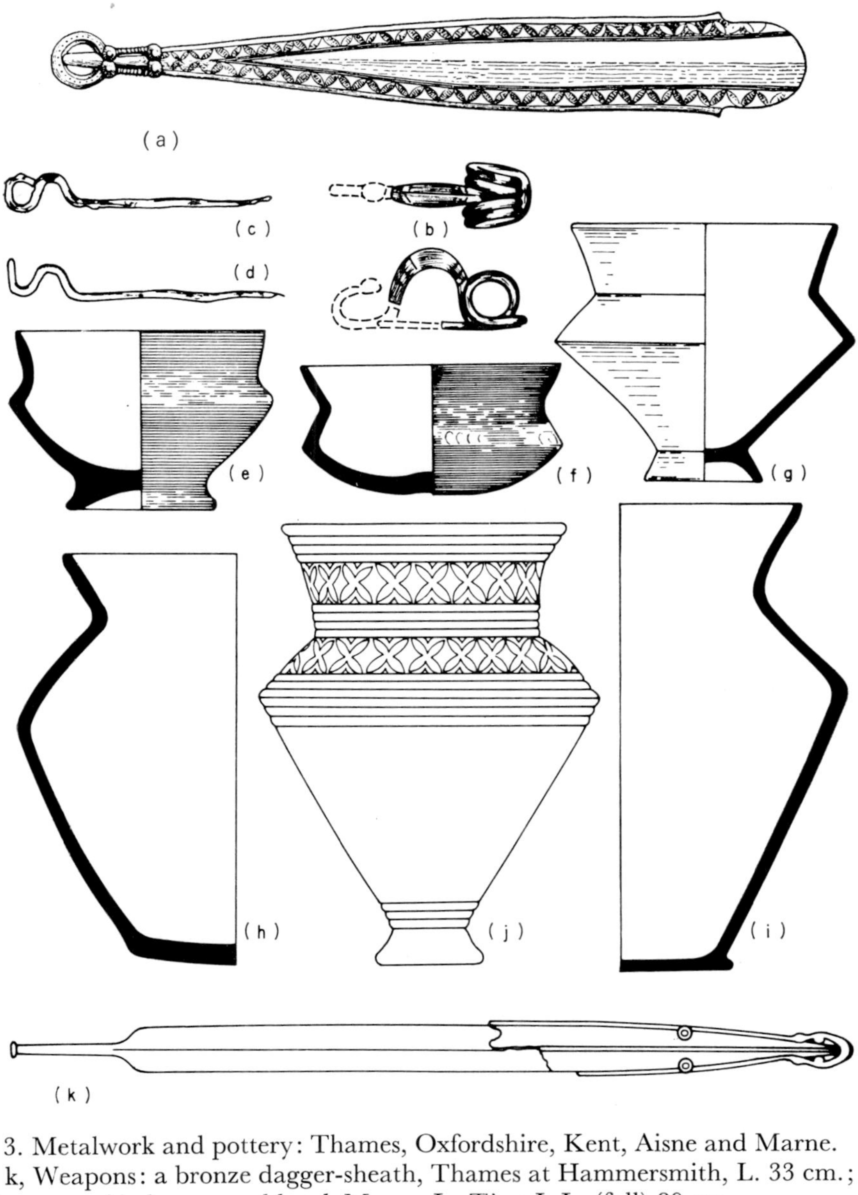

FIG. 3. Metalwork and pottery: Thames, Oxfordshire, Kent, Aisne and Marne.
a, k, Weapons: a bronze dagger-sheath, Thames at Hammersmith, L. 33 cm.; k iron sword in bronze scabbard, Marne, La Tène I, L. (full) 80 cm.
c–d, Pins, Oxfordshire ($\frac{1}{2}$): c Chinnor, iron: d Wood Eaton, bronze.
b, Fibula, bronze, Worth (E. Kent), La Tène Ia ($\frac{1}{1}$).
e–i, Pottery: near Oxford, f Long Wittenham ($\frac{1}{3}$), e Chinnor ($\frac{1}{3}$), h Dorchester, Mount Farm ($\frac{1}{4}$); g Aisne, Sablonnières ($\frac{1}{4}$); i–j Marne, ($\frac{1}{4}$), j Sogny grave 16 ($\frac{1}{2}$) (Sources: a Jope; c–f, h Harding; b, g *Antiq. Journ.* 1940, 1951; j Thiérot, i Bretz-Mahler pl. 103, 2; k *Brit. Mus. Guide* fig. 56, 3: see notes, pp. 17 ff.

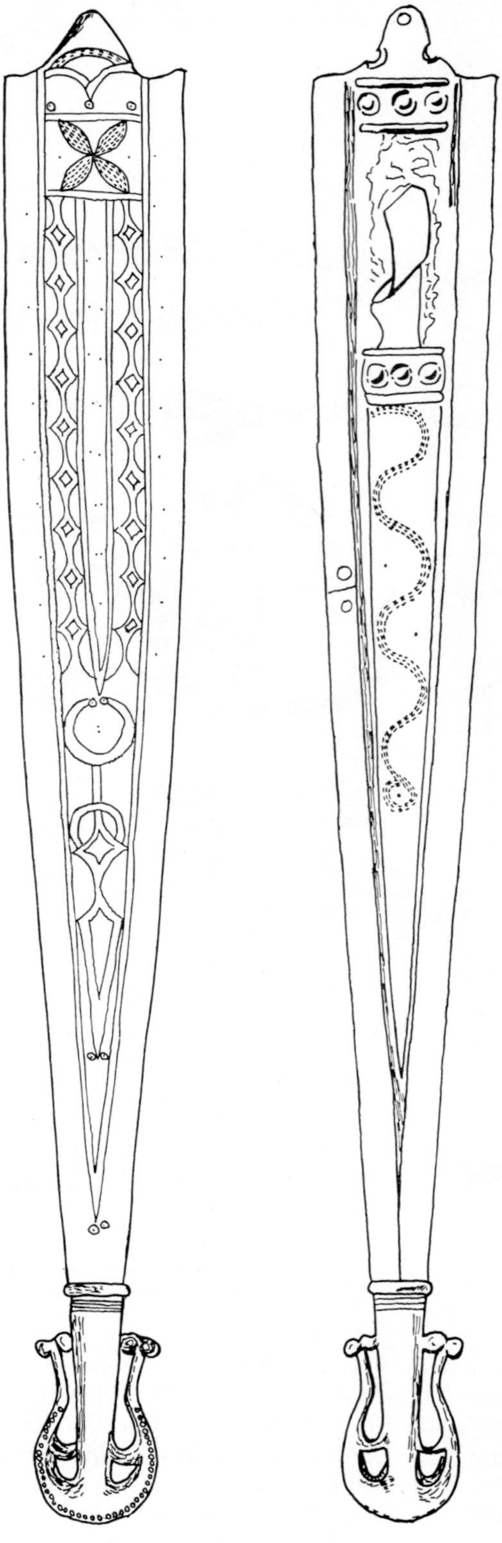

FIG. 4. Dagger-sheath, bronze, from the Minster Ditch at Oxford, Ashmolean Mus. ($\frac{1}{2}$). Drawn 1973 for author by T. Ambrose; compare *Archaeologia* 54, 497, C. J. Praetorius for C. H. Read, 1895, and Jope (as Fig. 2) 1961, figs. 7 and 5, 14.

the Romano-Celtic temple there, was pottery including forms still more like "Marnian": the carinated, sharply-shouldered "situla" shape of jar, and a goblet fragment and bowls looking "Marnian" equally. Due to invaders? But Worth was then a low-lying maritime cape; it might have been a Gaulish trading-post, not typical thus for Britain. So too, and a little earlier, might the coastal settlement at Eastbourne, close behind Beachy Head (where a Final Bronze Age find had gold)[19]; from its pottery, at least some of it manufactured on the spot, Eastbourne might be an outlying post of Gaulish Jogassians.[20] Thus excluding those

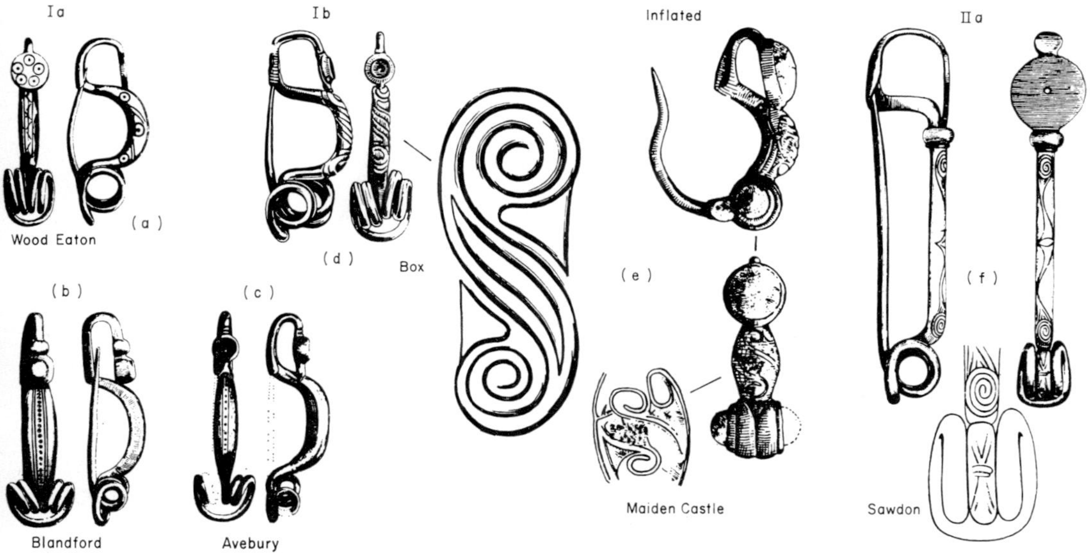

FIG. 5. British bronze fibulas, La Tène I and II ($\frac{1}{2}$).
a Oxfordshire, Wood Eaton (Ia); b Dorset, Blandford; c Wiltshire, Avebury; d W. Wiltshire, Box, with ornament on bow $\frac{1}{1}$ (all Ib); e Dorset, Maiden Castle ("inflated"; has red enamel settings), with ornament on bow-setting $\frac{1}{1}$; f E. Yorkshire, Sawdon ("flat" IIA), with ornament at head $\frac{1}{1}$.
Sources: a–d *Brit. Mus. Guide* figs. 94–7; e Wheeler *Maiden Castle*; f *Antiq. Journ.* 1947, Watson. Drawn: e W. F. Grimes, all rest C. O. Waterhouse (d enlargement specially for author).

two, we have remaining chiefly the Thames, with the men of the daggers, spread from its mouth to Oxford. On its flanks there are sites with pottery including forms defined as angular, which can resemble (Fig. 3, e, from Chinnor) the Early La Tène of the Aisne (Fig. 3, g). Some seem prior to it (f, Long Wittenham: omphalos base, not foot-ring); but all—like the daggers—suggest new arrivals amongst the inhabitants. Thus pottery and weapons alike, running out of Hallstatt into La Tène, show they had settled down already before the late Vth century. For the La Tène sites on the Aisne will have commenced towards 450, the earliest date available for the imported bronze situla, found with a strainer and Etruscan wine-bowl in the chariot-grave at Pernant.[21]

On the Aisne and Marne alike, La Tène begins then with pottery, mostly distinct from the Jogassian and with angular forms more prevalent.[22] Its carinated vases, where the neck is kept short, are just angular situlas copied in clay (Fig. 6, 1). Where taller (*col haut*) or flaring (*évasé*),

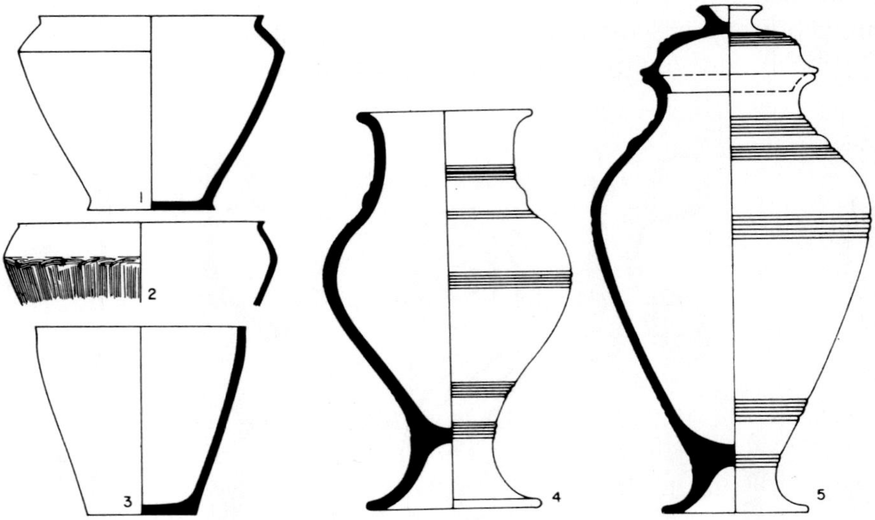

FIG. 6. Pottery, La Tène I, dépt. Marne and western Rhineland ($\frac{1}{5}$).
Marne: 1–2 carinated, like bronze situlas, 3 plain (Brit. Mus., coll. Morel). W. Rhineland (Nahe valley): 4–5 "piriform", cordoned, with pedestal (Kreuznach Mus., from excavated graves in the Hochwald).
Sources: *Antiq. Journ.* 1940, 117, Hawkes; *Katalog Kreuznach* (1938) Taf. 17, Dehn.

the feature is inherited: from the forms with similar necks, though not angular yet in body, of the Urnfield-Hallstatt wares that had there preceded them.[23] When Britain got some of the angular sort, it was mostly with necks made flaring:[24] compare Fig. 3, i (Marne) with h, from one of the Thames-side sites (Mount Farm at Dorchester) having bowls or cups like e; they recur together, small with large. But Britain got none with curving profiles, vases and bowls of early pear shape (*piriforme*), some with pedestal and all with cordons (*bourrelets*): Fig. 6, 4–5 resemble many from the Marne.[24] These in the Champagne are found in the centre of the Marne and in the north and east; their mode could have come from the first La Tène of the Rhineland[25]. Like the swords, the abundance of fibulas, and the advanced Early-Style art[26], all of them standard characters of a full La Tène I, they were not (within this time) received in Britain. Yet the name La Tène is employed nonetheless, in the Marne or the Aisne, for the simpler characters that really were received here. I conclude that "Early La Tène" is a name that at present has two connotations.

In both, it was Celtic culture, but only one was culturally full. The other was not so full, and was partly different in its forms. Hallstatt (as well as Urnfield) traits are perceptible in it still, though affected in its pottery-forms by newly-diffused bronze situlas. And as it was this, the not-so-full La Tène culture, that was passed to Britain, can the full La Tène of the Rhineland yet have reached into northern Gaul—the north and east and centre of the Marne—when the movement to Britain was happening?[27] Early La Tène in its fulness, in fact, of wealth and power and of art, cannot be co-extensive either with Celts or even with the name "La Tène", as used for the full and the not-so-full together. So I submit that the case of Britain, once it is better comprehended, must warn us against confusing protohistory by the terms—such as "Early La Tène" here—that we use for the cultures of its peoples.

Part III

Reverting to La Tène, and to Britain, one expects the sequel to be a movement which at last would bring in a fuller La Tène culture. Yet there was never such a single movement affecting Britain as a whole. The task is to sort out several, chronologically and regionally, whether or not bearing instalments of advance in La Tène art. Cases of this should have meant introducing fresh artisans; yet these can have done as much through having effect on older workshops, as through setting up craft traditions all their own.

Movement into East Yorkshire, starting doubtless around 400, may be viewed in an eastern-coastal context, extending from the Thames first to the Wash and then to the Humber. Hallstatt and earlier elements there were apparently less pervasive; yet it was long before any immigration passed to a sequel in Yorkshire art-work, though the current growth in our knowledge may bring surprises—and indeed has started to. A western-coastal context, stretching at least to North Wales, is cut by the Bristol Channel dividing Wales from the South-west—opposite to Armorican North-west Gaul. This peninsula, like Wales and its Marches with western England, had important earlier elements, both indigenous and immigrant. Openings given by fresh ones, for any La Tène artistic output, can nevertheless have begun well back within the IVth century. An example pointing to this is the fibula from Box (Fig. 5, d), just within Wiltshire but yet quite close to the Bristol Channel: with its fleshy-looking spiral leaf, it joins the Cerrig-y-Drudion bowl in recalling the Armorican "floral" vases (pp. 165, 214 below). The rest of Fig. 5 shows the Maiden Castle "inflated" fibula, still something of an oddity in Dorset, and hard to date, and the Sawdon (E. Yorkshire) example of the long and straight-bowed form, with rivet-attached foot, which grew out of La Tène I forms (Figs. 7 and 8c), and for quite some time excluded Continental La Tène II forms. The Sawdon brooch is of interest for its centrally-peaked scroll, and its tightly-coiled spiral, which both are matched on British shields, and so give links between minor and major British work; but this comes later. For those and other illustrations of British La Tène I and II work, chapter II of Sir Cyril Fox's *Pattern and Purpose* (1958: Cardiff, National Museum of Wales), continues to merit study, despite the progress made since then. But the title of that chapter, with its mention of "Marnians" in Britain, takes us back to the south and south-east, and to the question of further incursions, debated for the IVth and IIIrd centuries, and still unclear—though there were anyhow certainly changes, in which the Continent played some part.

Whenever exactly those changes came, and whatever the agencies bringing them, there are also some surprising imports, not at all "Marnian" exclusively. Figure 7, a fibula from Deal (East Kent), is closely

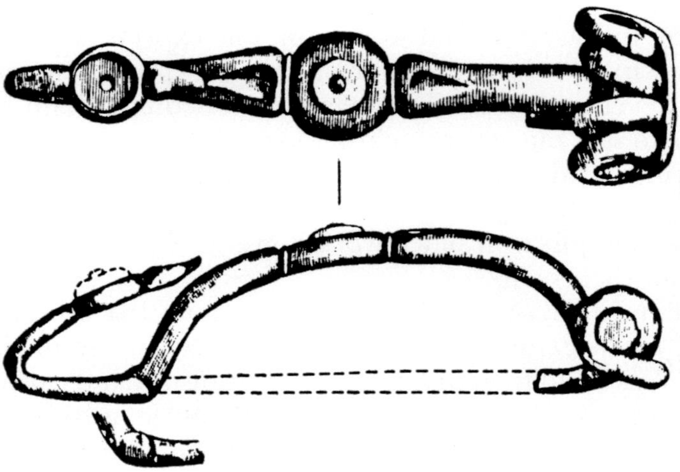

FIG. 7. Bronze fibula, Deal (E. Kent), of a La Tène Ib or c form ($\frac{3}{4}$). Deal Mus: *Antiq. Journ.* 1940, 276, Hawkes.

matched in Switzerland; so is the silver bent-ring (*anneau ployé*) from Park Brow in Sussex[28]. But besides these, the changes brought some novelty in pottery: as in Sussex (where its disputing[29] invites more efforts in excavation), and anyhow in southern Wiltshire, the heart of the chalk country of Wessex. Figure 8, from Swallowcliffe Down there, shows locally-made versions (a–b) of the pedestalled *vase piriforme*, now at last thus making an appearance after its spreading to the Aisne and Marne; it also shows (c) a local iron rendering of an advanced La Tène I fibula, like Fig. 7 but with simple bow and somewhat different foot.[30] Both represent phenomena calling for fresh consideration, now that the general scene and chronology will allow it to be more relaxed than when the notion of British "Marnians" first aroused discussion and argument.

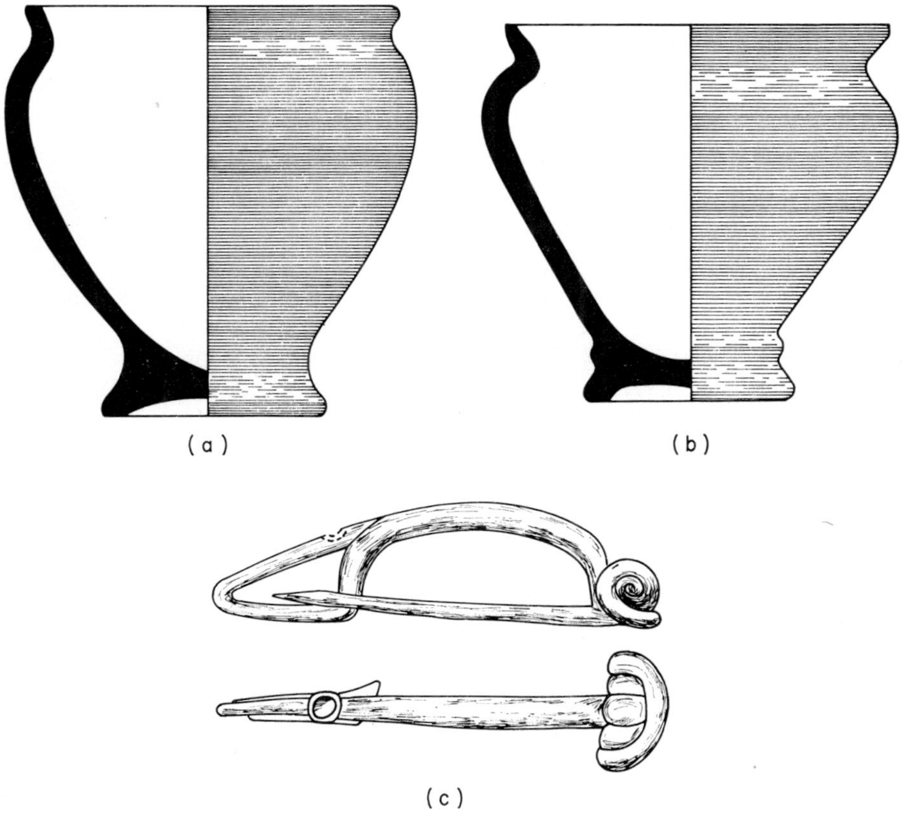

FIG. 8. From the Swallowcliffe Down habitation-site, S. Wiltshire
a–b, Pottery vessels, "piriform", with pedestal ($\frac{1}{5}$). c, Fibula, iron, of a La Tène Ib or c form ($\frac{4}{5}$).
Devizes Mus. (with a third pedestal, taller, from this site): *Catalogue* 1934, pots pl. XLVI, 4, 6, after excavator R. C. C. Clay, *Wilts. Arch. Mag.* 1925; fibula, his pl. XI, C36, p. 82.
All re-drawn for author by T. Ambrose.

Such changes in their further aspects, for example in weapons and in fortification, may here be passed by. Their strength will indeed have varied. Yet as marks of renewal in the older British social fabric, roughly within the century before the La Tène I–II transition, they merit noticing here as having afforded fresh opportunity for a higher artisanship, and a rising British art.

Such opportunity, social naturally, will have come through advances in power, based on varied but growing wealth in the dominant class. The basis in farming the land, with the traditional rural economy, could now support more enterprise, in politics, force, commerce; sustain more initiative, more arrogance. We know it was so on the Continent, as the Celts came more into history. And that brings me to my final point. Power will accumulate wealth as treasure—treasure in precious metal—as its sign and guarantee.

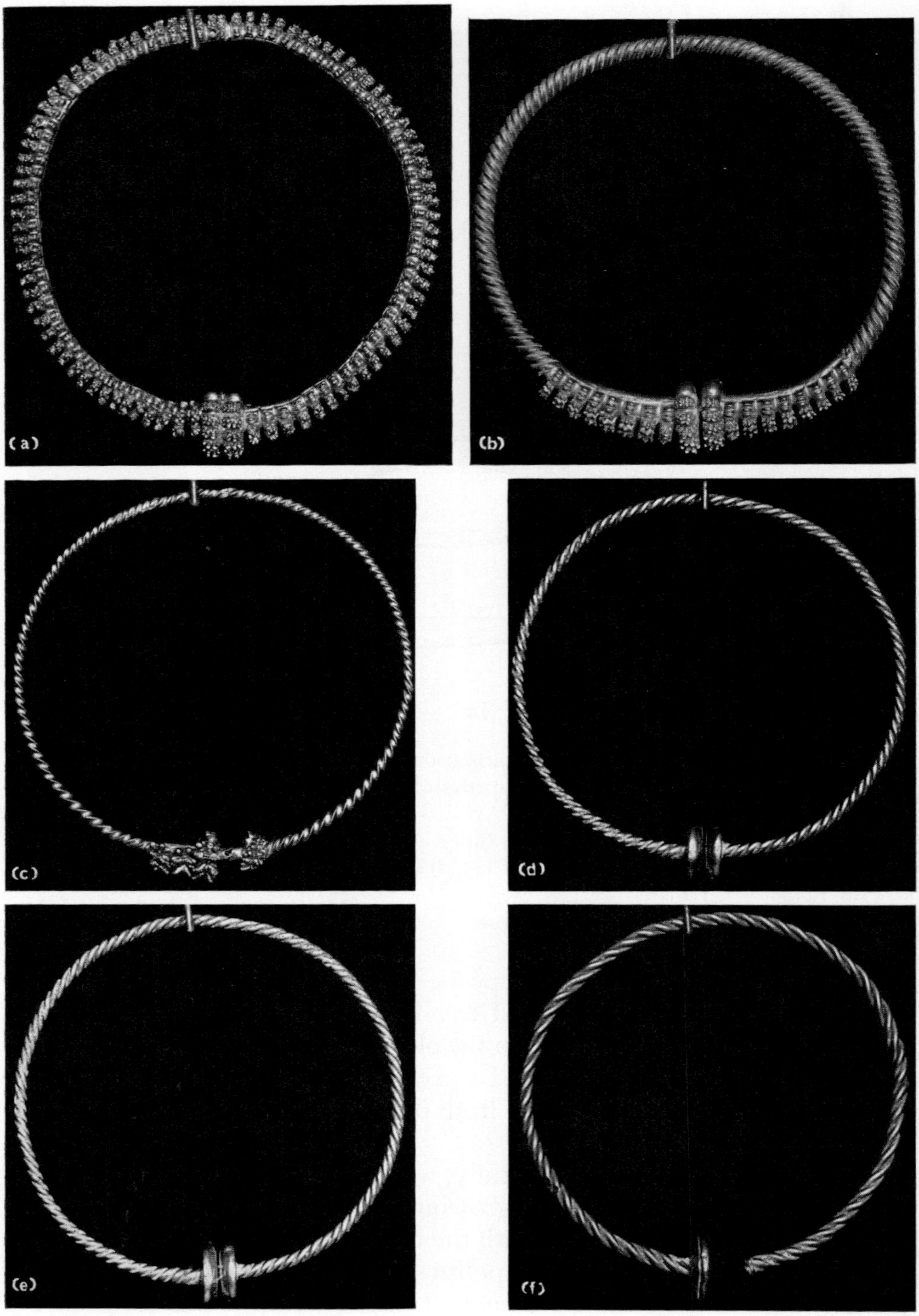

FIG. 9. Set of six gold torcs from Fénouillet (Haute-Garonne), south-west France. Toulouse, Musée Saint-Raymond: approx. $\frac{7}{16}$.
From photographs in the Paul Jacobsthal archive, Oxford; see note 31, p. 21.

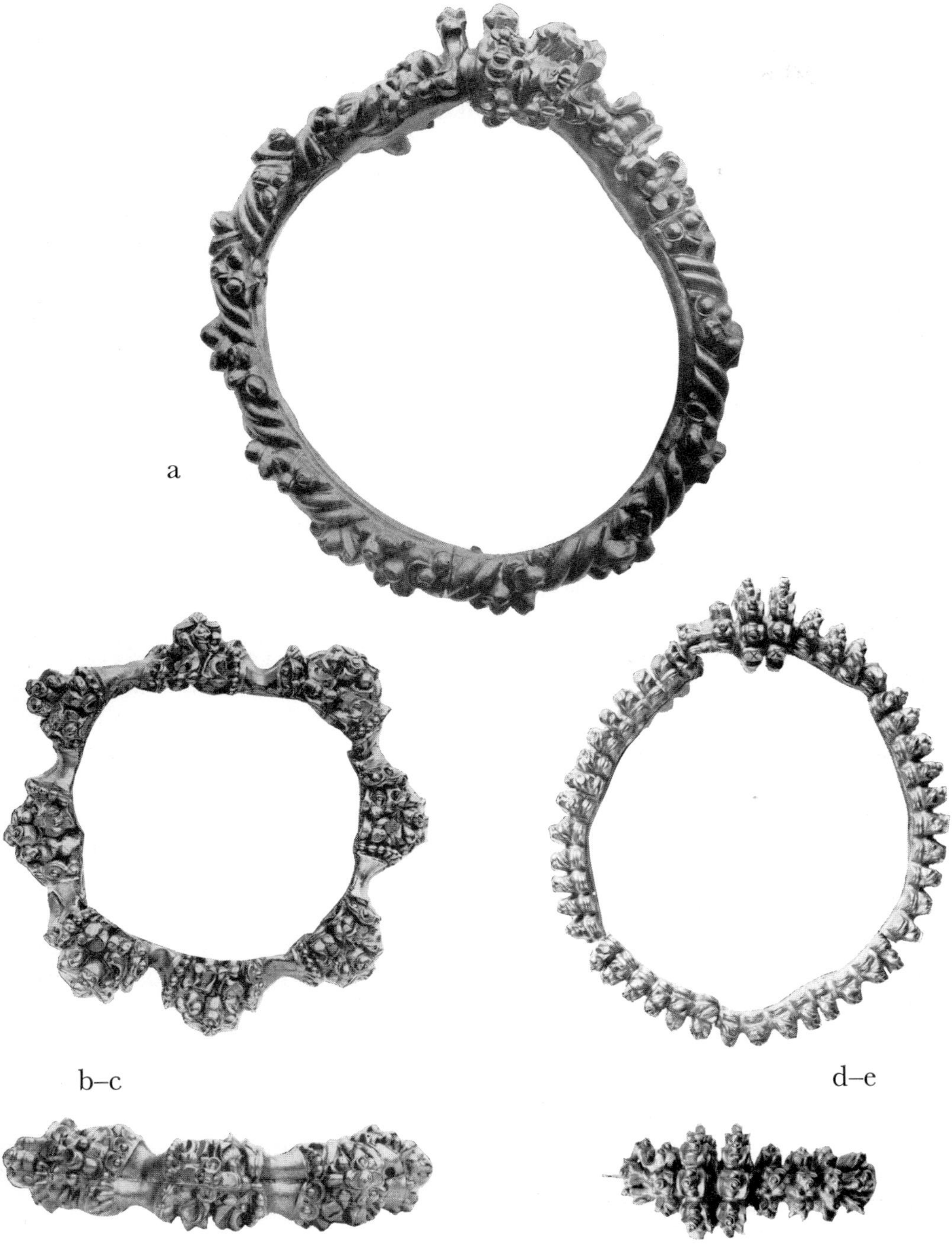

Fig. 10. Gold collar and bracelet from Lasgraisses (Tarn), south-west France; gold bracelet from Herczegmárok, meg. Baranya, south-west Hungary.
Toulouse, Musée Saint-Raymond (*a–c*) and Budapest, Nemzéti Muzeum (*d–e*): all approx. $\frac{2}{3}$; From photographs in the Paul Jacobsthal archive, Oxford; see notes 32–3, p. 21.

Precious metal here means gold. British and Irish finds of La Tène gold-work have been rare. Most have been single finds, of torcs or bracelets. Their dates have tended to be late; thus any to be noticed here by colleagues will have their contexts farther ahead, when the earlier phases have been passed. Of treasures with an ampler content, as most recently the Ipswich torcs (*Proc. Prehist. Soc.* **38** (1972), 219–34), two remain matchless: the treasure of Broighter in Northern Ireland, which its wonderful model boat implies was a votive group from a sanctuary, and the series of "hoards" comprising the eastern-British treasure of Snettisham (Norfolk), from a work-centre for goldsmiths, probably royal, among the Iceni. On the Continent, in proportion to the vaster size of the Celtic lands there, treasures (apart from the coin-hoards) seem still rarer. From Gaul, one recalls the enormous riches of precious metal which Caesar, in the years of the Gallic War, took away as booty. It was thus very right that Jacobsthal, in his *Early Celtic Art* gold catalogue, should have followed his "Plastic Style" so near to its later limits of date, in some of the rare treasures from the soil of France. And I may follow, to illustrate my point, by taking occasion to group together, in photographs from his archive, two of these—with a piece from Hungary.

One (Fig. 9) is the treasure of six fine torcs from Fénouillet (Haute-Garonne), photographed for him in the Musée Saint-Raymond at Toulouse by order of the Comte Henri Bégouen[31]. The other is the astonishing collar and bracelet of gold in the same museum, from Lasgraisses (Tarn): Fig. 10 shows the photographs used by Émile Cartailhac[32]. With them is the Herczegmárok bracelet[33], which the Comte Olivier Costa de Beauregard, in 1907, was the first to compare in detail with them, and with the Fénouillet torcs and the Aurillac (Cantal) bracelet and others, pointing on to international study of what Jacobsthal would call the Plastic Style[34]. Treated by art or not, such treasure—hoarded or dedicated gold, just as in the Bronze Age, but beyond doubt far more copious—was held by kings or sanctuaries of gods, as the "reserves" upholding power, and assuring continuity in a power-controlled society. In the end, they surely supplied the gold, or anyhow very much of it, that went into the minting of Celtic coins. To those we shall also come, for they have an art of their own for study. Thus from first to last, our subject of art, among the protohistoric Celts, may be seen as essentially art in its social setting.

Notes

(*Cross references within notes are indicated by bold italic type*)

1. Fischer, F. (1972), Die Kelten bei Herodot. *Madr. Mitt.* **13,** 109–124.

2. Hawkes, C. F. C. (1972). Europe and England: Fact and Fog. *Helinium* **12,** 105–116.

Idem. (1973). Cumulative Celticity in Pre-Roman Britain. *Etud. Celt.* **13,** 2, 590–611.

3. Cowen, J. D. (1967), *Proc. Prehist. Soc.* **33**, 377–454.

4. Hawkes, C. F. C. (1975), St. Catharine's Hill, Winchester. In *Hillforts of the British Isles* (Harding, D., ed.) Seminar Press, London and New York: on the pottery from that site in the article's Fig. 4 (A1–6).
Ibid. Dixon, P, Crickley Hill, Gloucester, with plans of house structures there (to compare with others).

5. Harding, D., Jesson, M., and Hill, D. (eds) *The Iron Age and its Hillforts.* Southampton University Monographs I, 1971.

6. Favret, P. M. (1925), *Revue arch.* 326 ff. (quotation, 331–332); 1926, 80 ff. *Préhistoire* **5,** 24–119.

For the final Hallstatt settlement at Thiverny (Oise), with pottery features of its own, see Durvin, P. (1961) *Ogam* **13,** 537–556; and *Idem,* (1964) *Celticum* (supplement to *Ogam*) **9,** 29–44.

7. Torbrügge, W. (1972), Vor- und frühgeschichtliche Flussfunde. 51–52. *Bericht der Röm.-Germanischen Kommission* 1970–71 1–146, with Beilagen 1–26.

8. Jope, E. M. (1961), Daggers of the Early Iron Age in Britain, *Proc. Prehist. Soc.* **27,** 307–343; 309–312, nos, 1–3 (329–330): Plates XVII–XIX, dates in Fig. 6.

Mariën, M. E. (1963). In *A Pedro Bosch Gimpera,* 307–312, dagger from Luttre (Hainaut), Belgium.

9. Favret, P. M. op. cit. *note 6.*

Joffroy, R. (1960), *L'Oppidum de Vix et la civilisation hallstattienne finale dans l'Est de la France* 166–173 (daggers, Plate 28);

Jope, E. M. op. cit. ***note 8***. 310–311, 312 ff., nos. 5, 6, 11–14 (331–333): following numbers show further series, suggested dates in Fig. 6.

10. Harding, D. W., following *The Iron Age in the Upper Thames Basin* (Oxford 1972, esp. 86–96), has in *The Iron Age in Lowland Britain* (London 1974) given this phase a wider survey for all these regions (157 ff.).

11. London Museum, photographs through kindness of Miss Jean Macdonald: Jope, E. M. op. cit. 317–318, no. 23 (337) and Plate XXI, D–E. British

Museum, Jope 313–314, no. 18 (335): Figs. 4 and 5 and Plate XXI, C, dates (for both) Fig. 6.

12. Bretz-Mahler, Denise (1970) *La civilisation de La Tène I en Champagne*, XXII, Suppl. à *Gallia*, 143, 282: Plate 125, 2.
Better: Thiérot, A. (1930). *Revue anthropologique* **38,** Fig. 3.

13. Oxford (Ashmolean Museum), drawing by courtesy of Department of Antiquities; Harding, D. W. op. cit. ***note 10*** Plate 79A, text 93–94, date as Jope;
Jope, E. M. op. cit. ***note 8*** (date from serpentine, IVth century), 314–317, no. 14 (332–333): Fig. 7, Plate XXII (chape's divergence, Fig. 5; his date Fig. 6).

14. British Museum; Jope 314 (not 316), no. 19 (335–336): Fig. 5, chape British in form; his date, Fig. 6; drawing Plate XIX after *B. M. Iron Age Guide* (1925) 110, Fig. 120.

15. Cyril Fox, classifying La Tène I fibulas for Britain, (Fox, C. (1927) *Archaeologia Cambrensis* 67–112), on the lines drawn by D. Viollier for Switzerland, adopted his Ia and in part his Ib; all with foot slanted and bow-curve low he called Ic, though such had started within Ib; e.g. the "Münsingen" and "Dux" (= Duchcov) forms. Recognition of this, long called for by Prof. F. R. Hodson, should in Britain be easier now with the elongation of chronology, though the overlap of dating for forms that in origin were regional needs to be watched here as well as on the Continent. See D. W. Harding cited above, ***note 10,*** and cf. warnings by Savory, H. N. (1970), *Antiquaries Journal* 121–2, reviewing Hodson's Münsingen Catalogue.

16. Figure 5, a–c and d, after *Brit. Mus. Guide* Figs. 96–97.

17. Pins, Fig. 3: d (bronze) swan-neck, Wood Eaton; c (iron) ring-head, Chinnor.

18. Worth: Klein, W. G. (1928), *Antiquaries Journal* 76 ff., 81 ff.;
Hawkes, C. F. C. (1940), *Antiquaries Journal* 115–121;
whence Childe, V. G. (1940), *Prehistoric Communities of the British Isles* 224–227, with Fig. 82, introducing the expression "Marnians".

19. Beachy Head: *British Museum Bronze Age Guide* (1920), 46, Plate IV, 51–52, 127;
Evans, E. E. (1930), *Antiquity* 157 ff, Plate I;
Find and primary literature, Curwen, E. C. (ed. of 1954), *The Archaeology of Sussex*, 207–208.

20. Eastbourne: Budgen, W. (1922), *Antiquaries Journal* 354–360;
Hodson, F. R. (1962), *Proc. Prehist. Soc.* 140–145; 142, he was the first to compare Les Jogasses, from the pottery forms having pedestal foot (impossible before VIth century; the painting on no. 1 occurs later as well as earlier). The forms

for comparing (with Favret op. cit. ***note 6***) include, with all these, also his nos. 8–17: not "situlae", but by Bretz-Mahler (op. cit. ***note 12***) called "vases tronconiques . . . flancs arrondis", lasting into initial La Tène from Jogassian; her text, 137–138, 281: Plate 117 nos. 6, 9, 12, 15, 16. Thus Eastbourne, not having any of the Worth La Tène forms, with carinated situla, seems certainly Jogassian (though perhaps not older than Worth by much).

21. Pernant: the entire cemetery, Lobjois, G. (1967), Celticum XVIII (Suppl. à *Ogam* 117–120: *Actes du VIme Colloque, Châlons 1967*), Rennes 1969, with maps of distributions for the Aisne; sites are only on course of the river, from La Tène Ia, no immediate antecedents, graves have no La Tène fibulas; La Tène III oppidum above Pernant is Pommiers (*Noviodunum Suessionum*). Chariot grave previously Joffroy, R. (1963), *Gallia* **21,** 1–9; Bretz-Mahler, cit. ***note 12,*** 264. Its bronzes: Pauli, L. (1971), Die Golasecca-Kultur und Mitteleuropa, *Hamburger Beiträge zur Archäologie* **I,** 1 as follows. Bronze bowl, Etruscan, or from Middle Italy anyhow, map (*Karte*) 2, list 3 (45) no. 5; to view with earlier-started scatter in France and SW Germany (with Switzerland normally richer) of objects from Italy or the Tessin (Golasecca region): maps 1, 3, –12, lists 1–2, 4 ff; bronze strainer (*Sieb=passoire*) not separately listed. Bronze situla, map 6, list 7 (51) no. 15; that from Melsbach (Neuwied), middle Rhine, is no. 12, and both are derived in the text (11–23, with Abb. 1 and nn. 74, 81, 90) from the Tessin—unlike the mass of "Rhine situlas" treated by W. Kimmig: **43–44** *Bericht d. Röm.-Germ. Komm.* (1962–1963), with rim-wire usually of iron, which will have been made by a daughter industry, commenced as "*succursale*", somewhere close to the middle Rhine itself. Ring-wire in Tessin is most commonly of bronze, as Melsbach, or of lead (*plomb*) as Pernant. Both these two situlas have decorated handle-attachments, whence their date from Margarethe Primas (1967), *Jahrbuch d. RGZ-Museums Mainz* **14,** 57: Tessin associations for such are not prior to about 450. Local production of situlas on the Rhine, ensuing on prior imports, can have earlier start (16), but the earliest of any there known (and in Switzerland) fall into a final Hallstatt (D2), not before late VIth century, which runs into the Vth: how far, remains a question (23). For the British reflections, compare D. W. Harding (***note 10***).

22. Bretz-Mahler, D. (op. cit. ***note 12***), 129–135: short neck, type B (plates 111–112) and bowls type b (Plate 114); tall and or flaring, type A (Plate 102–105) and bowls type a (Plate 108).

23. Aulnay-aux Planches (Marne) is the classic site, Brisson, A. and Hatt, J.-J. (1953), *Rev. arch. de l'Est et du Centre-Est* **4,** 193–233, with pottery from its four phases (each also figured separately) assembled in a tableau: 197, Fig. 40, proceeding from Urnfield forms of Hallstatt A and B, through C to D (Late Hallstatt); with Bretz-Mahler's A and a (***note 22***) compare the necks of nos. 1, 2, 6, 11, 12, 17, 22, 30.

Also: Sandars, N. K. (1957), *Bronze Age Cultures in France*, 167–169 Fig. 39; 196–8, Fig. 46; 218–221, Figs 56–57.

Such necks at Haulzy (Marne), Final Hallstatt and transitional.

Goury, G. (1911), *L'enceinte d'Haulzy et sa nécropole*, Les Etapes de l'Humanité I, II, Nancy, Figs 9, 10, 13, 17, 19, and 25; with text on all pottery, 60–70;

carried to conclusions and general essay on transitions, 93–108: has still much value.

24. Cordoned vases (*à bourrelets*): Bretz-Mahler op. cit. (***note 12***), 140–142, 281, 288: Plate 120; grave-groups Plate 177, 2–3 (where 2, like 1, is from the La Tène cemetery at Les Jogasses, not Hallstatt but La Tène Ia); distribution Plate 154; the Aisne department has none.

25. Where see W. Dehn, *Katalog Mus. Kreuznach* (1938), Taf. 17, from graves in the Hochwald-Nahe.

26. Early style of course included advanced compositions, their geometry growing floralized (cf. Schwappach below p. 61); the famous openwork bronzes from the Somme-Bionne chariot-grave (*British Museum Iron Age Guide* Plate IV, Jacobsthal, P. (1944), *Early Celtic Art* nos. 180, 192; cf 181–182, 190–191 from Rhineland) have their indication of date there (with Vth century beak-flagon (Brit. Mus. op. cit. Fig. 35), from its Attic Greek red-figure-cup, of around 420: Bretz-Mahler, D. (op. cit. ***note 12***), Plate 172. Round the neck of its La Tène jar was a *bourrelet* (visible, Brit. Mus. op. cit. Plate III); there was again a cordoned vessel in the La Gorge-Meillet chariot-grave (Somme-Tourbe), with Jacobsthal, P. ibid. nos. 157, 196–197, 199, and the helmet 135. Both are archaeologically La Tène Ia, yet not so early as its commencement in either the Marne or the Aisne (datable 470–450: Bretz-Mahler, 211, 219).

27. We know that there was an overlap in time with the Jogassian: Sangmeister, E. (1969), *Marburger Beiträge zur Archäologie der Kelten* (Dehn Festschrift,) has shown it as an aspect of the whole transition problem, as also on the upper Rhine and in the Haguenau Forest (Alsace). On Les Jogasses he should be read with Bretz-Mahler, D. (op. cit. ***note 12***), 223–225, with her plan on Plate 160 and map Plate 142. Yet the full extent of La Tène Ia in the Marne and down the Aisne (her Plate 162), with its carinated vases and angular bowls, passes west both of the Jogassian and of the Aulnay Urnfield zone. The Aisne has its own chariot graves, on from the time of that at Pernant, but only there has imported bronzes: the rest of these are east of the Marne (Bretz-Mahler Plate 145), with nearly all the other chariot-graves (Plate 144) and further features taking us to full-scale La Tène (Plates 146–150, 152–153, 155–157), including the cordoned *vases à bourrelets* (***note 24***). And of course that north-east quarter of the Champagne is the nearest to the Rhineland.

28. Smith, R. A. (1927), *Archaeologia* **76,** 19–20 with Fig. J;
cf. Viollier, D. (1916), *Les Sépultures du 2me Age du Fer* Plate 28, Figs 19–23: his La Tène Ic;
Hawkes, C. F. C. (1939), *Sussex Arch. Collections* **80,** 230–235, significant because so fragile; Hodson, F. R. (op. cit. ***note 20***), 146–147, merely "isolated trinket". Fibula from Deal, Fig. 7:
Hawkes, C. F. C. (1940), *Antiquaries Journal* **20,** 267 (stud on bow declared coral by H. J. Plenderleith); on the form, see ***note 15***, and Hodson, F. R. (1966), *Atti VI Congresso U.I.S.P.P. Roma 1962, III*, tav. XXVII, La Tène Ib and early c.

29. Hodson, F. R. (op. cit. ***note 20***), 145–155.

30. The Swallowcliffe Down pedestal-footed pots, no. 1–2 handsomely restored, are in Devizes Museum: *Catalogue* (1934), 152–153, nos. 4 and 6, among the ample material excavated by Dr. R. C. C. Clay:
Clay, R. C. C. (1925), *Wilts Arch. Mag.* **43,** 59–93; iron fibula, 82, C 36, whence Fox, C. (op. cit. ***note 15***) 90, Fig. 21; (see again ***note 15*** and Hodson, F. R. op. cit. ***note 28***).

31. Jacobsthal, P. (1944). *Early Celtic Art* nos. 64–67 are four of them; he intended to figure five (op. cit. p. 172) but did not, and the sixth is not so "very badly broken" as he stated. The six thus together show the treasure as a "set". His archive shows that the photographs from Bégouen were procured for Jacobsthal by Gerhard Bersu (letters from each, 6 and 12 May 1935).

32. *Early Celtic Art* nos. 68–69: Cartailhac in *Matériaux pour l'hist. nat. de l'homme* 1886, 182, pls. I–II.

33. Jacobsthal (1944). Ibid. nos. 68–69: Costa de Beauregard *Congrès préhist. de France, Autun 1907*, 824–827. On all, and on the Aurillac, Montans, Tayac, etc. finds of gold, see still Déchelette, *Manuel . . . La Tène* 1339–46 (in ed. of 1927=845–852).

34. *Vide infra*, pp. 182–4. It was that discussion that afterwards moved me to use these treasures to illustrate my point, instead of the British and Irish that I used at the Colloquy: Snettisham (Norfolk) and Broighter (Northern Ireland). For more on these and others, refer to: Jacobsthal, P. and Jope, E. M. (1974), *Early Celtic Art in the British Isles* Clarendon Press, Oxford: *v.s.* Preface p. xii.

Résumé

Celtes et culture : richesse, puissance, pouvoir, art

I

Ce colloque concerne une période de cinq cents ans (VIe–Ier siècles av. J.-C.) en Europe intérieure: la fin de la Protohistoire, suivant la terminologie française, ce qui précise le mot "ancient" contenu dans le titre anglais du volume. Après 600, des auteurs grecs nous font connaître des noms de peuples: Ligures, Ibères, Illyriens, Celtes, qu'on peut confronter avec les cultures révélées par l'archéologie. Après "Hallstatt", qui s'étend tout le long du Danube et du Rhin et passe à l'Atlantique, "La Tène" nous donne, jusqu'à l'époque de l'Empire romain, l'art celtique, sujet du présent livre.

Toutefois, on ne peut dire, d'après les découvertes archéologiques, que la celtisation de la Bretagne, et encore moins de l'Irlande, soit due seulement à l'immigration des Celtes laténiens. D'ailleurs, quels sont les conducteurs de l'expansion d'une culture ? Des chefs de guerre ou des marchands, des "voyageurs de commerce" ? "Les cultures archéologiques ne sont pas, en Protohistoire, les prisons des peuples" s'il ne faut pas enfermer les Celtes insulaires dans la notion de La Tène (pas plus, me semble-t-il, que dans celle de Hallstatt). La transition s'est-elle faite brusquement ? Et qu'est-ce que cela signifie en termes humains ?

II

On ne peut étudier l'art d'une culture sans connaître sa richesse ni—le mot est plus historique qu'archéologique—le pouvoir, la puissance, dont elle émane. La richesse est un facteur de ce pouvoir, la pauvreté, quand elle entraîne la faiblesse, en est un autre. Les Celtes avaient une classe dirigeante, comme la plupart des anciens peuples de l'Europe. Une situation favorable favorise les progrès techniques, perfectionne les parures des chefs et de leurs femmes et embellit les objets de culte—quels que soient les modèles, la valeur émotionnelle est la même.

Comment peut-on distinguer le Hallstatt final, en Bretagne méridionale, de La Tène ancienne ? N'oublions pas que dans cette région il n'y avait pas alors de sépultures avec mobilier: les seuls objets recueillis viennent du dragage des rivières—peut-être même n'y avait-il pas de sépultures dans la terre dans cette Europe du nord-ouest. Les armes ont d'abord des analogues dans les bassins de la Marne et de l'Aisne à la fin du Hallstatt (Jogassien) et au début même de La Tène Ia ; très belles, elles évoquent une aristocracie régnant dans la région londonienne. Il n'y a pas d'épées laténiennes proprement dites et le décor des fourreaux est encore en bandes continues, comme celles du Premier style. Il n'y a encore rien du style végétal ni même des motifs grecs floraux, ni des masques ou des formes animales. Pas de torques, très peu de bracelets comme de fibules du Ve siècle.

Quant à la poterie, on y trouve, à Worth sur le Pas de Calais et en plus sur la Tamise, des formes marniennes comme sur l'Aisne surtout, où le début de La Tène peut être daté maintenant vers 450 (tombe de Pernant). Lorsqu'à l'épaule plus ou moins carénée s'ajoute un col haut ou évasé, c'est par tradition antérieure comme à Aulnay-aux-Planches (Marne). Les profils incurvés piriformes et à bourrelets (anglais *cordoned*), absents de La Tène Ia dans l'Aisne et répartis pour la plupart vers l'est de la Marne, n'arrivent en Bretagne que vers la fin de La Tène I, comme les épées et le style végétal; et pourtant on parle de La Tène I en Bretagne! "La Tène ancienne" a donc ici deux significations: culture celtique dans son ensemble, elle est, d'une part, une culture pleinement originale, sur le Rhin moyen, qui bientôt se répandra en Champagne, d'autre part, une culture moins riche à son début, à traditions jogassienne et même antérieures, et dont la céramique prend le profil anguleux de la situle, mais pas encore le piriforme à bourrelets. Du Premier style elle n'a qu'une simple partie. Peut-être la pleine culture de La Tène, originaire de Rhénanie, n'avait-elle pas encore atteint le Nord de la Gaule quand la seconde atteignit la Bretagne. La richesse, le pouvoir et l'art qui en dépendent ne coïncidaient en fait ni avec les Celtes ni même avec le nom de La Tène.

III

Pour l'arrivée d'éléments laténiens moins restreints dans le Sud de la Bretagne, des sites importants se trouvent dans le Sussex et dans le Wiltshire. Peut-être à partir de 300, ils ont commencé à rayonner, le Sud-Ouest et déjà le Yorkshire ayant des éléments propres à eux. On verra par les communications du colloque que là, comme sur le Continent, le pouvoir a accumulé la richesse sous la forme de métal précieux. Traités ou non par l'art (Figs. 9, 10), ces trésors étaient détenus par les rois ou dans les sanctuaires des dieux comme garantie du pouvoir et de la continuité. Vers la fin, cet or fut en grande partie transformé en monnaie: le colloque traitera aussi de ce sujet. Du début à la fin, l'art des Celtes protohistoriques, notre sujet, sera envisagé dans son cadre social.

Discussion

Speakers:— Professor Duval, Dr Schwappach, Professor Hawkes

Opened by PROFESSOR DUVAL, who picked out, as main points, that of the linkage of art to social power, and that of the concept "La Tène I" as less homogeneous than is supposed, the discussion was taken up by DR SCHWAPPACH. Adverting to the two connotations discerned by Hawkes in "La Tène I", one fuller, as on the Rhine, in fact the Hunsrück-Eifel region, and one less full, as passed to Britain from the Marne or Aisne, he asked whether these implied a succession in time. For the beginning-date in the Hunsrück-Eifel for piriform vases there, in the Hochwald country of the upper Nahe river, is seen now as no earlier than that for carinated vases in the Marne. Hawkes confessed that he had thought it was, as claimed by Wolfgang Dehn; Schwappach explained that further work had made that opinion doubtful, and that the two series of vases could have begun contemporaneously. Their difference in character and form would then be due to the introduction of a new and faster-rotating potter's wheel. The curving-profiled and cordoned piriform vase would be made on this; the carinated not, for if it were, it would lose its shape, since the work on the wheel would round its angles out. He believed that in the Aisne and Marne, the carinated vase was started already, before this wheel and before the end of the Jogassian Final Hallstatt. But though the wheel and the piriform vase would thus be introduced there somewhat later, this would not be any later than their introduction in the Hunsrück-Eifel. Thus there need be no movement into the east of the Marne from there, but merely a distribution of the new potter's wheel. He admitted that the carinated vases long continued, from La Tène Ia through Ib, and even into Ic (V^{th} century, through IVth and into IIIrd); the Sogny vase was perhaps itself wheel-made. But he still judged the wheel sufficient to explain the piriform vases, and likely to have been introduced to the Rhine and Marne together, from a single southern source.

From this, the discussion was turned by PROFESSOR HAWKES to considering Britain. He repeated that in the early phase of connection with northern Gaul, Final Hallstatt to early La Tène Ia, any novel pottery was angular, and designs in art repetitive. Florescent designs appeared in Britain only later, and the *vase piriforme* not before late La Tène I. Until that later time, therefore, the connexion with Gaul was with a La Tène still lacking both advanced designs in its art, and also the piriform vase in its ceramics. Schwappach agreed that this postponement must be genuine: whereas the piriform came to Britain after a longer lapse of time, angular forms will have come when La Tène was beginning, alongside the Jogassian then concluding. But he doubted if their angularity could all be due to their copying situlas. The situla of bronze at Pernant, on the Aisne and apparently isolated, should not suffice to account for all the many carinated vases. The Urnfield culture preceding, from which could come the flaring necks, had already a shape of jar sufficiently angular in its body, to let their carinated body form be derived from this as well; the shape was to be seen at Arcachon, in south-west France by the Pyrenees, and could not there be connected with bronze situlas.

Hawkes replied by insisting that statistics, for any cemetery, depended on the community's choice of what to put in the graves. So where situlas in bronze were rare, their occurring seldom in graves tells us nothing of the prestige that could cause their frequent copying in clay. The short-necked carinated vase resembled situlas of bronze so closely, and any Urnfield flaring neck need affect the body so little, that he held to believing that this vase placed with the dead meant the same as one of bronze, namely a content of funeral liquor. In this, just as in the art, was a prestige that inhered in the culture.

Additional Note

Britain and the Hallstatt - La Tène Transition

The La Tène being Britain's first acknowledged decorative art on metal, since the time when the Bronze Age goldsmiths adopted massive rather than sheet work, acknowledgement in Britain is hard to gain for the Final Hallstatt craftsmanship which the La Tène of the Thames dagger-sheaths subsumed. Archaeology is busy re-valuing our transition to Iron from Bronze; and with aid from radiocarbon it is showing us unexpected aspects. Yet the Continental problems of the years from around 500, in which the changes in the Hallstatt world itself were enhanced by the change to La Tène, have links of importance—two-way links—with the British.

The Hallstatt changes, with the easterly onset of horse and wagon and iron-working, back in the VIIIth century, began also with iron-working, spread from the Alpine region, added to the gains accruing from Italy; yet the Alps were crossed not only in the iron-rich east. North through Switzerland from the Tessin into Germany and also France, branching thus to the north-west, scatters of finds give us signs of commerce. It will thus have brought the cordoned *cista* (or ribbed bronze pail) that we have from Weybridge, of course of Italian type and no doubt VIth-century. But the extension of Hallstatt westward and south-westward, into Spain, added commerce up the Rhône, where it fell to Greeks. Onward from their foundation at Marseilles around 600, it attained a range in which in notable ways it surpassed the trade from Italy. But this had its own resources and took new forms. At Vix, though principally Rhône-connected, it made its mark as well; the Champagne in turn has a Vix-connected culture, the Jogassian, yet Italy's prior access was not extinct when La Tène began there, as the bronzes from the grave at Pernant now have shown. And Britain brings to this moving picture two particular problems.

In what degree was Britain offering products esteemed commercially, and standing amongst the magnets attracting trade from the south north-westwards? And how did it come that immigration here, which till now had been crossing from Belgium (with interior Europe behind), moved to a phase when it came from France? It was this, within the gradual growth of the British Isles' Celticity, that brought here metal-artisans with skills from the Hallstatt–La Tène transition, commanding an initial Celtic art not fully exploiting its southern models. The artisans had masters who themselves had led them as immigrants, though set among kindred people along the Thames: so much seems clear. Yet why come across at all? Was a British commerce part of the reason?

British archaeology's work on sites, with house-forms, radiocarbon, pottery, and so on, is an aid towards answers even if not perceived by some of its workers. For part of the aid is chronology. The Continent, searching the south, seeks limiting dates for objects implying arrivals and influence northwards. Britain, with also neighbours working opposite and inland, seeks patterns of culture, regional and social, but again in need of dating. The patterns have a spatial and a time dimension too. And the excavator's pottery itself affords a contribution. For fifty years at least Britain has vaguely talked of "the situla", meaning distant metal prototypes for its pots with bent shoulder, yet is aware extremely seldom of what the Continent has to show of them. Producing angular pots is a craft, no less than producing pear-shaped; the impulse to either declares the prestige of the prototype (old or novel), just as ornamenting metalwork means admiring the master-patterns.

Respect for such things is social. Yet with societies in such transition, and power through wealth from products and trade so variably balanced, as Celtic Europe was finding them in the VIth and Vth centuries, their leavings in archaeology cannot be simple to interpret. Britain, especially now when its earliest Celtic art was appearing, has its problems to add to the complex, along with the Rhine and the Alps and France. Within the complex, the art was born. Studying it to-day, we need one another. This will be seen again for the IVth century and later. But it calls for notice already here at the outset.

C. HAWKES.

2

Coral in Europe: Commerce and Celtic Ornament

SARA CHAMPION
Oxford

THE RED CORAL, *Corallium rubrum*, used to decorate metalwork in Iron Age Europe, is a species found off the coasts of the Mediterranean Sea. Pliny, in Book XXXII of his "Natural History", explained that the coral most prized by the Celts came from the Îles d'Hyères, the Lipari Islands, Sicily, the Etruscan coast, and Naples, but a hardly inferior material may be found in most areas where the temperature is favourable. A brief discussion of when and by what route this coral began to be imported from the Mediterranean into Transalpine Europe, and in what manner it was used, is the theme of this paper.

It has always been accepted that coral plays an important part in the decoration of Early La Tène personal ornament and fine metalwork. What has been to some extent underestimated is the importance of this material in the decorative arts of the Hallstatt Iron Age, particularly of Hallstatt D. The discussion begins, therefore, in this earlier period, and will show how the techniques of using coral progress without visible breaks from the first to the second part of the Iron Age.

As a background for the history of the use of coral within the Celtic realms, we should perhaps look briefly at the areas using coral at this period outside them. In the 1890s four articles appeared in Italian journals dealing with the use of coral in Iron Age Italy. Pigorini[1] mentioned finds from Emilia, Umbria, Campania, Sicily and Sardinia, and argued for a date well previous to the Celtic invasions of Italy, citing evidence from Veii and Golasecca. Fogolari and Frey[2] strengthened the evidence for an early date for coral in Italy by showing its appearance in graves of the Late Este II period and the transition from Este II to Este III.

Reinach[3] discussed coral in Celtic industry, but also mentioned examples from Bosnia, Central Russia and the Caucasus. He did not treat of these finds in detail, however, concentrating mainly on the French La Tène material. The chronology suggested for most of the Scythian pieces with coral decoration rules out the possibility that the idea of using this substance was transmitted from the East to the West, for the Scythian dates fall mainly in the Vth and IVth centuries B.C., while in Central and Western Europe the use of coral was flourishing already in the sixth.

Coral occurs frequently in the Ticino (Tessin) cemeteries, which were used well into the La Tène period; it would seem, however, that we may

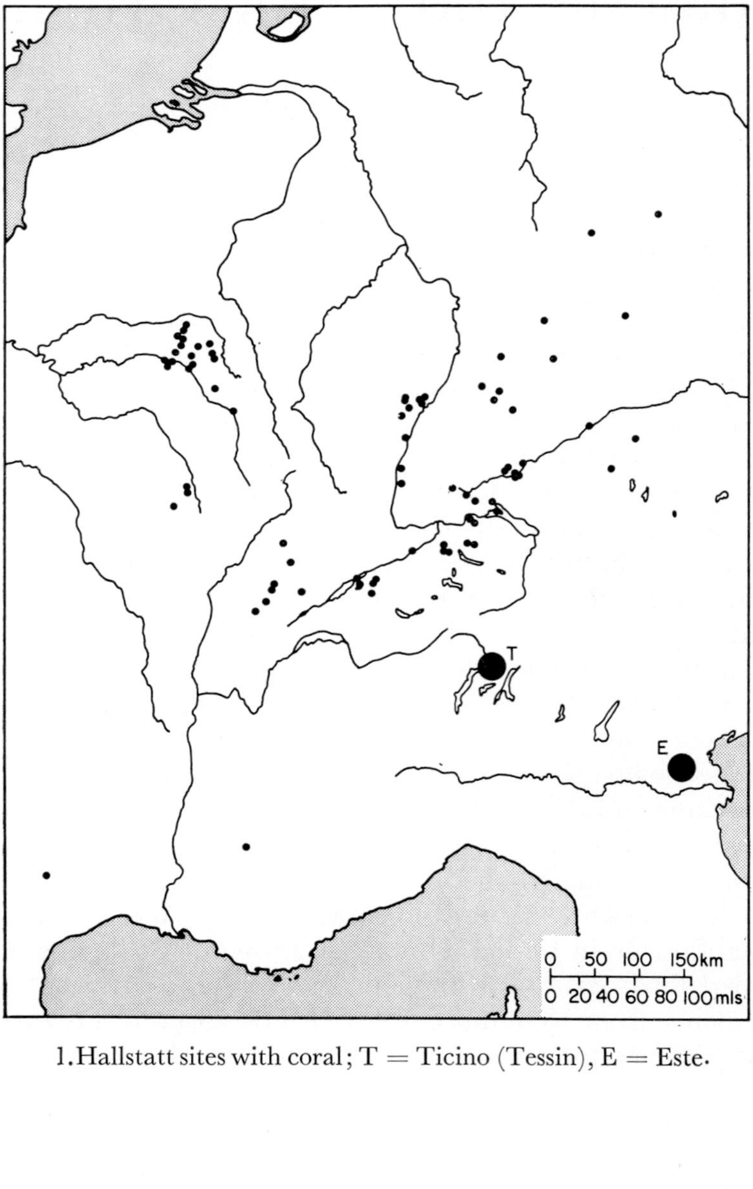

1. Hallstatt sites with coral; T = Ticino (Tessin), E = Este.

place at least some of the Golasecca fibulas with coral incrustation within the middle period of Este III, that is, at the end of the VIth century B.C. We have already seen that in Este itself coral occurs in Late Este II graves, in the second half of the VIIth century B.C., and continues in use throughout the VIth. We might then suggest that the *idea* of using it spread northwards from Italy to the Alps and beyond them during the Late Hallstatt period. Was the coral itself imported into Transalpine Europe by this route?

Figure 1 shows the distribution of sites of the Hallstatt period that have yielded coral. It includes no details of finds South of the Alps, but indicates the Este and Ticino cemetery groups mentioned in this paper. Each dot represents one findspot, and many of these sites have yielded more than one object with coral decoration. It can be seen that Switzerland, and the valleys of the Danube, the Rhine and the Marne have quite heavy distributions, while the South of France and the Rhône valley are almost empty of sites. The two exceptions are first, a find from St. Félix-de-Sorgues, Aveyron, consisting of a North Italian Golasecca fibula with coral incrustation found in a burial; the type is extremely rarely found in this area, and cannot be regarded as being of local manufacture. The second is the bird-head fibula from Ste. Colombe, Hautes-Alpes, which will be discussed later. The lack of findspots in the Rhône valley is in sharp contrast to the distribution of other imports during this period. Figure 2 shows the finds of "Phocaean" grey ware, as published by Kimmig and Gersbach[4]; this pottery is heavily distributed along the South French Mediterranean coast, and relatively thickly inland, up the Rhône valley and its tributaries. The site that is obviously outside the main distribution area is the Heuneburg, whereas this site, in Fig. 1, lies in the centre of the main area of coral finds. Although these contrasting distribution patterns may simply reflect a lack of interest by the inhabitants of the South of France in coral as a decorative material, they might also suggest that coral was imported over the Alps from Italy, perhaps via the Ticino valley and the Bernardino pass, along with other articles of Italian origin. This view is supported by the observation that a number of the finds from North of the Alps that are decorated with coral are North Italian in type, especially fibulas.

I have so far taken note of 190 finds of coral North of the Alps occurring either in Hallstatt contexts or on Hallstatt objects. Included in this number are a few pieces which no longer contain coral, but which, on the analogy of identical objects elsewhere, probably once did. By far the most numerous types decorated with coral are fibulas (140 examples), but it also occurs on pins, earrings, beltchains, rings, bracelets, daggers, plaques, and as beads and pendants. Most Hallstatt fibula types may be decorated with coral: Italian forms include serpentine and arched fibulas, which may have coral in a cup at the end of a long foot, or a small spot protruding from a solid foot end. The more frequent varieties

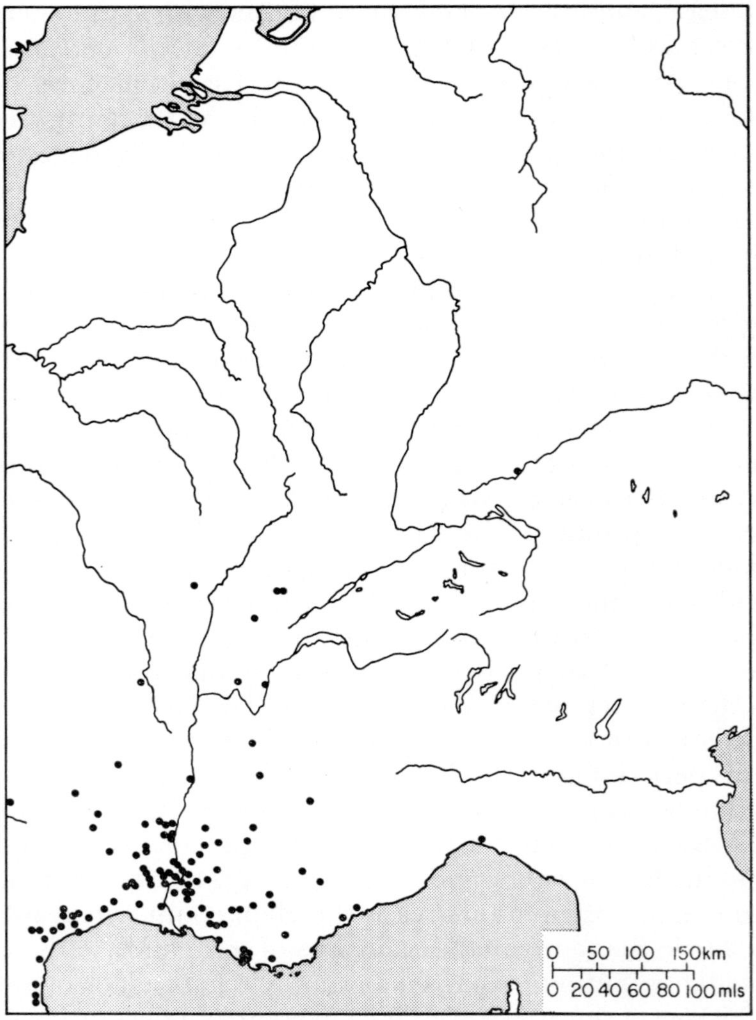

FIG. 2. Sites with "Phocaean" grey ware, after Kimmig and Gersbach.

of Hallstatt fibula North of the Alps, kettledrum, double kettledrum and *Fusszier*, may all be decorated with coral, either set into the top of the drum or placed in a cup on the end of the foot. In most cases the coral has been shaped and smoothed, but there are occurrences of unworked coral, as on the foot of one of the Mont Lassois *Fusszier* fibulas. A particularly interesting variety of Hallstatt fibula which is invariably decorated with coral is the "channelled bow" type. Generally of crossbow construction, this type has transverse grooves cut into the bow which in most cases still retain coral. A variation of the Transalpine type, with a long foot in the Italian style, was found in grave 14 at Pelà, in the Este group, dated to the transition from the VIth to the Vth century B.C. (Fogolari and Frey, op. cit.). The Transalpine type, when found in dateable contexts, is always associated with Hallstatt D material. These fibulas appear in the Cantons of Ticino and Bern in Switzerland, in Bavaria, Baden and the Rhineland in Germany, and in the French départements of Bas-Rhin, Jura, Haute-Marne, Marne, Doubs, and Hautes-Alpes. There are about three dozen examples in this extensive area, and similarities in construction and decoration suggest production from one or two workshops, or by a number of craftsmen working in very close contact. The foot may be in the form of an upstanding cup containing coral, as on the Swiss examples; of a flat plate with cross- or star-shaped cuts, sometimes containing coral, as at Jungnau, Baden[5], the Camp du Château, Jura[6], and Chamouilly, Haute Marne[7], though this latter is slightly different in having longitudinal bow channels as opposed to transverse; and of a bird's head, sometimes with coral eyes, as at Mark-Forst, Bavaria[8], Ste. Colombe, Hautes-Alpes[9], Fay-en-Montagne, Jura[10], and Les Jogasses, Marne[11]. The Camp du Château examples occur in levels containing Attic black-figure ware; and the fibula from Ste. Colombe was stratified with a VIIth century B.C. Attic lekythos, so that a date similar to that of the Pelà grave seems reasonable for this type.

Coral used as beads or pendants is common in France and Germany, particularly in the Marne and Rhine valleys. Beads may be made of a raw branch of coral with longitudinal piercing, or may be worked into a rounder shape; these can occur in great numbers, such as the 109 from Tumulus VI, grave 6 at Königsbruck[12], and were probably strung together as bracelets and necklaces. Raw branches of coral, transversely pierced, were worn as pendants, and in this context should be mentioned the apotropaic qualities ascribed to coral as recently as the XIXth century A.D., and recorded by Pliny and other ancient writers. Pinheads of coral were sometimes made of a rough bead, but there are at least three examples of large globular pinheads made up of interlocking segments of coral pinned together with bronze rivets: these come from Sirnau, Württemberg[13], Nordhouse, Bas-Rhin[14], and Mont Lassois, Côte d'Or[15]. Small pieces of coral were used to decorate bronze wire earrings, beltchains and Hallstatt daggers such as that from Les Jogasses.[16]

It can be seen from this brief summary that coral was plentiful in the Hallstatt period. It occurred generally in rather smaller pieces, however, than in the later period, and it was with the flowering of La Tène art that the fullest use was made of its decorative possibilities.

Among the surviving Early La Tène metalwork fibulas continue to be the types most often decorated with coral. In Hallstatt D, about 74% of the coral finds appear on fibulas; in La Tène, the percentage is slightly higher, 77%, although within specific areas the percentage may vary greatly. In Switzerland, for instance, where the great La Tène I flat cemeteries produce so much coral, nearly 95% of the coral finds are on fibulas, whereas in France only 43% of the total coral appears on fibulas, the greater percentage being distributed among chariot fittings and decorative metalwork of other types. In Germany, the decoration of fibulas is again more frequent, with 69%.

The distribution of coral in this period is more widespread, but is still concentrated in areas where it was already used during the Hallstatt period. Thus Switzerland produces nearly 40% of La Tène coral, France 27% and Germany 18%, with the other areas—Austria, Belgium, Czechoslovakia, East Germany, Great Britain, Hungary, Jugoslavia and the Netherlands claiming only 15% between them. The number of finds in the South of France has increased slightly, although the coral is still occurring on objects less characteristic of this area than of other parts of Iron Age Europe. Thus there is still no strong evidence for a consistent use of coral in these parts.

This is not the time to go into detail on the uses of coral in the La Tène period, and what follows is simply a summary of the types of object on which it may be found. Continuing directly from the Late Hallstatt period are the groups of fibulas decorated with the heads of birds, animals and humans. The example from Schwabsburg (Jacobsthal[17], No. 289—henceforth all references to this work quoted as *ECA* plus the number of the object) is a double bird-headed fibula with coral in all four eyes, on the ends of the two beaks, and in a channel down the bow. It is a typical example of this class of fibula, although many of the other examples have lost their inlay, and it is difficult with fibulas of this type to ascertain whether coral or enamel would have been used. A more elaborate version of this type is the fibula from Val de Travers (*ECA* 293) in Switzerland, where coral still remains in some of the birds' eyes, and was probably the inlay used in the other parts of the fibula. In both these examples the coral is either in the form of a small, round, smoothed bead, or a longer branch worked to fit the channel in the bow. The coral is not always fixed by small bronze rivets on to this type of fibula, but may be set into a cavity in the bronze and fixed by a black resinous material similar to that used for the same purpose in the Hallstatt period.

The form of the Münsingen fibula, with its large disc foot, is especially suitable for the application of coral. The example from Münsingen grave 49 (*ECA* 332) has a series of nine small beads, fixed with bronze rivets, surrounding a larger bead, also riveted, which has engraved decoration. There are also beads of coral on the ends of the spring. The fibula from grave 50 at Münsingen (*ECA* 333) exhibits another typical manner in which coral may be used—a ring is made up of two or more shaped coral branches riveted on to the disc, surrounding a central knob. The fibula from Steinheim (*ECA* 344), one of a pair, shows the extent to which the coral itself may be decorated. Another typical decorative scheme may be seen on the fibula from grave 80 at Münsingen, where, as well as coral on the disc, there is some in a channel down the bow. While the disc coral is normally fastened by means of rivets, that in the bow is secured by resinous material. A popular variation on this latter type is that consisting of coral in the bow and enamel on the disc, a combination of substances that occurs so frequently that it can no longer be accepted that enamel was *developed* as a substitute for coral. The coral fixed into the bow is often decorated with transverse lines, giving a rope-like effect; and sometimes a branch of coral decorated in this way may be placed on a spike protruding from the end of a returned fibula foot.

The fibula from the La Tène I cemetery at Pleurs (*ECA* 342) has often caused concern because of its formal resemblance to a La Tène III type. However, its context suggests an early date, and an identical fibula from a grave at St. Benoît-sur-Seine, Aube[18], was found with an amber ring of Early La Tène type. These two pieces were almost definitely made by one craftsman, and probably represent an attempt to produce fibulas looking as if they were made entirely of coral—this necessitating a variation on the usual form of the bronze component.

The disc fibula from Wargemoulin (*ECA* 348) is one of a group found frequently in France and Switzerland during La Tène I. As well as small beads of coral on spikes around the outside of the fibula, there is a ring of them around the central boss, which is decorated with longer pieces of coral inserted into hollows. Some of the variants of this type may be the prototypes for the English coral-decorated fibulas.

Torcs may also be decorated with coral, although this does not occur frequently. The disc torc from Leimersheim (*ECA* 226) is unusual in that the discs are of coral, whereas the great majority of this type have enamel discs. Other groups of torcs may have coral decoration in slots on the body, or in the eyes of birds attached to the front. Bracelets and other bronze ornaments can be similarly decorated; but what certainly go out of fashion in La Tène I are the large numbers of beads and pendants which were so common in Hallstatt times. There is a find of coral branches from Wérimont, Belgium[19], and a few beads and branches occur in Bohemia, but in general the use of coral on its own i.e. not attached to metalwork of some kind, becomes rare.

There is, however, an increase in its use on highly decorative objects like the Weisskirchen belt-plate (*ECA* 350), where there are lines of straight corals, and pear-shaped pieces filling in the gaps in the pattern. A similar use of coral to accentuate the voids in a design may be seen on the Laumersheim chariot-fitting. Chariot-fittings of many types from the Marne burials are decorated with coral, such as the pair of "hames" from La Bouvandeau (*ECA* 171). The most richly decorated pieces from this period are the flagons from Basse-Yutz (*ECA* 381), where again the pattern is picked out with large pieces of coral; these vessels are especially interesting because of the combination of coral and enamel.

There are a few La Tène II fibulas, apparently decorated with coral, from Northern and Eastern Germany, where previously there has been no tradition of coral-using; there is also a small homogeneous group of fibulas of Augustan date, allegedly with coral decoration, from Eastern Germany. Apart from these two small, anomalous groups which appear, culturally and chronologically, to have little to do with the main European series, there are no finds of coral North of the Alps in contexts datable later than the La Tène Ic–La Tène II transition period. South of the Alps coral may continue in use in the Ticino cemeteries. An explanation for the absence of coral later may lie in Pliny's statement that red Mediterranean coral was being exported to the Indians by his time. If coral was redirected to India, and was no longer available to the Celts, its absence on later objects would be explained.

Notes

1. Pigorini, L. (1896), "Uso del corallo nelle età preromane", *Bull. Palet. It.* Ser. 3, Vol. **II**, 305–306; *idem* (1897), "Uso del corallo nelle età preromane", *Bull. Palet. It.* Ser. 3, Vol. **III**, 18–19.

2. Fogolari, G. and Frey, O-H. (1965), "Considerazioni tipologiche e cronologiche sul II e il III periodo atestino", *Studi Etruschi* **XXXIII** (Ser. II), 237–293.

3. Reinach, S. (1899), "Le corail dans l'industrie celtique", *Rev. Celt.* **20**, 20.

4. Kimmig, W. and Gersbach, E. (1971), "Die Grabungen auf der Heuneburg 1966–1969", *Germania* **49**, 21–91.

5. Zürn, H. (1970), *Hallstattforschungen in Nordwürttemberg*, 108 and Taf. P, B5.

6. Piroutet, M. (1928), "Essai de classification du hallstattien franc-comtois", *Rev. Arch.* **27**, 220–281; Fig. 24.

7. Déchelette, J. (1913), *La Collection Millon*, 73 and Fig. 8.

8. Uenze, H-P. (1964), "Zur Fruhlatènezeit in der Oberpfalz", *Bay. Vorgeschichtsbl.* **29**, 77; 82 and Abb. 1, 1.

9. Courtois, J-C. (1968), "La stratigraphie de Sainte-Colombe (Hautes-Alpes)", *B.S.P.F.* **LXV**, 154–159.

10. Lerat, L. (1966), "Informations archéologiques, Circonscription de Franche-Comté", *Gallia* **XXIV**, 362; Fig. 25.

11. Favret, P. (1927), "La nécropole hallstattienne des Jogasses à Chouilly (Marne) (suite)", *Rev. Arch.* **XXVI**, 80–146; 123, Fig. 15, 106.

12. Schaeffer, C. (1930), *Les Tertres Funéraires Préhistoriques dans la Forêt de Hagenau*, II, L'Age du Fer; 28.

13. Paret, O. (1936), "Das Hallstattgrab von Sirnau bei Esslingen, Württemberg", *Germania* **20**, 246–252; Taf. 5C.

14. Forrer, R. (1912), "Die Grabhügel bei Nordhausen", *Anz. für Elsass. Altertumskunde* **IV**, 288–299; Taf. XLI, 12.

15. Joffroy, R. (1960), *L'Oppidum de Vix et la civilisation hallstattienne finale dans l'Est de la France*.

16. Favret, P., *op. cit.* ***note 11***, Fig. 5, 22.

17. Jacobsthal, P. (1944), *Early Celtic Art*, Oxford.

18. Joffroy, R. (1967), *in* Frézouls, E. (ed.), "Informations Archéologiques, Circonscription de Champagne-Ardennes", *Gallia* **XXV**, 277.

19. Mariën, M. (1961), *La période de La Tène en Belgique—Le groupe de La Haine*, Brussels; 195.

Résumé

Le corail de la Méditerranée tient une place bien connue dans le Premier art celtique, alors qu'on distingue moins bien son importance à la fin du Hallstatt. Pline atteste le goût des Celtes pour le corail. Les techniques de son emploi ont progressé à la première époque de La Tène. Il était largement en usage en Italie avant même les invasions celtiques du début du IVe siècle: il existe dans les sépultures d'Este II et III. En Gaule, l'emploi du corail a des antécédents occidentaux antérieurs à ceux que Reinach lui trouvait chez les Scythes: à Este, à Ticino, à Golasecca, du VIIe à la fin du VIe. Le corail décoratif a-t-il été transmis aux Celtes de la fin du Hallstatt, d'Italie à travers les Alpes?

Sur la Fig. 1, les points désignent des sites hallstattiens ayant livré un ou plusieurs objets ornés de corail. La plus grande densité est en Suisse, sur le Danube supérieur, le Rhin et la Marne. La France méridionale a seulement deux trouvailles, dans l'Aveyron et les Hautes-Alpes (à Sainte-Colombe, avec un lécythe attique du VIIe siécle). La Heuneburg est dans une région de grande densité, ce qui confirmerait la provenance italienne. 190 pièces relèvent de trouvailles hallstattiennes cont 140 fibules et 50 autres objets (pendentifs, perles). Le corail y est habituellement en forme et poli, notamment sur les fibules à arc cannelé.

A l'époque de La Tène, les morceaux de corail sont plus gros et leur emploi, plus décoratif, concerne à 77% les fibules (74% à la fin du Hallstatt). La distribution géographique est plus large. Il apparaît aussi avec l'émail, très fréquemment: on ne peut plus accepter l'idée que l'émail a remplacé le corail, en guise de succédané. Les objets et les techniques sont plus variés: fibules à disque, torques, bracelets et autres parures de bronze, vases métalliques (Basse-Yutz, avec corail et émail), agrafes de ceinturon (Weisskirchen), pièces de char. Par contre, les pendentifs et les perles deviennent rares, comme les branches de corail brut.

Après La Tène I, on ne trouve plus de corail, sauf sur quelques fibules de La Tène II, au nord des Alpes, tandis qu'il existe encore dans le Tessin. Pline atteste l'exportation de corail méditerranéen jusqu'en Inde: est-ce la raison de sa disparition dans la décoration des objets celtiques?

Discussion

Speakers:— Dr Kruta, Mrs Champion, Professors Frey, Piggott, Hawkes, Dr Schwappach.

Amber and coral

Dr Kruta recalled that amber was used for decoration already in late Hallstatt times, sometimes together with coral, sometimes instead of it. The Maňetin fibula from Bohemia, moreover, showed amber used apparently in just the same manner as was coral in the Hallstatt fibulas from Marx-Forst: in discoidal settings and in transverse grooves across the bow. Bohemia has also a fibula set with coral in this manner, found near Slaný, and not yet published.

Mrs Champion replied that though unable to treat of them in the short time available, she was well aware of these uses of amber, and particularly of the numerous fibulas and other objects showing amber as well as coral.

Enamel and coral

Dr Kruta next raised the question of the relation between coral and enamel. It had always been tempting to believe the old idea that enamel replaced coral, when the sources of this were no longer so widely accessible. But enamel makes its earliest and most abundant appearance in Switzerland, on the fibulas and on torcs like those of Nebringen, Andelfingen, etc.; Switzerland is a region which ought to have been well supplied with coral. Why then did it make so much use of enamel? On the other hand Bohemia, and the parts of Central Europe from Bavaria eastwards, made no use of enamel at all but did use coral—which from Italy should have been traded to them through Switzerland. Furthermore, the La Tène "baroque" employment of coral, as in rosettes (for example, on the large discs of the reverted foot of "Münsingen" fibulas), did not come into vogue till after enamel had made an appearance.

On the other hand, the pair of iron cones studded with coral, from the Marne (museum, Saint-Germain), which Mrs Champion had taken as fibulas, have a parallel in a similar pair from a grave-group in Bohemia, where a further such cone was published by J. L. Pič, found at Leitký. Examining these has shown them not to be fibulas at all, but cones to apply to the surface of wooden shields. This use for coral could thus be primarily Central-European; it should anyhow be considered apart from fibulas.

Mrs Champion replied, first as regards the commencement of enamel work, that she was sure it had not been solely to give a substitute for coral, in the sense of a replacement, because the two run side by side. Fibulas might show enamel, she thought, already in Hallstatt times, and the use and methods of mounting of the two materials continued, sometimes both on the same object, through the La Tène times ensuing—though with partly different distributions. She was pleased to learn of the iron cones with coral as meant for shields. When coral went out of use, with the transition from La Tène Ic to II, enamel seemed to decline quite sharply, and then take different forms. Its late uses in Gaul were surpassed on the British side of the Channel, but this was a matter beyond her present scope. Professor Frey confirmed that coral, so late, seemed never to re-appear.

Colour of coral

Professor Piggott, recalling that the colour of the coral was most often now white, and supposed to be bleached from red through age, enquired if use had ever been made of genuinely white coral. This did exist in nature; and if used on bronze with enamel that was red, would make a polychrome decoration. Mrs Champion's reply was to lament the timidity of most authorities of museums, which impeded recourse to laboratory testing. A proof of genuinely white coral would enlarge the geography of possible sources: she believed, for example, it occurred on the coast of Scotland. But the fact remained that on any Celtic object where the coral had a surface not totally white, the perceptible or extant colour was pink or red. Reminiscence was offered by Hawkes of seeing white-coloured coral, on a famous Celtic object, restored to pink by being moistened; he agreed however that any such interferences with coral were anathema to nearly all curators.

Chronology and distributions

Professor Frey stressed the importance of the evidence from Este: whereas coral was used for a long time in Italy more generally, at Este it became frequent just when it did so north of the Alps. The new Ticino cemetery, carefully excavated and published, was a further aid to chronology, especially of the characteristic fibulas with mask. He added that although this route, Este-Ticino-Central Europe, was the chief and prior means for distributing coral beyond the Alps, there were connections, shown by fibulas already within the Vth century, between Central Europe and Southern France. This could account for beginnings of the use of coral appearing there, not just from rare imports now, but genuinely Southern French. Only a start, but within the same century as it had started also in Champagne. Dr Schwappach, speaking last, repeated the priority of Northern Italy; his own work on fibulas there, and the Este-Ticino-Late Hallstatt links, reinforced his conviction of its importance, just as now had Mrs Champion's, with her special place for coral in its history. Yet the North-Italian connexion afforded links with France besides; and these, quite surpassing the route by the Rhone, had a broader range. In a survey of the centuries to the Vth (La Tène A) from the VIIIth (Hallstatt B), lately published—*Hamburger Beiträge zur Archäologie* I, 1, 1971—this range has been displayed by Ludwig Pauli. Transalpine influence on central-eastern France (Mont-Lassois region) and also on the Champagne (to Marne and Aisne) had importance farther. In the north-west, for Armorica: Late Hallstatt finds in Brittany had come that way, over inland France from Switzerland, with Golasecca and Este as sources. Bronze situlas, such as he discussed with Hawkes, had examples included too. And the route is important also for the British Isles.

3

Orient and Orientalizing: Recent Thoughts reviewed

N. K. SANDARS
Oxford

TERENCE POWELL wrote not long ago, in an article full of insight and alive with fresh ideas, that "from the viewpoint of those conditioned geographically to look back at European prehistory from the north-western periphery, the occurrence, at almost any chronological horizon, of 'eastern' manifestations, tends to carry implications of suddenness and of disturbances among the peoples".[1] I take this comment as my text for a few remarks on the eastern manifestations that have been observed in early La Tène art. I shall not repeat the arguments which I have put forward elsewhere, concerning the historical background to any direct Celtic involvement with oriental people and arts at this time, that is to say in the Vth and IVth centuries B.C.[2]

The existence of an orientalizing aspect of La Tène art, that was neither specifically Scythian nor Greek nor Etruscan, was accepted by Jacobsthal as real, and at the same time as raising great difficulties. His failure to find a satisfactory explanation for its existence arose from the lack of imported objects in either direction, to give it a solid basis; and the distances to be covered. It had too much of those uncomfortable appearances of "suddenness" which we so often, and unnecessarily, account for as "disturbances among the peoples." I have tried to show that a good historical basis *is* provided by the Persian presence in Thrace, between Darius's Scythian raid of about 513 and the retreat of Xerxes' army in 479. There was a full generation of contact, which continued, in a diminished form, until almost the middle of the Vth century, during which time there were friendly exchanges between the Persian garrisons of towns like Eïon on the Struma and Doriskos further east, and the native Thracian population; with opportunities for traffic in precious objects, as well as, and before, the dispersal of the great loot of the defeated Persian army. I want now to make two points; first that these good relations between the Persians and Thracian natives, so different to Persian relations with the Greeks, were historically appropriate and a thing to be expected; and that there is reason to think that they may have reached further north than at first appears likely. Secondly I want to look at the reason for the very different character of the orientalizing aspects of Thracian and Dacian art in the Balkans and Rumania, from that of orientalizing La Tène art.

The fact that "eastern" meant principally Scythian in Jacobsthal's great exposition, along with a supposed Scythian presence in Hungary, was what caused the greatest difficulty; for there was the apparent paradox that most of the "eastern" traits were not found on objects from the eastern extremities of the early La Tène world, but rather in the princely burials of the rich centres in the Rhineland, Austria and west of the Vltava in Bohemia. But this is explained by that commonplace of economic history: that wealth and art follow the market, even into the wildernesses of Mongolia and remote valleys in the Urals or the Elburz.

We now tend to play down the Scythian presence in eastern-central Europe and the Balkans. Some "scythian", in the sense of steppe or "northern nomad" objects are scattered over the whole region, but in early La Tène art an overtly "Scythian" element is confined to few objects, and those not the earliest. For example the Basse-Yutz flagons and Parsberg fibula, which are so closely allied, have it; but the Dürrnberg flagons and Panenský Týnec fibula do not.

Those who now question Jacobsthal's eastern or "Iranizing" component, while accepting the "southern" (Greek and Etruscan) and the "native", credit the Etruscans with an almost exclusive rôle as intermediaries between Celtic workshops and those of western Asia[3]. Without diminishing the Etruscan contribution to the formation of early Celtic art, I think that there *is* room for more direct oriental participation. It is well to remember that Etruscan art is itself derivative and provincial, and that, though it may have acquired some of its oriental manifestations direct from Anatolia and the Levant, it was deeply indebted to orientalizing Greeks, so that whatever the Etruscans had to pass on to their neighbours over the Alps was already at a double remove from its sources; not second but third-hand *orientalia*. A more difficult problem is to distinguish the oriental elements reaching the Celts more directly from east Greek workshops. I think that the real problem lies in this direction.

There are certain hints that can be followed, though with caution. One is the taste for drinking horns, admittedly Iranian and never adopted by the Greeks except when working directly for a barbarian clientèle; and the animal handles of flagons are another. Jacobsthal singled out as "Persian" or "Iranizing" the Glauberg torc, the Rodenbach gold bracelet and the Weisskirchen belt clasp. To these can be added, for a start, the Klein Aspergle horns, the Panenský Týnec fibula, the Stupava plaque, perhaps the Dürkheim openwork "net", and the four Erstfeld gold torcs. But this is not the place to deploy arguments and stylistic comparisons; moreover we must remember that, as well as identifying his three sources for Celtic art, Jacobsthal insisted further upon its *unity*.[4] It is generally unprofitable to tear to pieces individual objects and say this or that motif or treatment comes from here or there because, with few exceptions, they have been so assimilated and fused that the final product retains little of its origins.

To return to the first of the two points that I want to discuss here: Herodotus was the author of the great myth of Europe against Asia. Born into a world intellectually and emotionally still dominated by the Greco-Persian wars of the early Vth century, it was inevitable that he should construct his historical geography around the conflict of Asia and Europe, as of Barbarians and Greeks. This polarity he projected back to the time of the Trojan War, but Homer knew nothing of it. The idea that began in a local and brief conflict soon ossified and became so much a part of ordinary thinking that today, when we draw our archaeological maps and write our archaeological histories, they halt too often at the Bosphorus, separating not only the Balkans, but also the Aegean, from Anatolia and the Levant. At different times this attitude has misled to a greater or less degree. The turn of the second and first millennium B.C. is one of those periods when it has done much damage.

Recent "dark age" studies have shown how very different was the history of Macedonia from that of the rest of Greece at this time. Dr Anthony Snodgrass in his *Dark Age of Greece* has a very interesting review of the arrival and distribution of iron technology. He draws a real frontier through Thessaly, rather than on the Bosphorus or Hellespont. South of this line Greece and the islands received their iron technology from Cyprus in the late XIIth and XIth centuries, just before the severing of the sea-lanes. Thereafter isolated, they became self-supporting. At the same time Macedonia and Thrace were indebted to Anatolia for *their* precocious iron, which is XIIth century at Vardaróftsa and Xth, or more certainly, IXth century at Vergina near the Haliakmon[5]. At this time the rest of Greece, apart from Crete and Ionia, has nothing to compare with the material prosperity of Vergina which was also open to the northerners.

A map of iron in the IXth century is instructive (Fig. 1). The points in Europe north of the Alps are taken from Professor Kimmig's list of 1964,[6] so there may by now be a few more. Italy is not covered. These scattered objects do not imply a real dependence on iron, anymore than do occasional third and early second millennium iron objects, or references in texts, in western Asia. Their immediate source was probably, like Mycenaean iron, Cyprus; but in this case, by way of Italy. The real change to an iron-dependent economy comes afterwards in the later VIIIth (Hallstatt B 3) and VIIth centuries. The argument usually runs that it was introduced from the Caucasus round the north of the Black Sea. But this takes no account of iron in Macedonia, nor iron smelting in the middle levels of Babadag in the Dobrogea which, in the terminology of Dr Morintz, is B 1 or Xth century[7]. Moreover at this time iron was still very scarce in the Caucasus; but there is no need to go to the Caucasus with the iron of upland Anatolia, which had already been worked during something like a millennium, so much nearer.

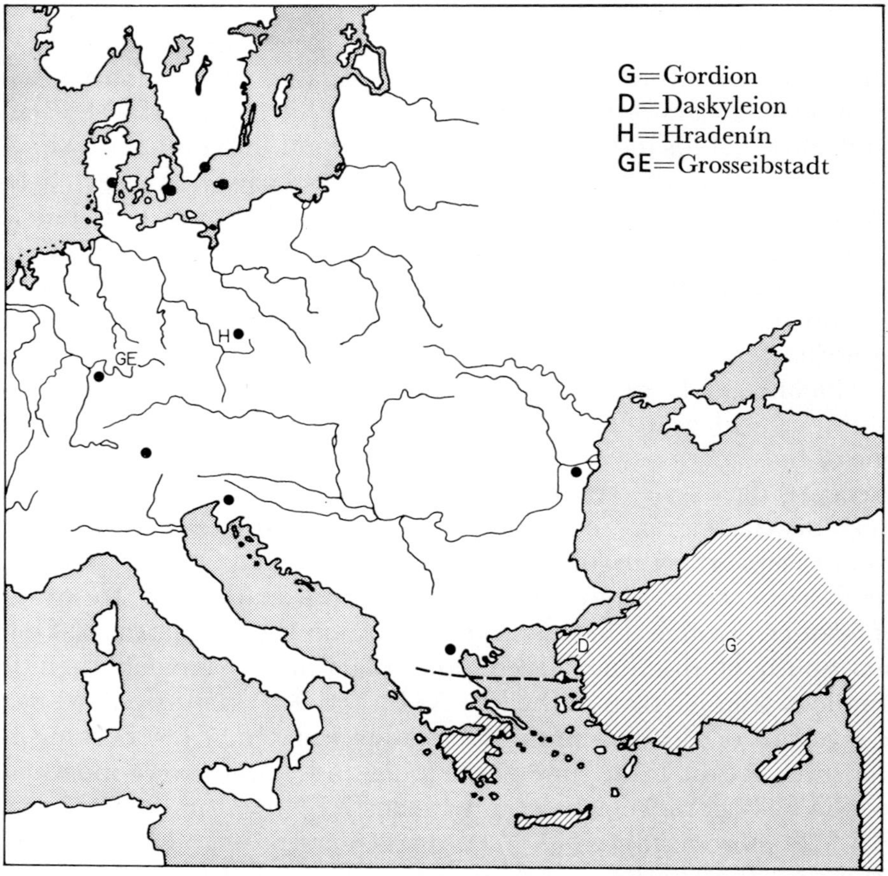

FIG. 1. European iron before 800 B.C. (except Italy): black dots ●; Aegean and Anatolia: shaded; also some later sites mentioned in the text.

It is not only iron that points to Anatolia, there are those strangely conflicting Greek legends about the origin of the Phrygians: that they came from Thrace to Anatolia; but also that they came *from* Anatolia *to* Thrace; while Midas and his 60-petalled roses are at home in both[8].

Turning from legend to history, in Anatolia we have Phrygians as the western name for a body of warlike people called, in the Assyrian texts, Muski and Tabal. Muski are mentioned first about 1160, but late Hittite texts refer to a Mita of Pakhuwa who is usually identified as a Midas. Pakhuwa is probably Divrigi on the upper Euphrates, at the centre of an iron producing area[9]. There is no question of *these* people having come from Europe. They appear first in *eastern* Anatolia. They may have been related to the Gasga, who were old enemies of the Hittites, living in northern Anatolia in what was later reputedly the country of the iron-working Chalybes, and certainly an area very rich in iron. Not enough is yet known about the Gasga, but it is clear that the Muski, the Tabal and the Phrygians were, even more than the Urartians, the heirs of the Hittites. Moschians (Muski) and Tibarani (Tabal) were still together in Xerxes' army.

Given the partial identity and practical connections between Tabal, the most eastern, Muski or Moschi, and Phrygians, the most western, this alliance can be stretched a little further to explain the conflicting Greek traditions concerning Bryges or Phrygians. The problem only exists if the Bosphorus is taken as a serious barrier; it vanishes if Thracians and Phrygians are related, like Tabal and Muski, mingling and moving back and forth between Europe and Asia. There is no difficulty then about a Midas at Edessa, nor about iron-working in XIIth century Macedonia, and again in the Xth and IXth centuries, so close as it is to old Hittite and Gasga lands. In the Persepolis inscriptions of Darius I there are Thracians on both sides of the Bosphorus. Phrygian pottery may have eastern links, but owes more to the Hittites, and like the Hittites the Phrygians became masters of metallurgy; the bronze bowls and cauldrons of Phrygian Gordion are proof of it, and much of this work was exported to Greece in the VIIIth and VIIth centuries, and some also to the Balkans. It is worth noting that according to John Boardman the Xth century painted pottery from Vardaróftsa and Boubóusti was closer to Phrygian styles than to Greek Geometric[10]. There are also marked similarities between the painted and animal decorated pottery of Gordion, and the painted and animal decorated Hallstatt C pots of Gemeinlebarn in Lower Austria and Nové Košariská in Slovakia[11]. Perhaps more to the point is the work of Central European archaeologists, noted by Powell, especially M. Párducz in Hungary and M. Dušek at Chotín in Slovakia[12]. They argue that in the mid-VIth century, from the Rhodope mountains to the eastern Alps, there was a broadly-based unity of population which they call Thracian. Throughout this whole region wheel-thrown pottery was already in use, and it is suggested that the Celts, far from introducing this skill to their eastern neighbours, had learnt it *from* the Thracians who had acquired it from the Black Sea Greeks (Fig. 2).

If iron technology came to Macedonia, Thrace and even the Dobrogea, from Anatolia, and we are only talking about a technology not

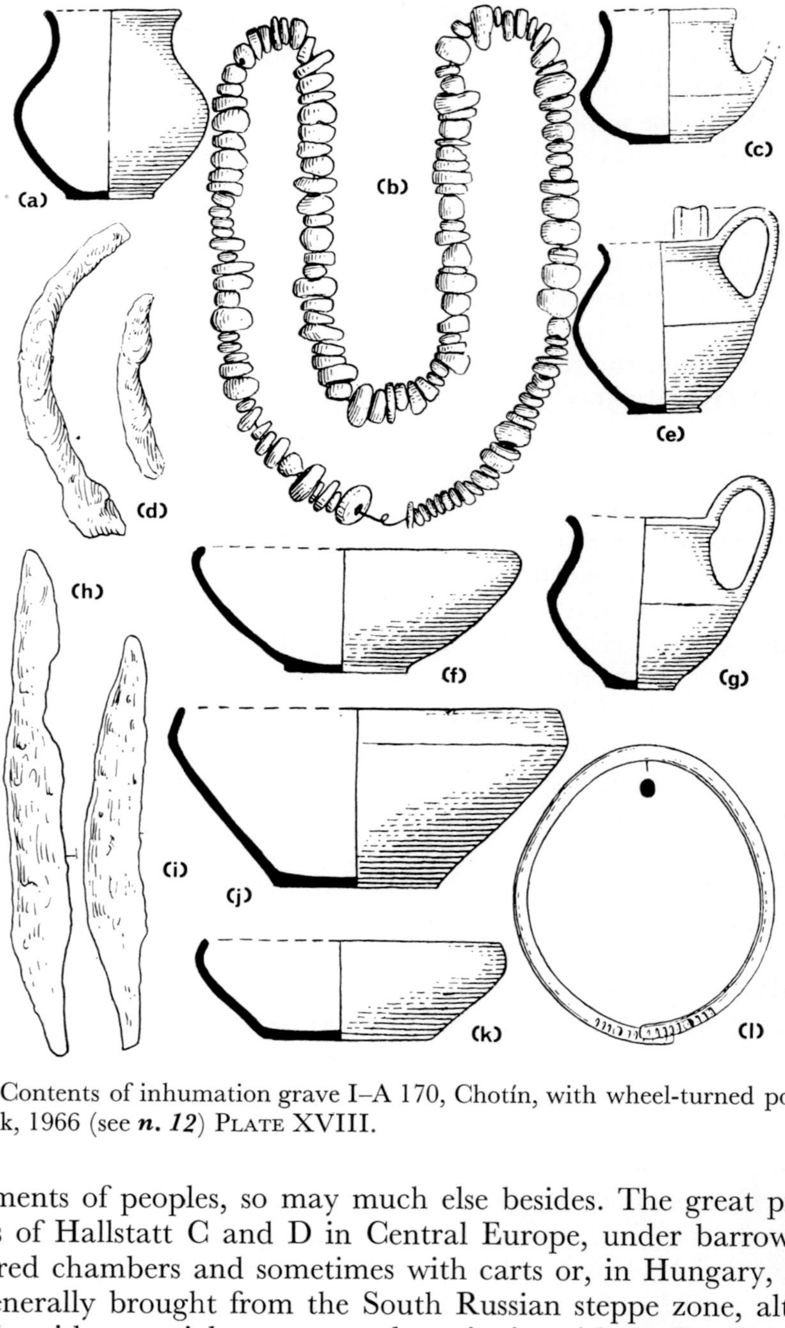

FIG. 2. Contents of inhumation grave I–A 170, Chotín, with wheel-turned pots, after Dušek, 1966 (see ***n. 12***) PLATE XVIII.

movements of peoples, so may much else besides. The great princely graves of Hallstatt C and D in Central Europe, under barrows with timbered chambers and sometimes with carts or, in Hungary, horses, are generally brought from the South Russian steppe zone, although there is neither spacial nor temporal continuity with the Russian timber graves. But VIIIth to VIIth century tombs of Phrygian kings at Gordion are also timber graves of especial magnificence, and in one tumulus two horses with their ornamental bronzes were buried in the grave-pit next to the timbered chamber (Fig. 3)[13].

Carts in Hallstatt graves have recently been subjected to a brilliant analysis by Prof. Kossack[14]. He has shown that the Hallstatt C hearses

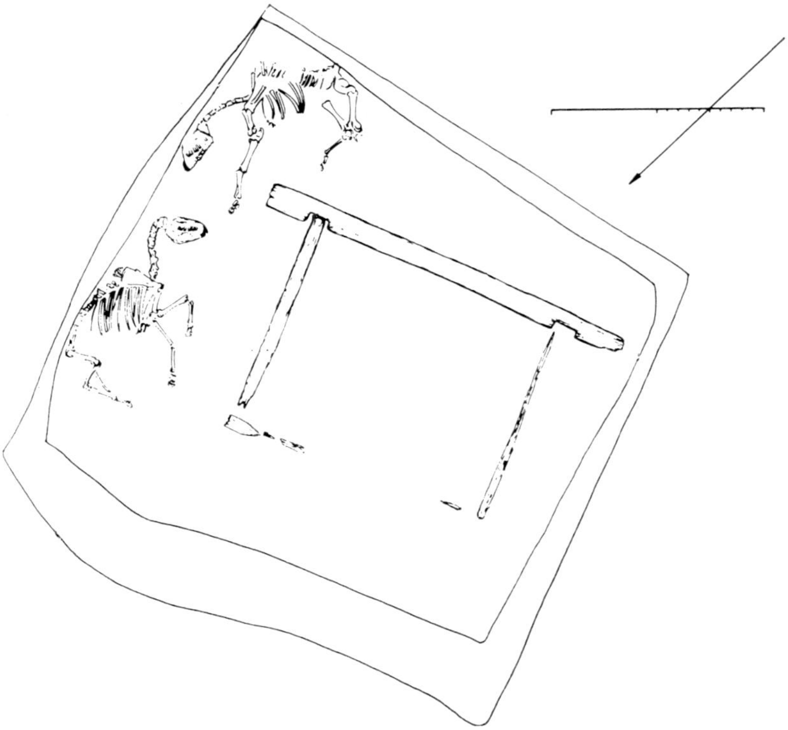

FIG. 3. Grave with two horse-burials, Gordion Tumulus KY, (after R. Young, 1956, PLATE 96, fig. 57; see *n. 13*).

of Grosseibstadt in Lower Franconia and Hradeník in Bohemia, have wheels constructed in a way that is quite different from earlier Urnfield period wheels. They have board felloes with U and T-shaped iron attachments, and except for the wholly European iron tyres, they are the same as the large wheels of VIIIth century Assyrian carts as we see them on the palace reliefs (Figs 4, 5b), and actually surviving in VIIth century graves at Salamis in Cyprus. Kossack thinks the technique came round the Black Sea from south of the Caucasus where the cart wheels of Lachashan on Lake Sevan are similarly constructed and earlier[15]. As usual with this argument it means bridging great gaps.

It is also a great distance from the sphere of Assyrian chariotry to Bohemia over the Bosphorus, but not *so* great, and there is a possible point between. Carved grave stelae from Aksakal-Daskyleion, south of the sea of Marmara, still a Thracian area, show a loaded hearse on its way to the grave, and the funeral feasting. The wheels of the hearse are of the same general Assyrian type, which was adopted by the Persians. The dates of the stelae are around 500, later than the other wheels we have been discussing, but the same type of wheel was still in use in the XIXth century on the light carts of Chinese officials in Manchuria[16]. (Fig. 5a and map Fig. 1).

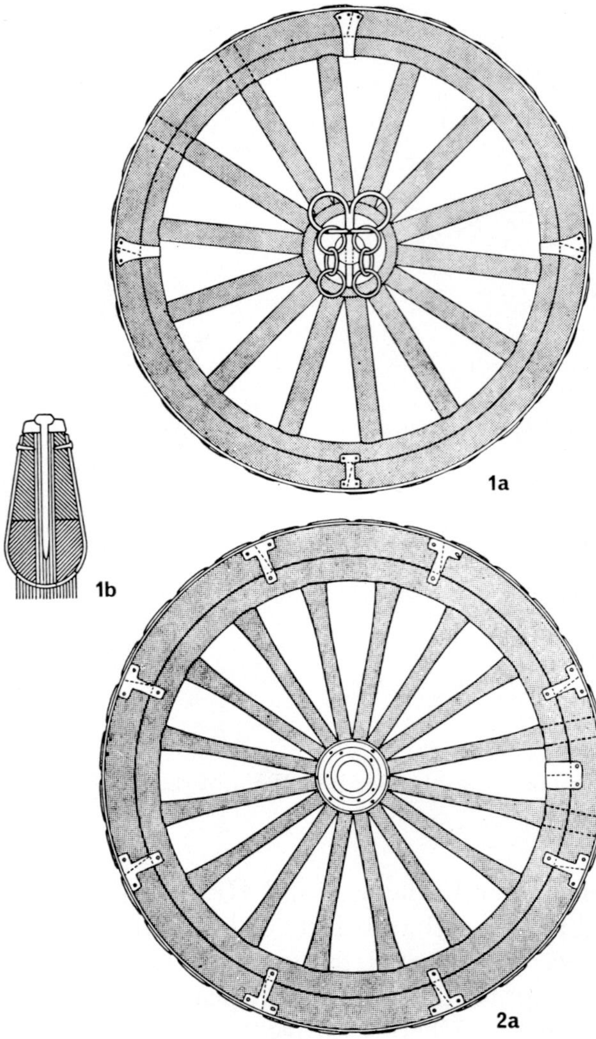

FIG. 4. Wheels with board felloes and iron attachments, 1. Hradenín, Bohemia; 2. Grosseibstadt, Lower Franconia (after G. Kossack, 1971, Fig. 31, see ***n. 14***). Diam. no. 2: 83 cm.

It may seem that none of this has very much to do with Celtic La Tène art, but I think that in fact these rather remote archaeological and historical matters *do* have a direct bearing on the proto-history of the Celts, also of their art, for not only do they show how the Persian army, with its Phrygians, Lydians and Thracians from both sides of the Bosphorus, would have contained relatives of inland Thracian tribes up the Struma and the Maritsa; but also that Thracian and Dacian society and culture was physically a continuation of that of Anatolia, and that a physical continuity in popular arts on both sides of the Bosphorus might be expected. This leads me to my second point concerning the fundamental difference in the nature of the oriental aspect of

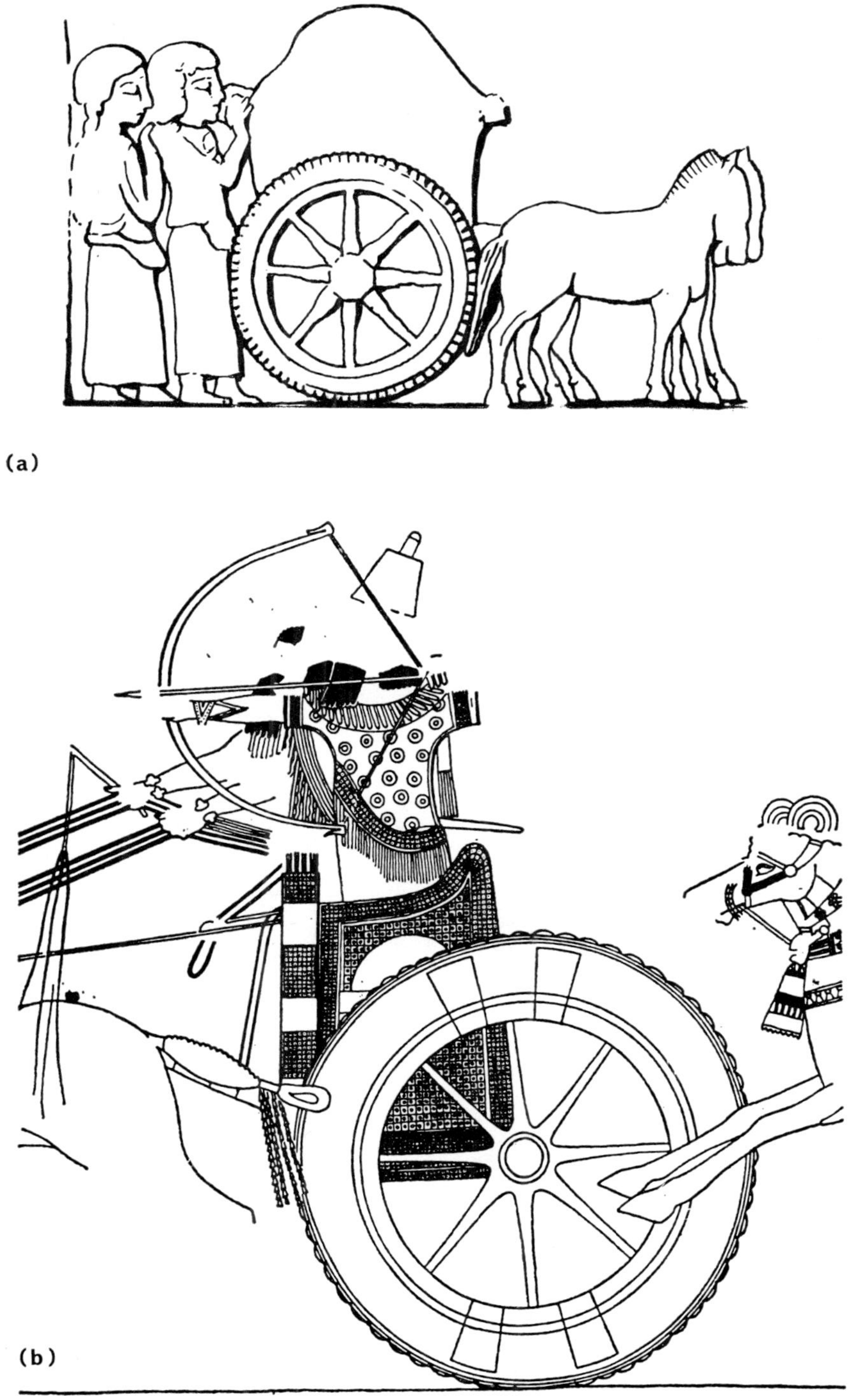

FIG. 5. (a) Grave stela from Aksakal-Daskyleion (after J. Borchhardt, 1968, PLATE 50 see ***n. 16***) *c.* 500 B.C.
(b) Assyrian war-chariot, Til Barsib (Tell Asmar), (after G. Kossack, 1971, Fig. 35, 3 see ***n. 14***), second half of eighth century.

Thracian and Dacian art, and that of La Tène art. It is a matter of a different history and antecedents.

I think I have said enough elsewhere about the Achaemenian contribution to La Tène art (note 2 above), but I want now to illustrate one or two points relating to Thracian and Dacian art which were then ignored. Their connections are with essentially provincial oriental styles, whether they come ultimately from Amlash or Hasanlu or Gordion. Others have drawn attention to the inspiration of Marlik and Ziwiyeh[17]. I shall confine myself to a few objects rather nearer at hand. The Phrygians inherited the old oriental motif of the bird or griffin with a fish hanging from its beak[18]. There is an ivory from Gordion, found in the inner room of a building (Megaron III) of the Phrygian city, that has it; and on the spout of a painted pot from Tumulus III, also at

Fig. 6. (a) Painted design on pot with sieve-spout, Gordion Tumulus III (after E. Akurgal, 1955, Plate 20 see ***n. 19***).

(b) Ivory from the Phrygian city, Gordion (after R. Young, 1960, Plate 60, Fig. 25 see ***n. 19***).

(c) Haghigiol, base of silver goblet (after *Revista de Preistorie* . . . București, 1937, Plate XV see ***n. 21***).

(d) Haghigiol, silver goblet (after *Treasures from Rumania, Catalogue* p. 39, see ***n. 20***). Scales various.

Gordion, and dated around 700 B.C., an indeterminate animal, perhaps a bear or pig, hangs by its tail from the mouth of a large predator (Fig. 6, a and b)[19]. We find the same motifs in Dacian art on the silver goblets from Haghigiol (Fig. 6, c and d)[20]. The Phrygians seem to have hung whole animals, not limbs, from the mouths of their predators. It was the Etruscans who had a peculiar predilection for severed limbs, and this is followed in two cases by Dacian art; on the base of the Haghigiol and "Iron Gate" goblets and on the neck of the gold tiara from Poiana-Coţofeneşti[21]. As far as I am aware a small animal on the rim of the Dürrnberg flagon is the unique early La Tène example of this severed or gobbled-up limb motif (according to J. V. S. Megaw it is a beard).

Phrygian vase-painters often portrayed plumage by bands of alternating hatching, and this could be the source for a similar treatment by Dacian metal-workers, seen best, perhaps, on the "Seven Beast phalera" in the Cabinet des Médailles, which is evidently late work (Fig. 7, a

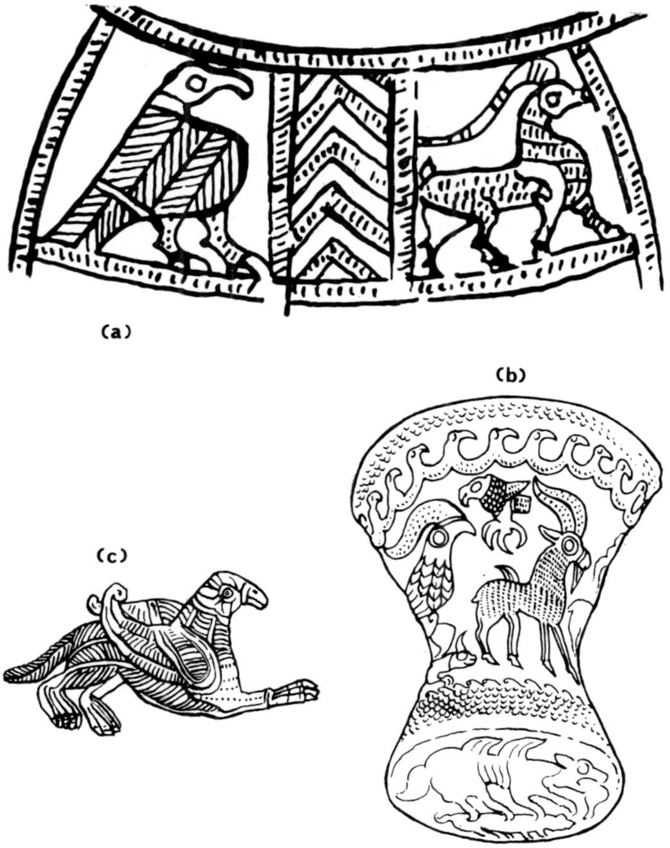

FIG. 7. (a) Painting on pot from Tumulus III, Gordion (after E. Akurgal, 1955, PLATE 19 a see ***n. 19***).
(b) Silver goblet from Haghigiol (after R. Florescu, 1968, PLATE 8 see ***n. 23***).
(c) One of a pair of griffins on the "Seven Beast Phalera" in the Bibliothèque Nationale, Paris, silver gilt (after D. Allen, 1971, PLATE XIV see ***n. 22***). Scales various.

and c)[22]. The goat or ibex on the same pot as Fig. 7 a, from Tumulus III at Gordion, is not unlike the Haghigiol goat (Fig. 7, c)[23]. A similar style can be recognised in Thracian gold and silver work from Letnica, Vratsa and Lovec in Bulgaria; as well as on the Gundestrup cauldron[24].

Against this native and rather provincial tradition, Achaemenian art is a court style, produced in a number of different centres, but bearing exactly the same stamp whether it comes from Afghanistan or Armenia[25]. There is very little of this "official" Achaemenian style to be seen in Thracian and Dacian art, either at its best in the great silver and gold tiaras with their barbaric splendour, or at its worst when it appears rather "wooden". The reason I think is that this art was strongly rooted in a native population which was itself a continuation of that of Anatolia, with traditions very different from those of Persepolis or Susa; so that this whole region from the Taurus to the Danube was closely linked, each unit spilling over a little further westwards and following a little later. This is what gave Dacian and Thracian art its strength and its staying power, for it did stay a very long time; well into the first centuries A.D.; while the official Achaemenian style had as little influence upon it as official styles usually have on popular art.

On the other hand to the Celtic craftsmen in central or western Europe all oriental objects were equally fascinating and alien, whether Scythian, Achaemenian, Phrygian or Thracian. Theirs was the originality and the audacity to transform and combine all these oddly assorted manifestations, making of them something different: the early La Tène orientalizing style.

Notes

(*Cross references with the notes are indicated by bold italic type*)

1. Powell, T. G. E. (1971), From Urartu to Gundestrup. in *European Community in Later Prehistory, Studies in Honour of C. F. C. Hawkes* (Boardman, J., Brown, M. A. and Powell, T. G. E., eds.) pp. 183–210 London.

2. Sandars, N. K. (1971), Orient and Orientalizing in Early Celtic Art, *Antiquity* **XLV**, pp. 103–112.

3. Megaw, J. V. S. (1972), Style and style groupings in early La Tène art, *World Archaeology* **3/3** pp. 276–292.

4. Powell, T. G. E. (1966), The Winged Beasts from Stupava, *Sborník Národního Muzea v Praze*, **22,** 1/2 pp. 133–136; Jacobsthal, P. (1944), *Early Celtic Art*, especially chapter 6, p. 156 f. Oxford.

5. Snodgrass, A. M. (1971), *The Dark Age of Greece*, Edinburgh, *passim*, especially chapters 5 and 6; Davies, O. (1926–27). *Annual of the British School at Athens*, **28,** 197–199, for Vardaróftsa, chemical analysis.

6. Kimmig, W. (1964), Seevölkerbewegung und Urnenfelderkultur, in *Studien aus Alteuropa*, pp. 220–282, Köln-Graz.

7. Morintz, S. (1964), Quelques problèmes concernant la période ancienne du Hallstatt . . . fouilles de Babadag, *Dacia N.S.* **VIII** pp. 101–118.

8. Dascalakis, A. (1965), *The Hellenism of The Ancient Macedonians*, pp. 98 and 139 (***n. 4, 5.***) Salonica; comments on Euphorion Fragment 15.
Herodotus, VII, 75, VIII, 138.

9. Barnett, R. D. (1967), Phrygia and the Peoples of the Anatolian Iron Age. In *Cambridge Ancient History* (rev. ed), Vol. II, Chapter XXX p. 56, Cambridge University Press, Cambridge. I am grateful to Mrs K. R. Maxwell-Hyslop for advice on the early history of iron technology in western Asia in general, and in Anatolia in particular.

10. Boardman, J. (1964), *The Greek Overseas*, p. 242. Harmondsworth, London.
Young, R. (1962), *Am. J. Archaeol.*, **66,** pp. 153–168.
see also: Young, R. (1963). *Gordion on the Royal Road*, and: *Proc. Am. Phil. Soc.* **107,** 4., 349–364.

11. Sandars, N. K. (1971). Cimmerians, Phrygians, Achaemenians and South-East Europe, *Actes du Congrès Internat. Sciences Préhist. Protohist.* (*Prague 1966*) pp. 873–877.

12. Dušek, M. (1966), *Thrakisches Gräberfeld der Hallstattzeit in Chotín*, Bratislava. According to Dušek the well known type of iron horse-bit usually called "scythian" is in fact better called "thracian". *See* ***note 7***; *see also:* Párducz, M. (1965), Graves from the Scythian Age at Ártánd, *Acta Arch. Acad. Sci. Hung.* **17,** 137–231.

13. Young, R. (1956). The Gordion Campaign 1955, *Am. J. Archaeol.* **60,** pp. 249–266 (PLATE 96, Fig. 57.)

14. Kossack, G. (1971), The construction of the felloe in Iron Age spoked wheels, in *European Community in Later Prehistory* ***note 1,*** 141–163, and Kossack, G. (1970), Gräberfelder der Hallstattzeit an Main und fränkischer Saale, *Materialhefte zur Bayerischen Vorgeschichte*, **24,** 98–186; *compare* the construction of the timber chambers at Villingen,

Spindler, K. (1972), Fürstengrabhügel Magdalenenberg bei Villingen, *Germania* **50,** pp. 56–73, (PLATES 12, 13;) *with* the great tumulus at Gordion: Young, R. (1958), *Am. J. Archaeol.* **62,** pp. 139–154 (PLATES 23–25).

15. Manatsakanian, A. (1960), Vehicles from Bronze Age Barrows on the Shores of Lake Sevan, *Sovet. Archeol.* **2,** 139–152 (Russian).

16. Borchhardt, J. (1968). Epichorische gräko-persisch beeinflusste Reliefs in Kilikien, *Istanbuler Mitt.* **18,** pp. 161–211 (especially pp. 196–199, PLATES 40, 47, 48, 50.)

17. Powell, T. G. E. (1966 and 1971): *see* ***notes 4 and 1.***

Venedikov, I. (1970), L'art thrace et l'art achémenide. *Acte Ier congr. internat. études Balkaniques et sud-est-Européennes* **II,** Sofia, pp. 381–396.

18. Goldman, B. (1963), A Scythian Helmet from the Danube, *Bull. Detroit Inst. Arts*, **42,** 4, pp. 61–72.

Goldman, B. (1966–69), Late Scythian Art in the West: The Detroit Helmet, *IPEK*, **22,** pp. 67–76.

"Scythian" is used by Goldman in a far wider sense than it is in this article.

19. Akurgal, E. (1955), *Phrygische Kunst.* Ankara (pots from Gordion, Tumulus III, PLATES 19–20).

Young, R. (1960). Gordion Campaign 1959. *Am. J. Archaeol.* **64,** pp. 227–234 (PLATE 60 and Fig. 25).

Young, R. (1964), *Am. J. Archaeol.* **68** (small ivory of uncertain date PLATE 84, FIG. 14) and *idem* (1968), *Am. J. Archaeol.* **72,** p. 231 (PLATE 76, Fig. 20, bird and fish).

20. British Museum (1971). *Treasures from Rumania, Catalogue* (Trustees of the British Museum), no. 157, p. 39 (illustration), *c.* 400 B.C.

21. *Revista de Preistoriei şi Antichită ţí Nationale*, Sept. 1937. Bucarest University, Faculty of letters and philosophy, Bulletin I, 1, Bucurşeti, PLATE XV.

22. Allen, D. (1971), The Sark Hoard. *Archaeologia* **103,** pp. 1–31 (PLATES 7, 8, 14 etc.)

23. Florescu, R. (1968). *L'Art des Daces*, Bucarest (Fig. 8.)

24. Venedikov, I. (1966), *Bulgaria's Treasures from the Past*, Sofia,
and (1972) *L'Art Thrace*, exhibition catalogue on the occasion of the First International Congress of Thracology, Sofia (in Bulgarian with a French summary).

25. Examination of the Duvanlij flagon and comparison with other Achaemenian work, especially the handle animals, convinces of its metropolitan character. The problem referred to above of distinguishing Greek work for a barbarian market from the true Achaemenian imperial style does not apply to this superb object, and I cannot agree with the suggestion made by Mr Brian Shefton to the contrary: in a paper read to the *VIth International Congress of Iranian Art and Archaeology* at Oxford in 1972. The later *phialai* and greaves from Bulgaria and Rumania are quite a different matter, however.

Acknowledgements

I owe my greatest, indeed an overriding, debt of gratitude to Prof. T. G. E. Powell, for conversations which stimulated the thoughts set out in this short article; any value they may have is owing to him. Needless to say he is not responsible for any errors or misrepresentations. I have also been fortunate in receiving great help from Mrs K. R. Maxwell-Hyslop in areas of which I knew little. I have had valuable advice as well from Prof. G. L. Huxley, Mr John Boardman and Mr Philip Lowery, to all of whom I am very grateful. Mrs Marion Cox made the drawings from photographs of the originals.

Résumé

Oriental et orientalisant : quelques réflexions recentes

Jacobsthal a admis, sans pouvoir l'expliquer, un aspect orientalisant de l'art laténien, qui ne fut jamais ni scythe ni étrusque : on manquait alors d'objets importés pour appuyer cette vue, malgré les échanges multiples provoqués jusqu' au milieu du Ve siècle par la présence des Perses en Thrace entre l'expédition de Darius (vers 513) et la retraite de Xerxès (479) ; et les Perses et les Thraces s'entendaient bien : les effets s'en sont fait sentir plus loin vers le Nord qu'il n'apparaît à première vue ; mais pourquoi les arts thrace et dace ont-ils des caractères orientalisants si différents de ceux de l'art laténien ?

Par "oriental" Jacobsthal entendait essentiellement : "scythe", alors que les caractères "orientaux" se remarquaient sur des objets laténiens trouvés entre le Rhin et la Vltava et non aux extrémités orientales du monde celtique. En fait, dans l'art le plus ancien de La Tène, l'aspect scythe ne se reconnaît que sur quelques objets, et non les plus anciens (vases de Basse-Yutz et fibule de Parsberg, non les vases du Dürrnberg et la fibule de Panenský Týnec) : il y a aussi l'élément iranisant, qui entrait aussi dans l'influence orientale reconnue par Jacobsthal. Entre l'Iran et les ateliers celtiques, l'intermédiaire étrusque n'est pas le seul : les ateliers de la Grèce d'Asie ont dû jouer un rôle important.

Par exemple : le goût celtique pour les cornes à boire, qui existe chez les Iraniens mais non chez les Grecs (sauf quand ils travaillent pour une clientèle barbare) ; les animaux qui forment les anses de vases. Au torque du Glauberg, au bracelet de Rodenbach et à l'agrafe de ceinture de Weisskirchen, reconnus comme "iranisants" par Jacobsthal, on peut ajouter les cornes à boire de Klein Aspergle, la fibule de Panenský Týnec, la plaque de Stupava, peut-être le "filet" ajouré de Dürkheim et les quatre torques d'Erstfeld.

Le fer d'Anatolie a dû jouer un grand rôle dès le IXe siècle et la métallurgie gagner la Macédoine, la Thrace et même la Dobrogea. Les Celtes ont dû apprendre des Thraces, puissants du Rhodope aux Alpes orientales au milieu du VIe siècle, l'art de faire au tour la poterie, qui venait des Grecs de la Mer Noire. Les tombes à char du Hallstatt C–D en Europe centrale remontent, plutôt qu'aux tombes en charpente de la steppe russe, aux sépultures royales de Phrygie (VIIIe–VIIe siècles). Les chars hallstattiens[14] étudiés par G. Kossack ont des roues qui ressemblent à celles des chars assyriens du VIIIe siècle, technique qui a pu venir par la Mer Noire jusqu'en Bohême et en Franconie au Hallstatt C ou plutôt par le Bosphore ou l'Hellespont.

L'aspect oriental des Thraces et des Daces n'en est pas moins très différent de celui de l'art laténien. Il est essentiellement d'origine provinciale et populaire, tandis que l'art achéménide est un art de cour, beaucoup plus uniforme. Les artistes laténiens ont eu l'audace de combiner toutes ces manifestations hétérogènes et d'en faire quelque chose de nouveau: l'art orientalisant laténien.

Discussion

Speakers:— Professor Duval, Miss Sandars, Dr Schwappach, Professors Hawkes, Duignan, Frey.

PROFESSOR DUVAL, looking back from Miss Sandars to Jacobsthal, and his thesis that Oriental elements came into La Tène through Italy, began by asking MISS SANDARS if she judged it still valid. She at once expressed doubts of this as the sole route of transmission and also doubts whether Jacobsthal was convinced of it himself. For some amongst those elements in La Tène, it was certainly valid. But others reflected Oriental work that was purer, and more sophisticated; and it was so difficult to see how this could get to approach any Scythian work, and therefore hint at some kind of transmission by land as a possibility, that he felt it might have had its influence passed through Italy like the rest. Duval supposed Etruria; but though she thought some influence possible, Miss Sandars saw in Italy nothing Achaemenian specifically. DR SCHWAPPACH declared that we ought to view the whole, but proceed to separate: while parts had Italian influence clear, the impression from others was different. The Dürrnberg flagon's animals, with jaws chewing something like legs (*carnassiers androphages* in French), could have passed to the Celts through Este. Subtracting such things as these and assigning them to Italy, and subtracting the Hallstatt find of sword and scabbard (*fourreau*) with figures, we could then better consider what remained. Miss Sandars replied that such things, which she was ready enough to subtract, seemed to her not directly Oriental: rather, Italianate-orientalizing. To turn from motifs to objects and take the drinking-horn, for instance (seen in the horns of the Klein-Aspergle), one found it an Oriental thing, which Italy had not got; nor had Greece. And would a flagon-handle formed as an animal come through Italy to the Celts, or come to them as something directly Oriental?

Personal memories of Jacobsthal were recollected here by PROFESSOR HAWKES. In the classes he had given in the last years of his life, when his book had been published, he showed that its treatment of these affairs had left him still not satisfied. In the winter of 1946 he gave them a whole succession of classes; those attending included Hawkes and Brian Shefton. He subtracted, precisely as Schwappach would, the Dürrnberg flagon's *carnassiers*, and the Hallstatt sword-sheath figures, the one as from Italy, the other as peripheral to the figure-art of situlas. Having taken out all he could, he said "We have all the rest remaining. What do we do with these?" And so he turned the class to the Scythians. The table was piled with Rostovtzev, Minns, Borovka, Ebert, Schefold. Yet in the end this answer failed: what it gave was either too remote from any Celts, or too dissimilar, or too late, to bring together with their earliest works. As Persian art had been also found too remote for direct connection (Hawkes continued), I remember I said to him "Look, what about the army of Xerxes? Herodotus gives its contingents, each with its own costume and armament, from all over the Persian Empire, coming and assailing the Greeks; when they drove it out, wouldn't there be stragglers, left behind? If the bronze ring from the Glauberg (in Oberhessen) is Persian, can't you fancy that a Persian straggler somehow brought it there?" Jacobsthal took it as a joke. Ah, my amusing English humour! He cracked a joke of his own and laughed very much. Really I had meant, quite generally of course, to suggest a historical context; but Jacobsthal's thought was on quite another plane . . . Many years passed. Then in 1970 at Edinburgh, to the Celtic Exhibition conference, Nancy Sandars gave in a primary form the lecture she had now developed. Its published form was in *Antiquity* 45, 1971 (June), 103–12. Far on beyond comparison with the sally I made to Jacobsthal, it brought forward again the idea of the same historical context, on a plane of thought original and all her own.

Dr Schwappach asked for locations of the Eastern influence's impact. Most of the works adduced had been found in Germany near the Rhine. How did Celts further east, in Bohemia or Austria, or along the Alps in Switzerland, connect with the people there? Was he to think of warriors marching, from Greece to the west and then to east? Miss Sandars answered no, but of precious objects taken to a market, where there was wealth supporting people who enjoyed fine things, who could therefore pay for finery and would always be sure of getting it. The distance, covered to reach them, did not necessarily matter. The Rhine was no farther to west than was the site of the Oxus Treasure, east of the Caspian Sea, from effective posts of Persian power. Schwappach again requested proof of the earliest locations, for pieces most resembling their Oriental sources, whether really around the Rhine or in (say) Bohemia. Miss Sandars replied that proof must stand on absolute chronology. In graves on the Neckar or Rhine, at the Klein Aspergle or at Rodenbach, this was given by Attic vases, well back in the Vth century. Admitting their absence from Bohemia, which had only bronze beak-flagons, Schwappach suggested that early date could be claimed from these alone; but he agreed that Etruscan bronze bowls there, the sole such imports otherwise, could not support such a claim. He regretted the lack of Attic cups.

Hawkes interposed by recalling the weighty study by Jürgen Driehaus, in the *Bonner Jahrbücher* 166 for 1966. It insisted that the strength and wealth of the people we knew from the western graves—the *Fürstengräber* of the Middle Rhine and Hunsrück-Eifel country—will have been drawn from their command of the great Saar-Mosel ironfield. And he himself would go further: he believed these powerful princes had not been bred from the older Hunsrück-Eifel population, but had won command by a "take-over" bid—in history's terms, a conquest—launched from a Celtic home of their own that was somewhere nearer to Eastern contacts. These were in consequence brought to extend to the Rhine, for trade in the iron. Hence the start, 480–450 B.C., of the influences and imports, from Italy including Etruscan and Greek, and also from sources of influence that were Persian. These, through Europe if they came that way, might be carried by water up the Danube; or if they came by sea, what map could chart the route by spots in the water of the Adriatic? If Orientalizing Etruscan, 200 years before, was not to be linked with the East by spots in the Mediterranean water, need our Celtic situation be thought so very different? So in principle he supported Miss Sandars's Persian historical context. Professor Duignan here added that Celtic homes well east of the Rhine, so nearer to Eastern contacts, would suit the linguistic geography, as in Heinrich Wagner's recent works on the cradle of the Celts in general. Up the Danube and to the Rhine they moved by shifts of population, starting long before La Tène, yet still with a bearing on the present question.

Finally Professor Frey, returning to Early La Tène itself, stressed the rarity of definite imports other than those which came from Italy. The Achaemenian Persian question, like the Scythian arising after it, was one of influence seen in the Celtic work, much rather than of actual imports. So it was hard to determine the way by which these influences arrived. Yet there was one piece, he believed, that was made in the East and came as an import: the band of thin gold from the grave at Weisskirchen (Saarland), embossed, between borders, with a frieze of helmeted sphinxes. Jacobsthal in *ECA* (Plate 254, *d*; text, p. 140) took it for Etruscan. But Etruria had no drinking-horns, and this was a band from a drinking-horn's mouth—in his own belief and also Dr Haffner's (of Trier) who at present was studying drinking-horns as a whole. Eastern in its origin as a type for costly mountings, the drinking-horn could have Greek or Greek-influenced decoration. That was true of this Weisskirchen mouth-band; it was not Achaemenian, but the whole horn must have been an import to the West. Further discussion might suggest it a place in the questions here at issue.

4

L'art ornemental du "Premier style" celtique

FRANK SCHWAPPACH
Hamburg

LES RECHERCHES de Paul Jacobsthal sur ce qu'il appelait l'"Early Celtic Art"[1] sont demeurées fondamentales pour toute étude sur ce sujet et le tableau qu'il en a tracé dans les années 30 n'a été, depuis lors, que légèrement modifié. Bien que son travail soit tenu en haute estime, la recherche dans le domaine protohistorique a depuis lors donné la priorité à d'autres directions d'enquête. Fait remarquable car, aujourd'hui, un matériel plus abondant s'offre ainsi à l'étude et la façon dont Jacobsthal a abordé le sujet rend possible une analyse plus exacte de nombreux aspects des premiers styles de La Tène. Parmi les importantes découvertes récentes, citons le riche trésor d'Erstfeld (Suisse)[2], qui contenait une série de lourds anneaux d'or de qualité exceptionnelle, ou la tombe princière de Reinheim (Sarre)[3], l'une des plus riches connues de la première période de La Tène, ou encore les importantes et riches découvertes celtiques du Dürrnberg, près de Salzbourg (Autriche)[4].

Les objets que Jacobsthal a utilisés pour définir ce qu'il appelle le "Premier style" ("Early Style") viennent dans une large mesure de la zone occidentale du domaine de la Tène, spécialement les régions du Rhin et de la Marne[5]. Là, sur des pièces venant des tombes princières, il a constaté la présence d'éléments de décor floral grec, qu'il a isolés dans sa "Grammaire" du décor celtique (par ex. Fig. 1)[6]. Cependant, il n'a pas souligné que ce décor végétal n'est caractéristique du "Premier style" que dans la zone *occidentale*. Comme le montre l'index des provenances de son ouvrage[7], il n'a pu citer que quelques pièces de la zone

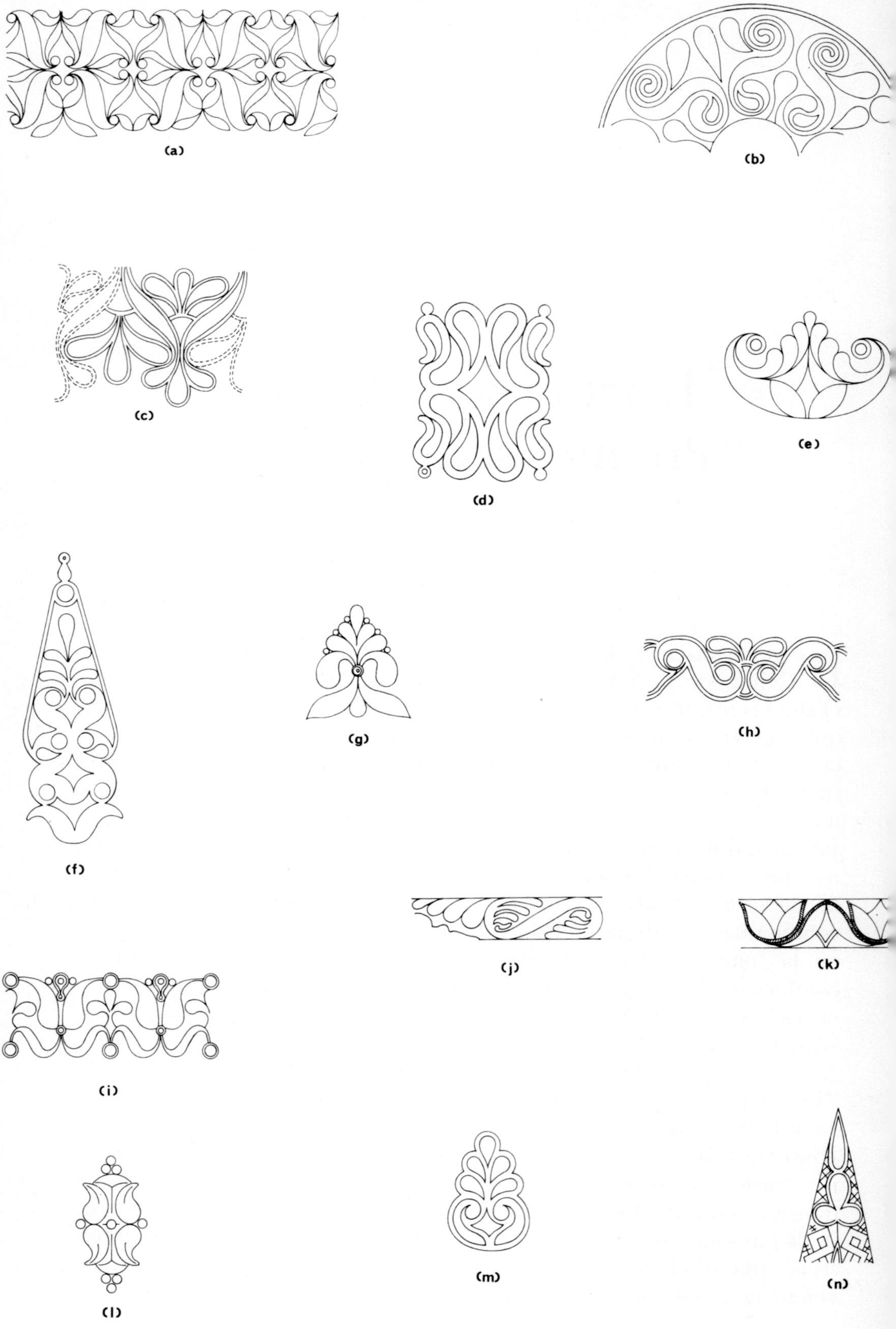

FIG. 1. Motifs végétaux du "Premier style" occidental[6].

orientale de La Tène (Bavière, Thuringe, Autriche, Bohême et Moravie) portant une ornementation florale, par exemple une feuille d'or (Figs 18, e; 26, d) de Chlum (Bohême)[8] ou la frise estampée (Fig. 12, a) d'un vase d'argile du Dürrnberg[9].

Or, les motifs végétaux tels que les palmettes, les feuilles, les lotus ou les lyres (Fig. 1), ne sont pas du tout communs dans cette zone orientale. Au IVe congrès international d'études celtiques, à Rennes en 1971, j'ai déjà attiré l'attention sur ce fait[10]. Les artisans des ateliers orientaux préféraient les ornements géométriques, fondés principalement sur des formes abstraites, arc, cercle et esse (Fig. 2)[11]. Des motifs constitués par ces éléments curvilignes se trouvent sur de nombreux exemples céramiques (par ex. Fig. 3, k)[12] et diverses pièces en métal (par ex. Fig. 3, a–b)[13], provenant tous de la zone orientale de l'Europe centrale.

Comme cet aspect spécifiquement oriental du "Premier style" est pauvrement représenté dans la "Grammaire" de Jacobsthal, ses planches de motifs se référant à cette phase stylistique sont surtout valables pour les centres occidentaux, ceux du Rhin et de la Marne. Jusqu'à présent, les archéologues qui se sont efforcés de classer les pièces celtiques décorées ou de les attribuer à différentes "écoles" artistiques n'ont pas tenu compte de ce fait incontestable. C'est ainsi que, pour J. V. S. Megaw[14], les motifs d'arcs et de cercles entrecroisés (Fig. 6), tracés au compas sur de nombreuses pièces orientales, telles que la phalère (Fig. 3, a) de Želkovice (Bohême) ou le vase en bronze de Dürrnberg (Fig. 9, i) "doivent représenter une importation occidentale"; Megaw a même supposé que le propriétaire de la phalère de Želkovice était "probablement originaire de Rhénanie"[15].

Au contraire, si l'on reporte sur une carte les exemples de ce motif caractéristique (Fig. 5)[16], il est clair qu'il s'agit d'un décor typique des premiers ateliers celtiques de Bavière, Thuringe, Bohême et Autriche. La carte démontre aussi que ce motif était étranger aux centres du Rhin et de la Marne, où le "Premier style" était entièrement dominé par des motifs floraux (palmettes surtout, carte Fig. 4).

En fait, parmi les innombrables pièces de La Tène A (Reinecke) et Ia (Wiedmer-Viollier) trouvés dans la zone occidentale, il n'existe que de rares exemples de décor purement géométrique et abstrait. Si l'on examine le couvercle de bronze de la tombe princière de Bad Dürkheim (Rhénanie-Palatinat), l'influence du "Premier style" oriental devient évidente (Figs 7, c; 24, d)[17]. Les fourreaux de Bussy-le-Château et de Châtillon (Marne) montrent aussi l'adaptation exceptionelle des motifs orientaux (Fig. 7, a–b; Fig. 24, a–c)[18].

D'autres pièces de métal occidentales offrent des exemples particulièrement frappants du contraste entre le "Premier style" floral local et sa version, si différente, de la zone orientale. Un contact direct entre les deux manières stylistiques apparaît sur l'applique de Laumersheim

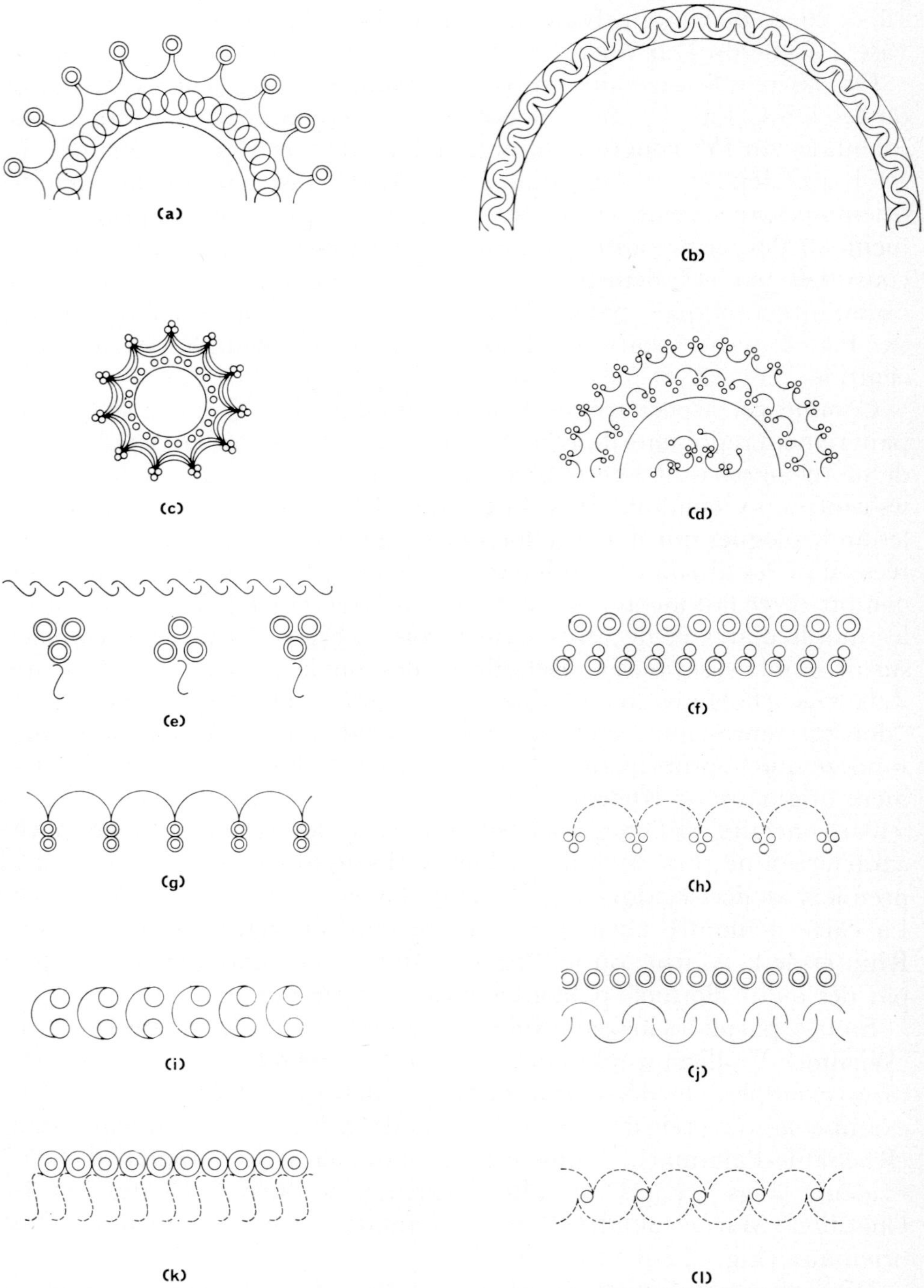

Fig. 2. Décorations géométriques abstraites propres au "Premier style" oriental[11].

(Rhénanie-Palatinat: Figs 8, a; 24, e)[19]: deux lyres remplies de corail sont aisément reconnaissables sur la partie supérieure, motifs qui se retrouvent sur de nombreuses pièces du Rhin et de la Marne[20]. Mais ce qui semble tout à fait particulier est la décoration marginale en arcs entrecroisés, tracés au compas, qui se retrouve sur l'agrafe de ceinture trouvée récemment par H. Zürn à Mühlacker (Bade-Würtemberg: Fig. 8, b)[21]. En revanche, le motif qui surmonte le motif des arcs est certainement, lui aussi, floral: il serait facile de le mettre en rapport avec d'autres motifs typiques qui se trouvent sur des pièces d'origine occidentale[22].

Le même contraste de styles se retrouve sur l'oenochoé à bec tubulaire de Waldalgesheim (Rhénanie-Palatinat)[23]. Un décor nettement floral entoure entièrement le vase d'un réseau complexe (Fig. 8, d), sur lequel l'artiste a mis fortement l'accent, mais un motif abstrait, du "Premier style" oriental, a été adapté dans le décor gravé (Fig. 8, a). Cependant, il est clair que le petit bandeau de rangées opposées d'arcs tracés au compas n'était pas considéré comme un élément essentiel de la composition. On pourrait aussi comparer la décoration semblable, combinée avec des motifs floraux, du casque d'Ecury-sur-Coole (Marne)[24].

Sur le tamis de Hoppstädten (Rhénanie-Palatinat)[25], le décor principal (Fig. 19, d) est composé d'éléments floraux caractéristiques (lyres, feuilles etc.), tandis qu'un motif d'arcs tracés au compas entoure la douille (Fig. 9, b). Un décor géométrique semblable se retrouve sur le vase d'Eigenbilzen (Limbourg, Belgique)[26]; cependant, sur cette pièce, la chaîne d'arcs opposés est divisée en éléments isolés faits de deux "feuilles" lancéolées, couronnées elles-mêmes de petits cercles (Fig. 9, e). On ne peut douter que les motifs essentiellement géométriques de ces deux objets dérivent des motifs à arcs de la zone orientale tels que ceux de la Fig. 9, d. Cependant, les décors de Hoppstädten et surtout ceux d'Eigenbilzen peuvent aussi être interprétés comme des représentations simplifiées de fleurs de lotus, les sépales seuls étant conservés. Pour une meilleure intelligence de cette interprétation florale, une frise d'une hydrie de Caeré (Fig. 9, a)[27] et un détail du décor de la coupe de Schwarzenbach (Fig. 9, c)[28] pourraient être étudiés à titre de comparaison. En outre, sur le vase d'Eigenbilzen, nous trouvons des rosettes à quatre et six feuilles, tracées au compas selon la technique dite "à figures rouges" (Fig. 9, g; 10)[29]. Des motifs semblables, mais traités selon la technique "à figures noires", sont connus sur quelques poteries estampées de Bohême, à Sedlo, à Láz (Fig. 9, h) et à Dýšina-Nová Huť (Fig. 9, k)[30]. Quelque interprétation abstraite ou florale qu'on donne de ces motifs géométriques, le "processus de floralisation" n'est caractéristique que des motifs tracés au compas du "Premier style" de la zone occidentale[31]. Ce trait extraordinaire du "Premier style" de l'art décoratif dans la région du Rhin et de la Marne est particulièrement souligné par les disques de Cuperly (Fig. 10) et de Somme-Bionne (Marne)[32].

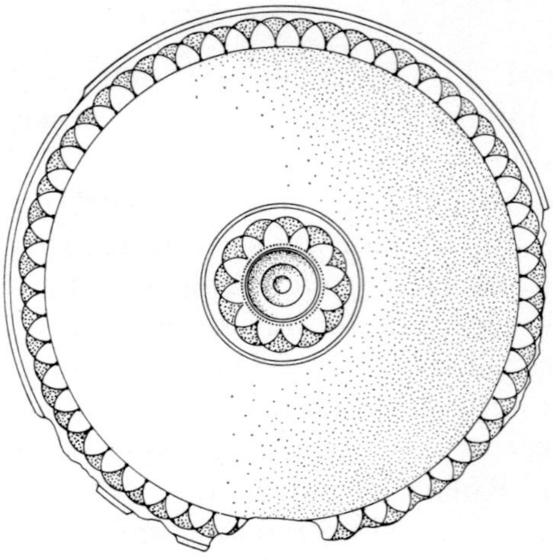

(a)

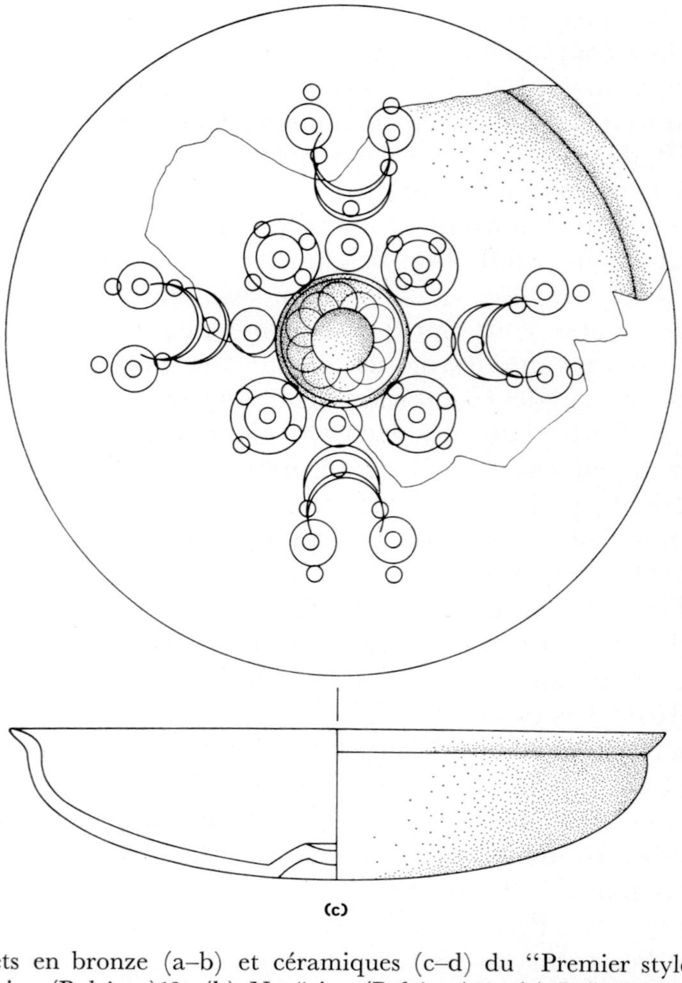

(c)

FIG. 3. Objets en bronze (a–b) et céramiques (c–d) du "Premier style" oriental: (a) Želkovice (Bohême)[13]; (b) Nevězice (Bohême)[13]; (c) Počerady (Bohême)[12]; (d) Dürrnberg (Autriche)[12].

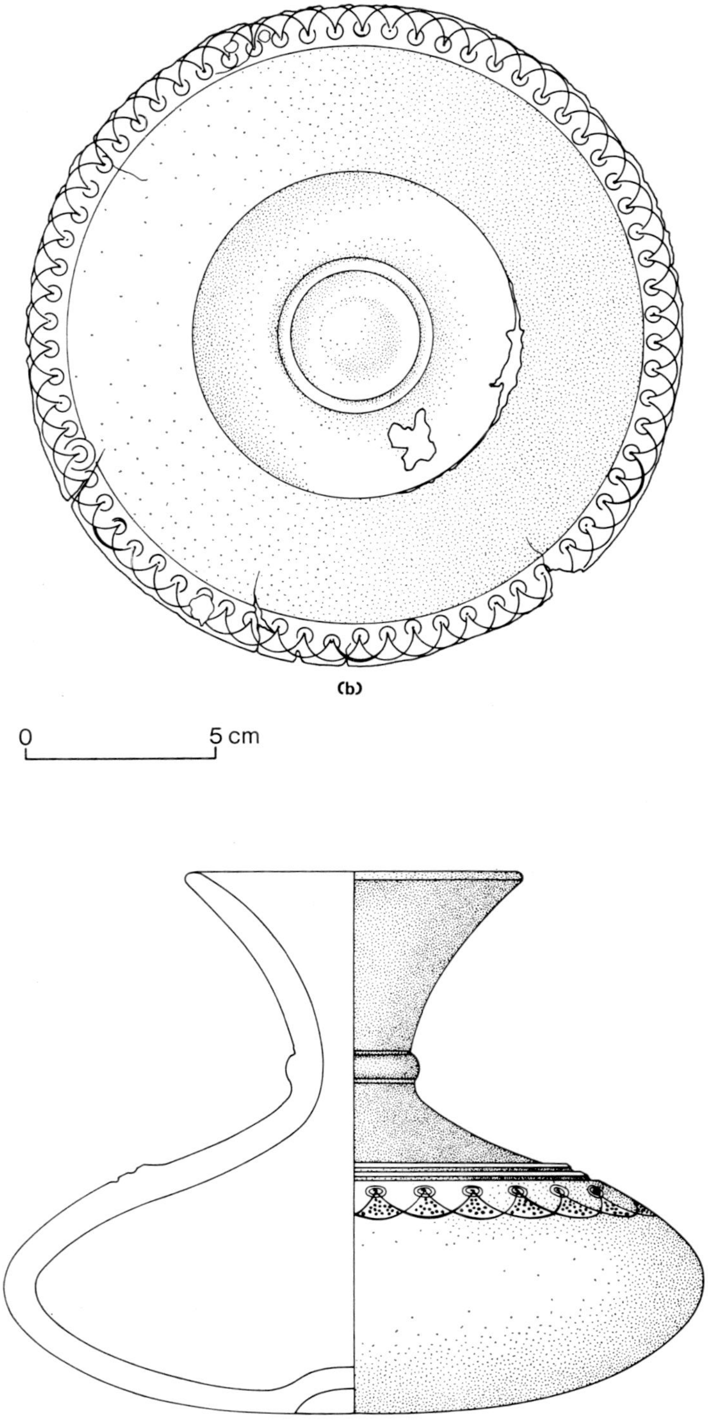

Fig. 3. (b) and (d). Voir page 66.

Afin de mieux marquer la distinction entre les deux principales provinces du "Premier style", que séparent des répertoires décoratifs essentiellement différents, nous présentons ici une autre carte de répartition (Fig. 4)[33]. Il est clair que les motifs à palmettes celtiques propres au "Premier style" de la période La Tène A (Ia) appartiennent aux

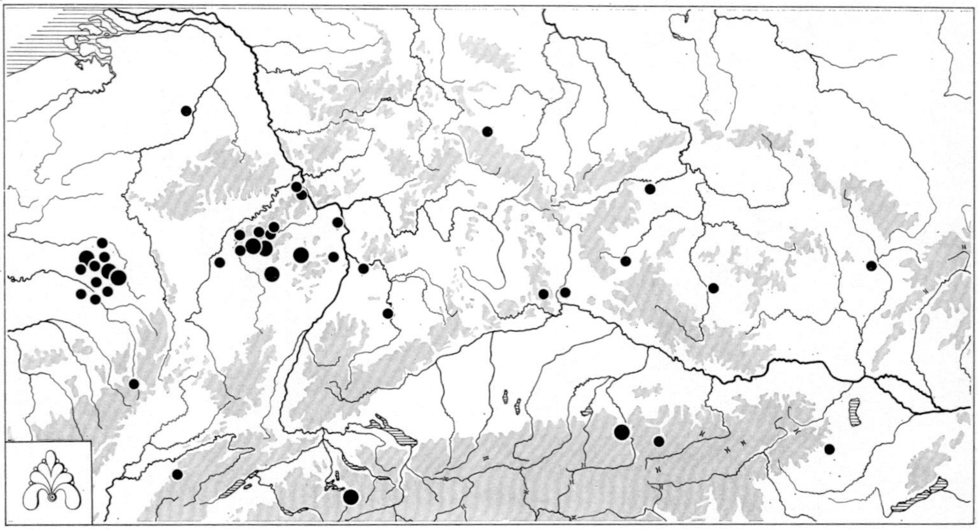

FIG. 4. Carte de répartition des palmettes celtiques propres au "Premier style" occidental[33].

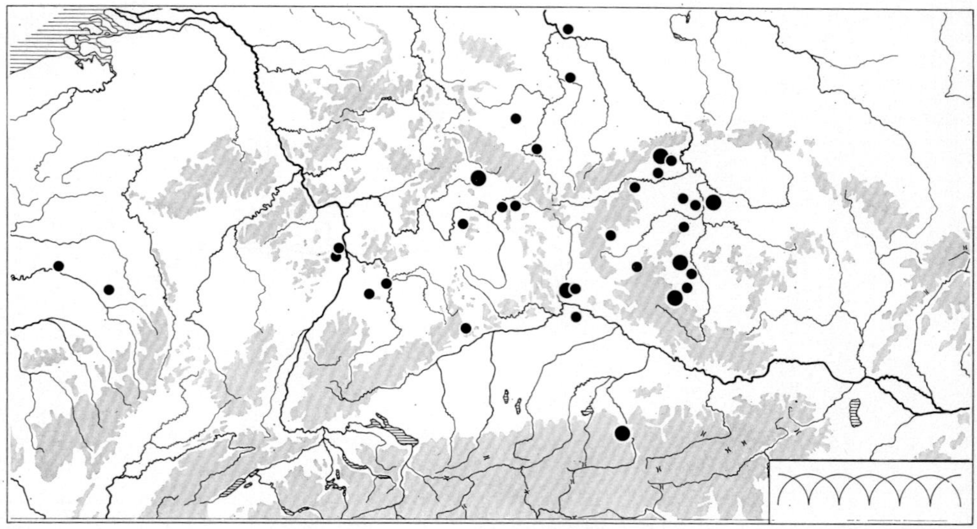

FIG. 5. Carte de répartition des motifs d'arcs et de cercles entrecroisés du "Premier style" oriental. Voir le répertoire Fig. 6[6].

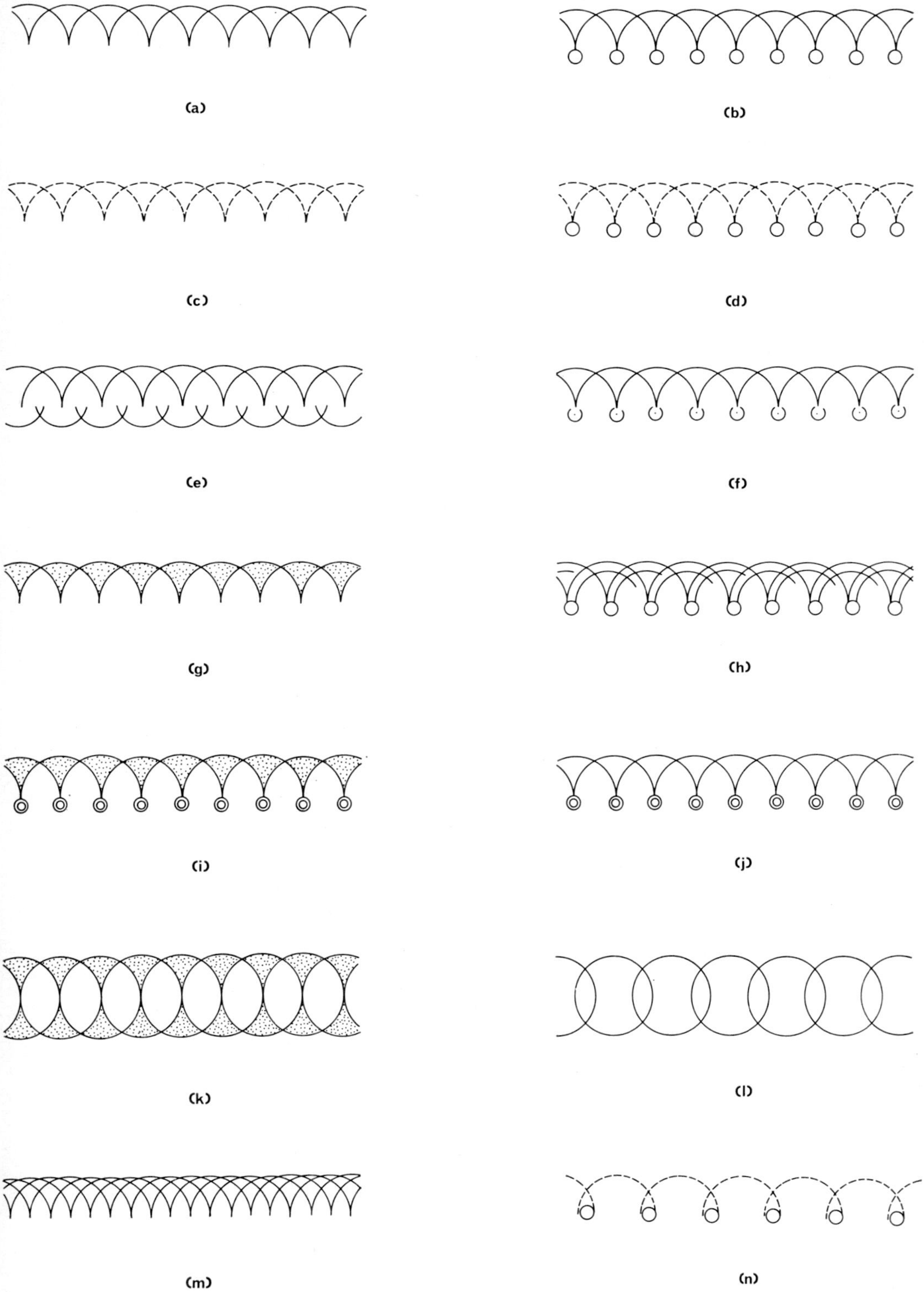

FIG. 6. Répertoire des motifs d'arcs et de cercles entrecroisés du "Premier style" oriental[16].

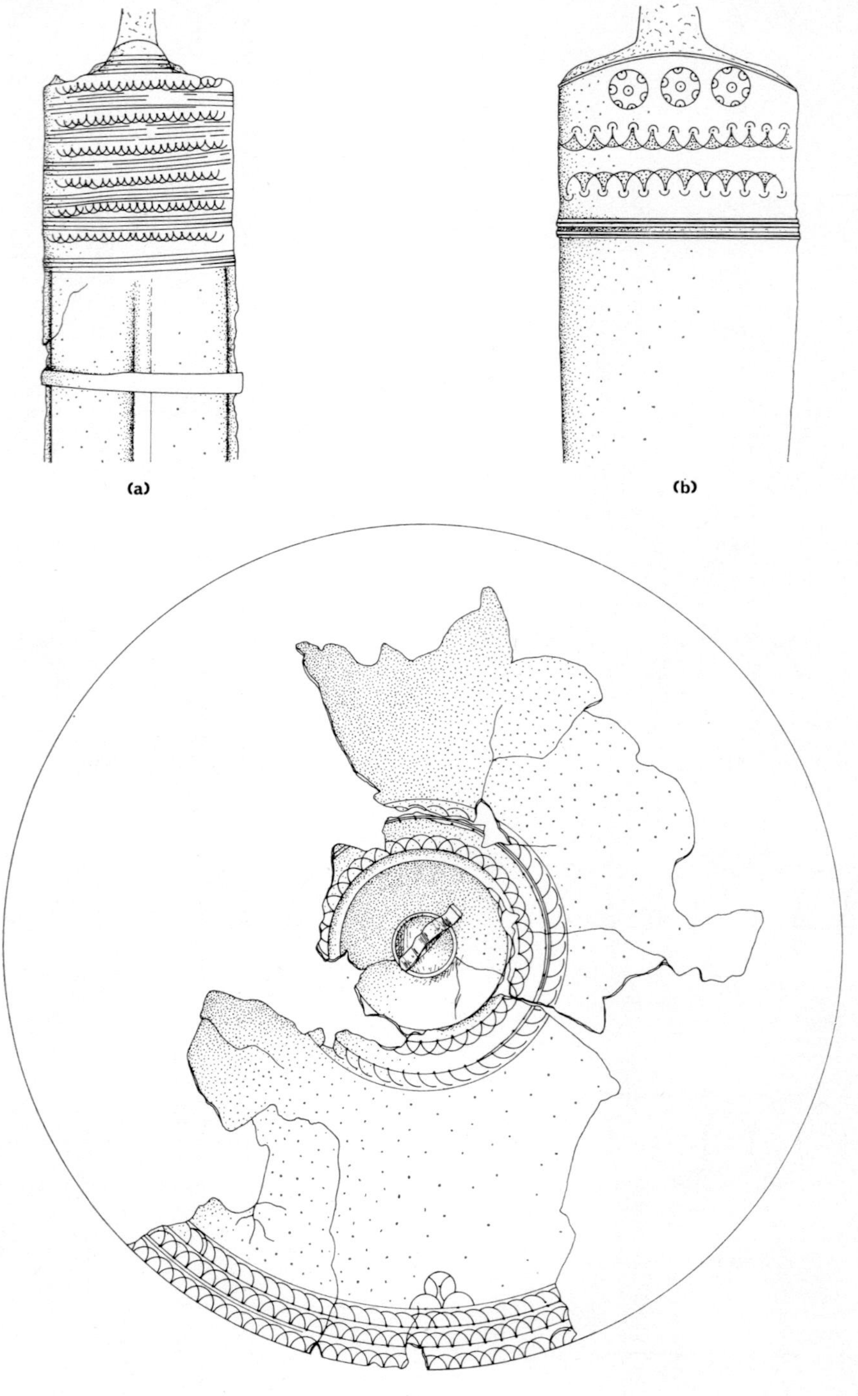

Fig. 7. Motifs abstraits curvilignes du "Premier style" oriental représentés sur objets en bronze de l'Ouest: (a) Châtillon (Marne)[18]; (b) Bussy-le-Château (Marne)[18]; (c) Bad Dürkheim (Rhénanie-Palatinat)[17].

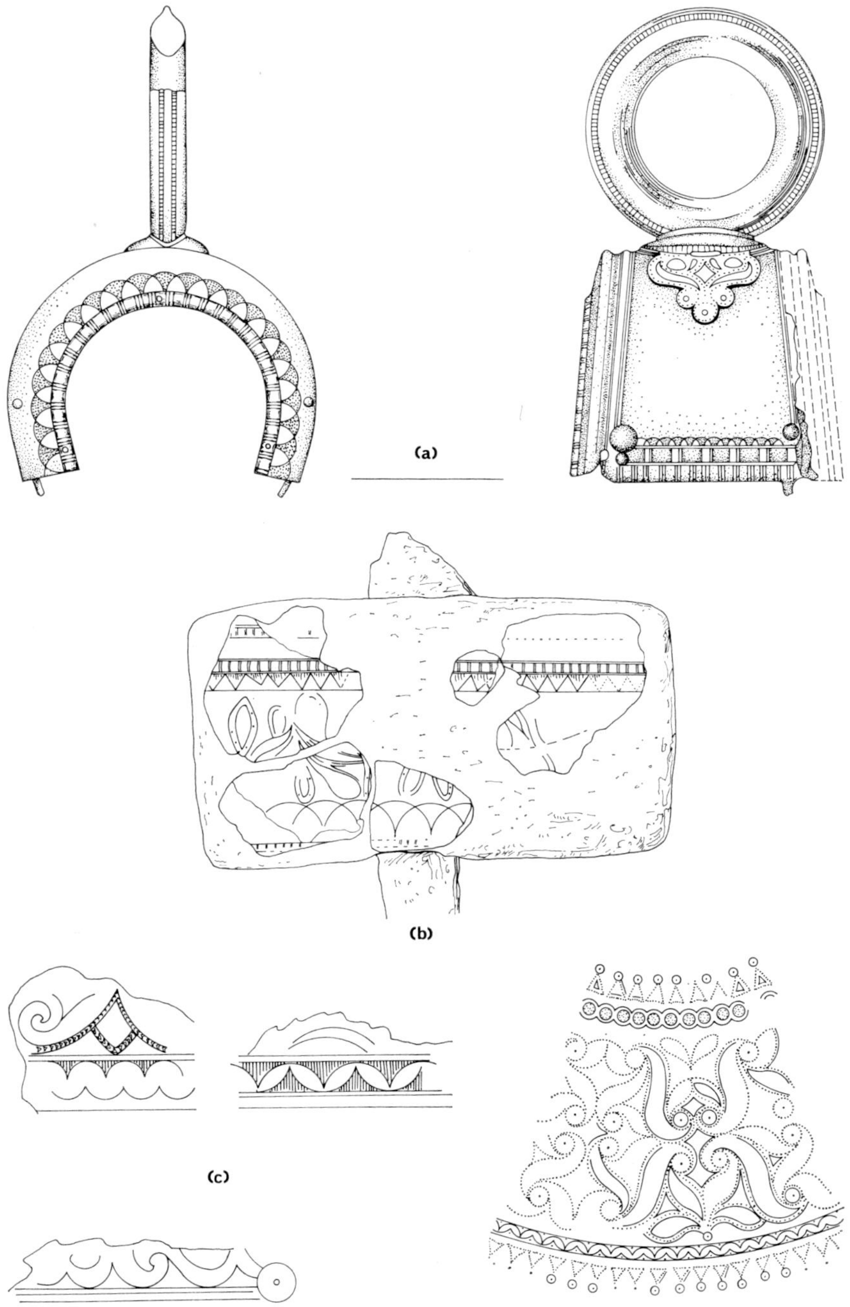

FIG. 8. Motifs abstraits du "Premier style" oriental combinés avec des ornements végétaux sur pièces en bronze de l'Ouest: (a) Laumersheim (Rhénanie-Palatinat)[19]; (b) Mühlacker (Bade-Wurtemberg)[21]; (c) Ecury-sur-Coole (Marne)[24]; (d) Waldalgesheim (Rhénanie-Palatinat)[23].

régions du Rhin et de la Marne et que la zone orientale de La Tène se distingue par la rareté des pièces comportant des motifs comparables. Non seulement les motifs à palmettes, mais les éléments floraux en général se trouvent rarement à l'Est. Les observations qui suivent, concernant quelques pièces majeures du "Premier style" oriental à décoration végétale, tendent à mieux préciser cette différence.

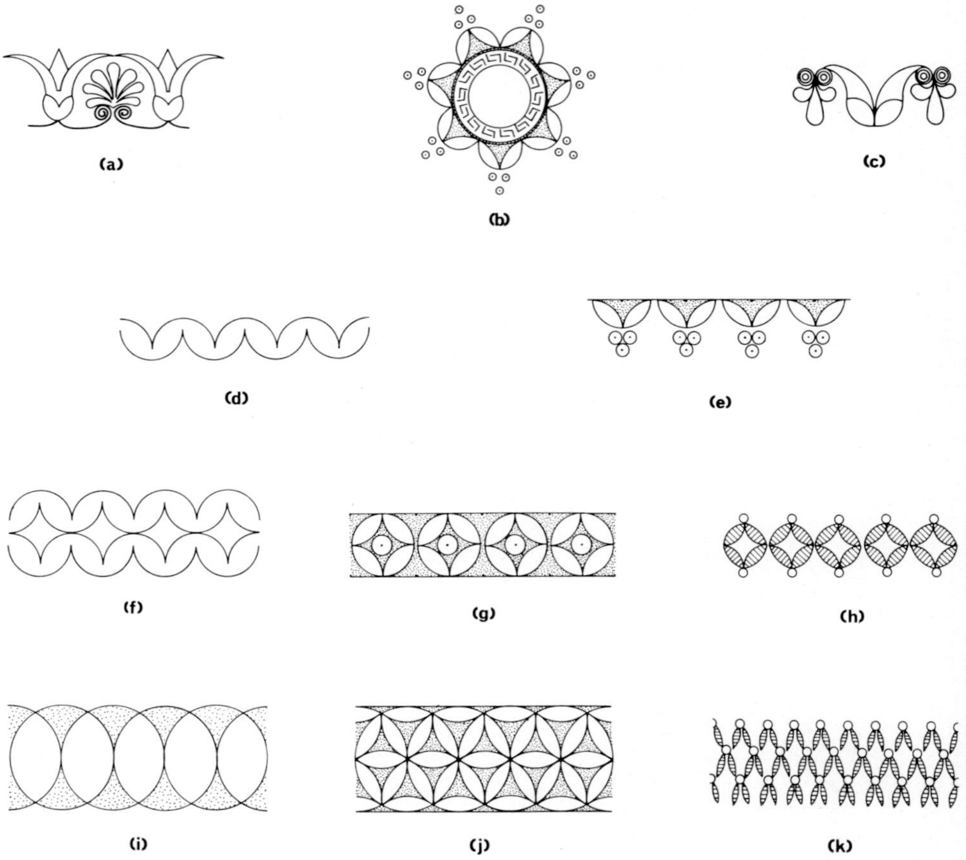

FIG. 9. Motifs (a) d'une hydrie de Caeré[27], (b) du tamis de Hoppstädten (Rhénanie-Palatinat)[25], (c) de la coupe de Schwarzenbach (Sarre)[28], (d et f) d'une céramique estampée de Prague-Podbaba (Bohême)[29], (e, g et j) de l'oenochoé d'Eigenbilzen (Belgique)[26], (h) d'une poterie estampée de Sedlo (Bohême)[30], (i) d'un vase en bronze du Dürrnberg (Autriche)[15] et (k) d'une céramique de Dýšina-Nová Huť (Bohême)[30].

Typique de l'art décoratif oriental du "Premier style" est un abondant répertoire de motifs à arcs, cercles et esses ("*Bogenstil*")[34], qui peuvent s'expliquer par l'introduction de l'usage du compas. Bon nombre de ces motifs sont des créations celtiques purement abstraites mais pour beaucoup d'autres il faut supposer une tradition hallstattienne ou même une origine méditerranéenne[35].

De tels motifs géométriques apparaissent sur d'innombrables céramiques (Fig. 3, c–d; 11)[36] et aussi sur un bon nombre de pièces en bronze, phalères, flacons, etc., (Fig. 3, a–c)[37]. Ou bien ils entourent en chaînes les récipients (Fig. 3, d; 11) ou bien ils sont disposés de manière concentrique (Fig. 3, a–b; 11, j, e, m). Les arcs, cercles et esses sont tracés en lignes simples, doubles et quelquefois multiples, continues ou pointillées (Fig. 11). Les compositions elles-mêmes sont variées: très communes sont les simples rangées d'arcs, de cercles et d'esses (Fig. 2); en outre, les motifs en chaînes ou en étoiles avec des arcs et des cercles entrecroisés sont fréquents (Figs. 3, 6)[38]. La richesse de la décoration propre au "Premier style" oriental s'explique par le fait que des motifs curvilignes sont isolés de leur contexte et permutés, et que leur disposition peut varier énormément.

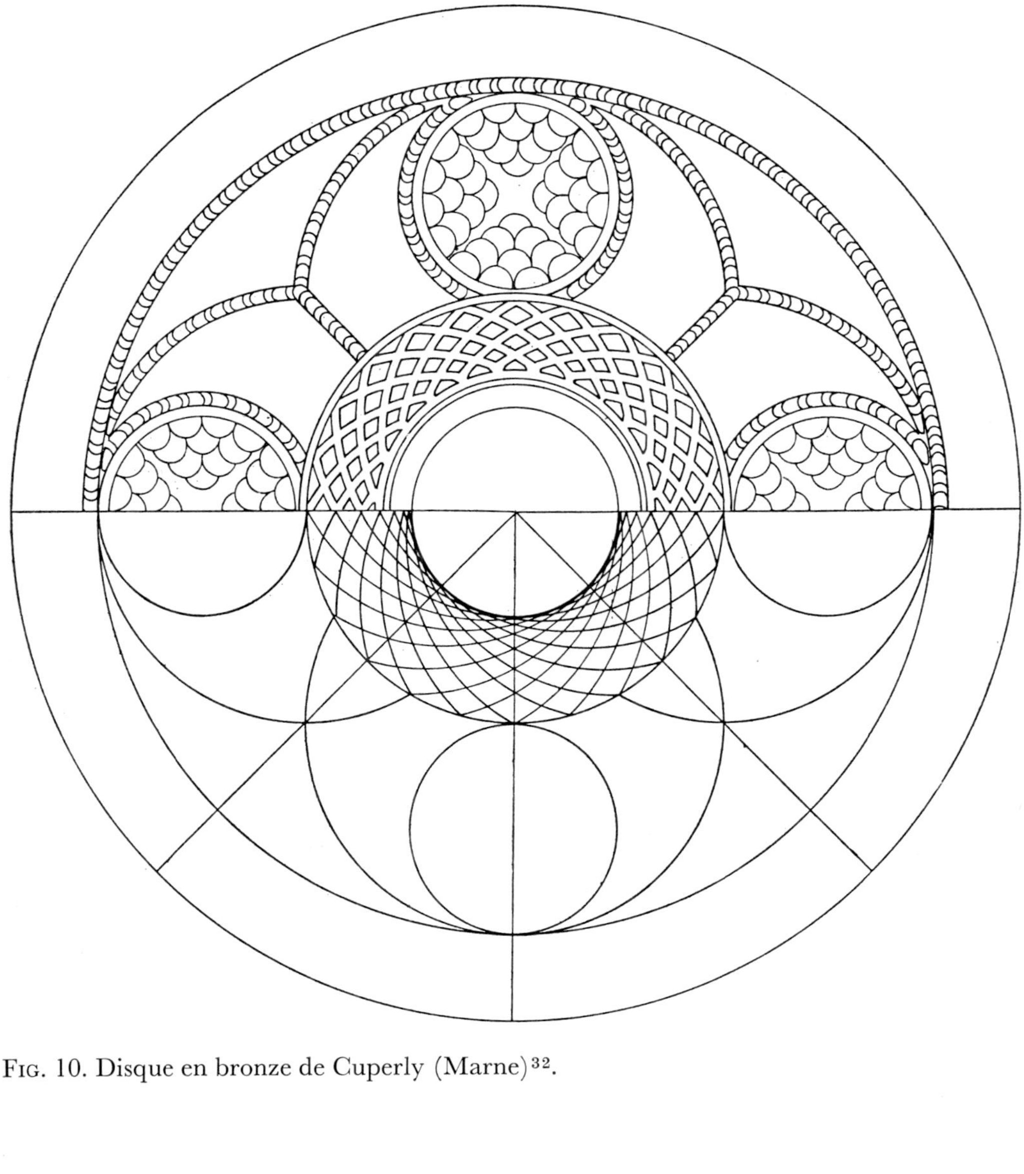

FIG. 10. Disque en bronze de Cuperly (Marne)[32].

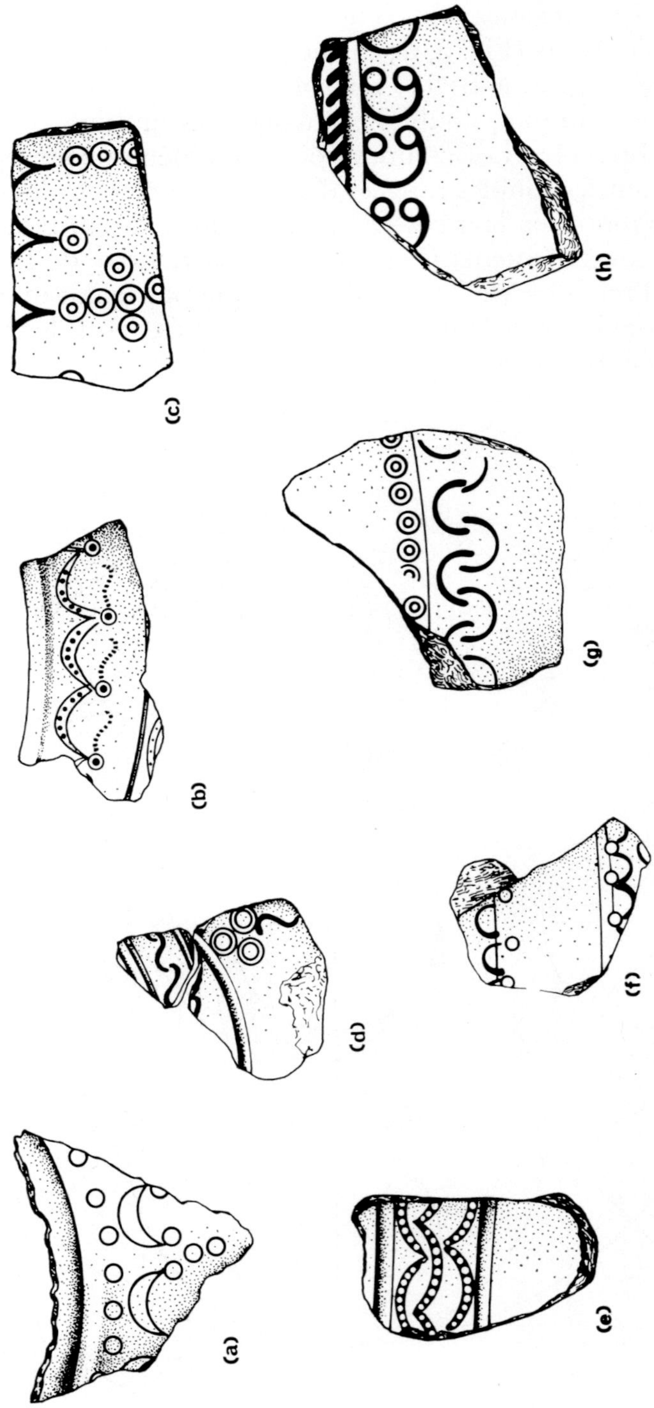

Fig. 11 (a)–(h). Voir en bas.

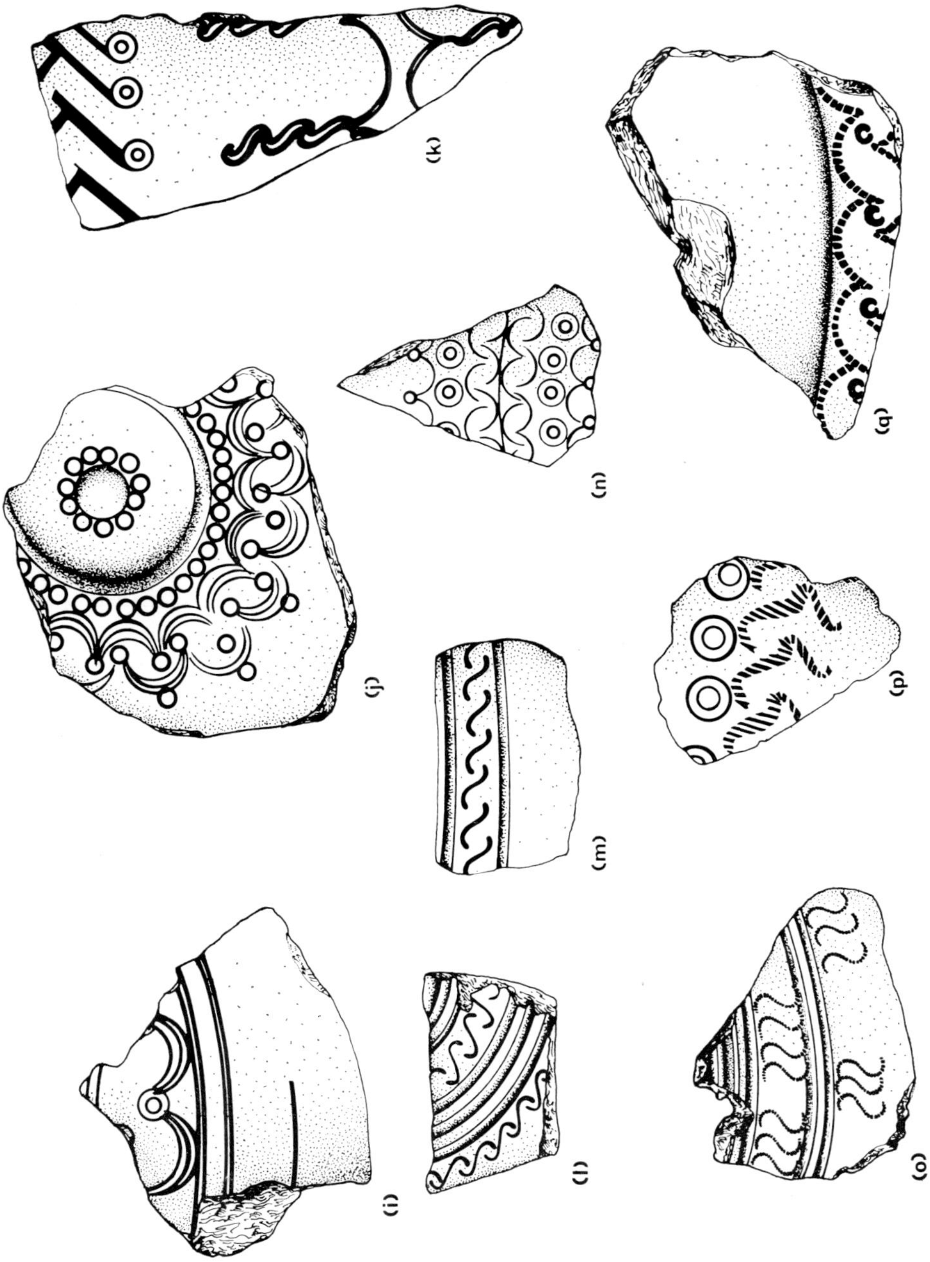

Fig. 11 (i)–(q). Céramiques estampées du "Premier style" oriental de Bohême, Bavière et Autriche[36]. (e, sens dessus dessous).

Les motifs à arcs, ou bien continus—par exemple les décors en bandes —ou bien disposés concentriquement en étoiles, ont en général leurs extrémités marquées par des cercles (Figs. 2–3). Dans quelques cas seulement, ces terminaisons sont remplacées par des éléments végétaux —palmettes, fleurs et feuilles—en général si étrangers au "Premier style" oriental[39]. Par exemple, les chaînes d'arcs estampés en pointillé sur trois vases en argile du Dürrnberg portent de petites palmettes à trois feuilles aux jointures (Figs. 12, a; 25a)[40]; deux feuilles se balançant à partir d'un petit cercle apparaissent sur un autre pot du Dürrnberg (Fig. 12, b)[41]; sur un flacon trouvé en fragments à Chlum-Bezdědovice (Bohême), deux feuilles sont attachées l'une à l'autre (Fig. 12, e; Pl. 25, b)[42], tandis que la frise de poterie de Prague-Bubeneč porte un motif à arcs avec des fleurs de lotus aux extrémités (Fig. 12, c; Pl. 25, c)[43]. Etroitement similaires sont les empreintes qui apparaissent à l'intérieur d'une tasse d'argile (Fig. 12, d)[44] trouvée à Prague-Hloubětín mais l'interprétation des deux petits sépales d'une fleur de lotus (cf. Fig. 9, a; 15, j) est déjà incertaine.

Des éléments floraux incorporés dans un décor géométrique à arcs—en général purement abstrait—se trouvent aussi sur un vase de Ratzersdorf (Autriche)[45], où l'on relève une rangée de motifs à feuilles accouplées, rattachés à des empreintes circulaires (Fig. 12, g1). Certes, ces éléments constitutifs peuvent aussi être groupés autrement, de telle manière que les deux feuilles s'inclinent l'une vers l'autre (Fig. 12, g2), mais, quelle que soit la façon dont on choisit de décrire ce décor, nous avons là un motif floral qui est incontestablement rare dans le "Premier style" oriental. Il est intéressant de noter que les cercles de la frise de Ratzersdorf sont estampés et les chaînes d'arcs, tracées à l'aide d'un compas, tandis que les contours inférieurs des feuilles étaient dessinés à la main. Semblable à la frise de Ratzersdorf est la remarquable frise du flacon de Hlubyně (Bohême) (Fig. 12, f)[46]. Il n'est pas nécessaire de la décrire ici en détail.

Les motifs à arcs d'Autriche et de Bohême discutés plus haut, avec leurs parures florales[47], comme les décors des bronzes occidentaux mentionnés ci-dessus (Fig. 8), constituent la presque totalité du matériel reflétant les deux tendances stylistiques du "Premier style", plus ou moins profondément mêlées. Outre ces pièces de la zone orientale à style composite nous trouvons aussi quelques pièces qui paraissent présenter des éléments floraux occidentaux dans une version beaucoup plus pure. Une tasse d'argile de Stehelčeves (Bohême)[48] comporte une frise d'empreintes à deux feuilles disposées concentriquement (Fig. 13, k). Bien que les empreintes fussent disposées en rangées symétriquement opposées et les feuilles hachurées, ce décor ne diffère pas fondamentalement de celui que nous avons déjà trouvé sur le vase de Ratzersdorf (Fig. 12, g). La frise estampée se trouvant sur l'épaule d'un récipient (Fig. 13, j) trouvé à Nynice (Bohême)[49] est en rapport étroit avec cette dernière. Une agrafe de ceinture de Linz (Autriche)[50], par exemple, porte un motif floral semblable (Pl. 26, f).

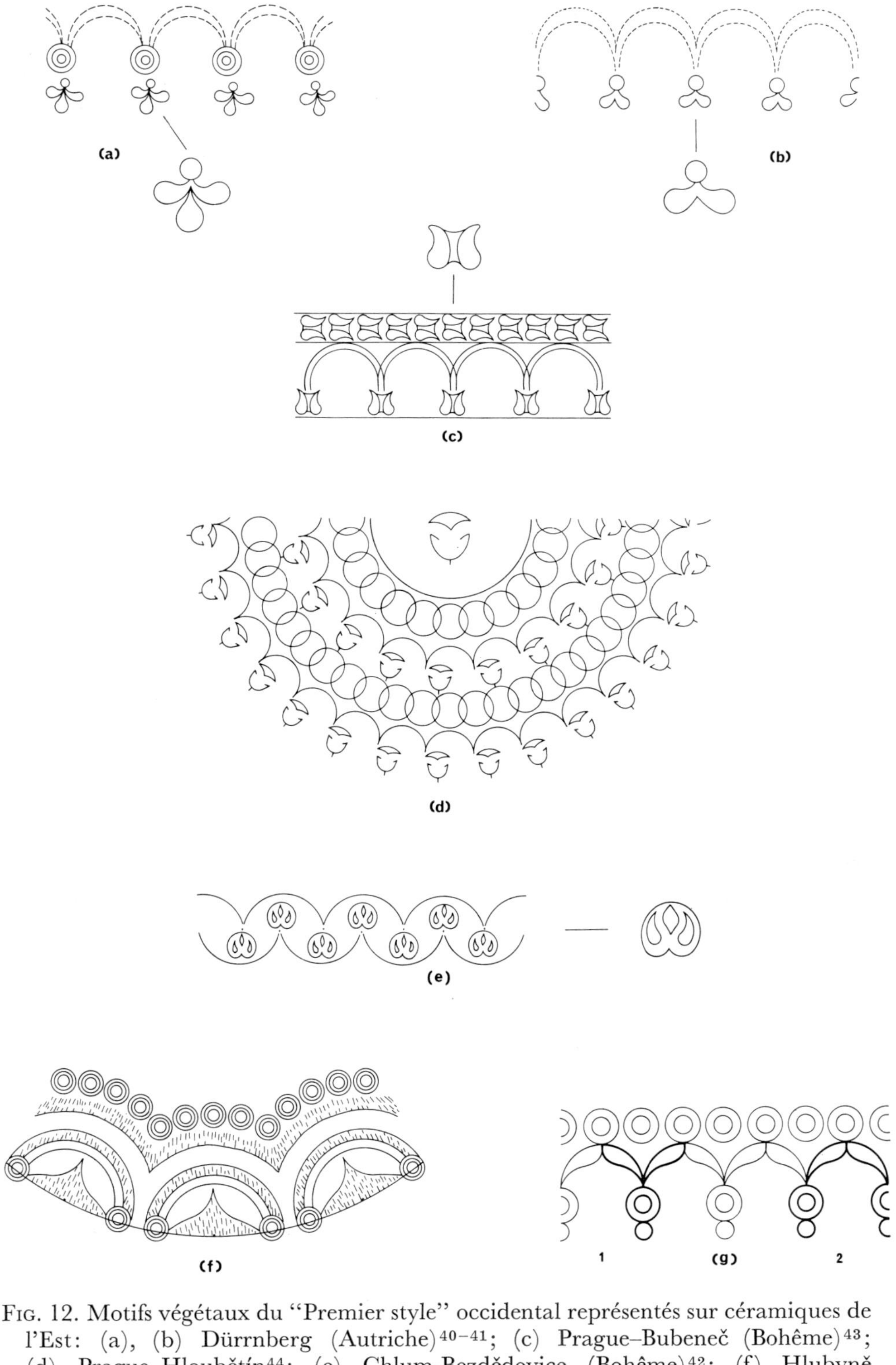

FIG. 12. Motifs végétaux du "Premier style" occidental représentés sur céramiques de l'Est: (a), (b) Dürrnberg (Autriche)[40–41]; (c) Prague–Bubeneč (Bohême)[43]; (d) Prague–Hloubětín[44]; (e) Chlum-Bezdědovice (Bohême)[42]; (f) Hlubyně (Bohême)[46]; (g) Ratzersdorf (Autriche)[45].

Des palmettes isolées à trois feuilles se voient sur une paire de branches en U (Fig. 13, c) associées à des mors dans la tombe d'un guerrier de Sedlec-Hůrka (Bohême)[51], un fragment en bronze (Fig. 13, b) de Velem-Szentvid (Hongrie)[52] ou sur la base de la poignée de l'oenochoé du Dürrnberg (Fig. 13, a)[53] et le fourreau d'épée de Hallstatt (Fig. 1, n)[54]. On peut citer encore à ce propos un torque découvert récemment au Dürrnberg (Fig. 13, d)[55], où une palmette à trois feuilles apparaît entre des esses.

Si l'on compare à la décoration estampée de Prague-Bubeneč (Fig. 12, c) les agrafes de ceinturon ajourées (Figs. 13, e–f, 26, a) de Nynice (Bohême)[56] et de Liebau (Saxe)[57], on peut y reconnaître des fleurs de lotus semblables, qu'on voit répétées sur des boucles de ceintures (Fig. 13, i) du Dürrnberg[58] et de Höresham (Bavière)[59] et en rangées, reliées à leurs extrémités par de petits cercles estampés (Fig. 13, g) sur des récipients d'argile découverts à Richterskeller et Hannersgrün (Bavière)[60]. Cependant, dans ce cas, les éléments estampés isolés consistent en deux feuilles en forme de gouttes surgissant d'un cercle (Fig. 13, g1). On voit bien comment, pour des yeux celtes, ces motifs n'avaient pas à être considérés comme un ensemble ayant une signification. En réalité, comme on peut le constater sur de nombreuses pièces, notamment pour le "Premier style", à l'Ouest aussi les artistes celtes brisaient en éléments isolés des fleurs et d'autres motifs floraux qui pouvaient, à l'origine, avoir une signification particulière[61].

Les pièces d'une tombe de Velká Turná (Bohême) comprennent des fragments d'un bol d'argile sur lequel se voient les empreintes de couples de feuilles accrochées l'une à l'autre (Fig. 13, h)[62]. En outre, des empreintes à quatre feuilles emplissent les bandes concentriques de la tasse de Velká Turná, tandis qu'un décor à peu près semblable fait toutefois de feuilles lancéolées et de cercles, signale le centre du bol.

Dans quelques exemples, les palmettes à trois feuilles ont rattaché directement à leur base, par un petit cercle, le motif de deux feuilles se balançant, que nous avons déjà vu sur le vase de Ratzersdorf (Fig. 12, g1). A l'intérieur d'une tasse d'argile trouvée à Lobodice (Moravie)[63], ce décor fait partie d'un motif fondé sur des esses qui entourent le centre circulaire de la tasse (Figs. 14, a; 25, e). Au dessus du motif de la feuille hachurée, apparaissent une remarquable empreinte à svastika, avec un cadre et des branches courbes, et, en outre, trois cercles. Une applique de bronze du Dürrnberg (Figs. 14, b; 25, f)[64] correspond, elle aussi, étroitement à l'empreinte à feuilles de Lobodice; cependant, un élément fait défaut au bronze autrichien: la hachure des feuilles. Les motifs floraux de Lobodice et du Dürrnberg peuvent etre comparés à ceux de Kallmünz (Bavière) (Fig. 14, d)[65] et aussi du Dürrnberg même (Fig. 14, f)[66], en dépit du fait qu'ici l'une des feuilles de la base est détachée. Mais ce qui semble spécialement intéressant est un trait de l'empreinte de la poterie de Kallmünz (Fig. 14, d): elle est remplie de

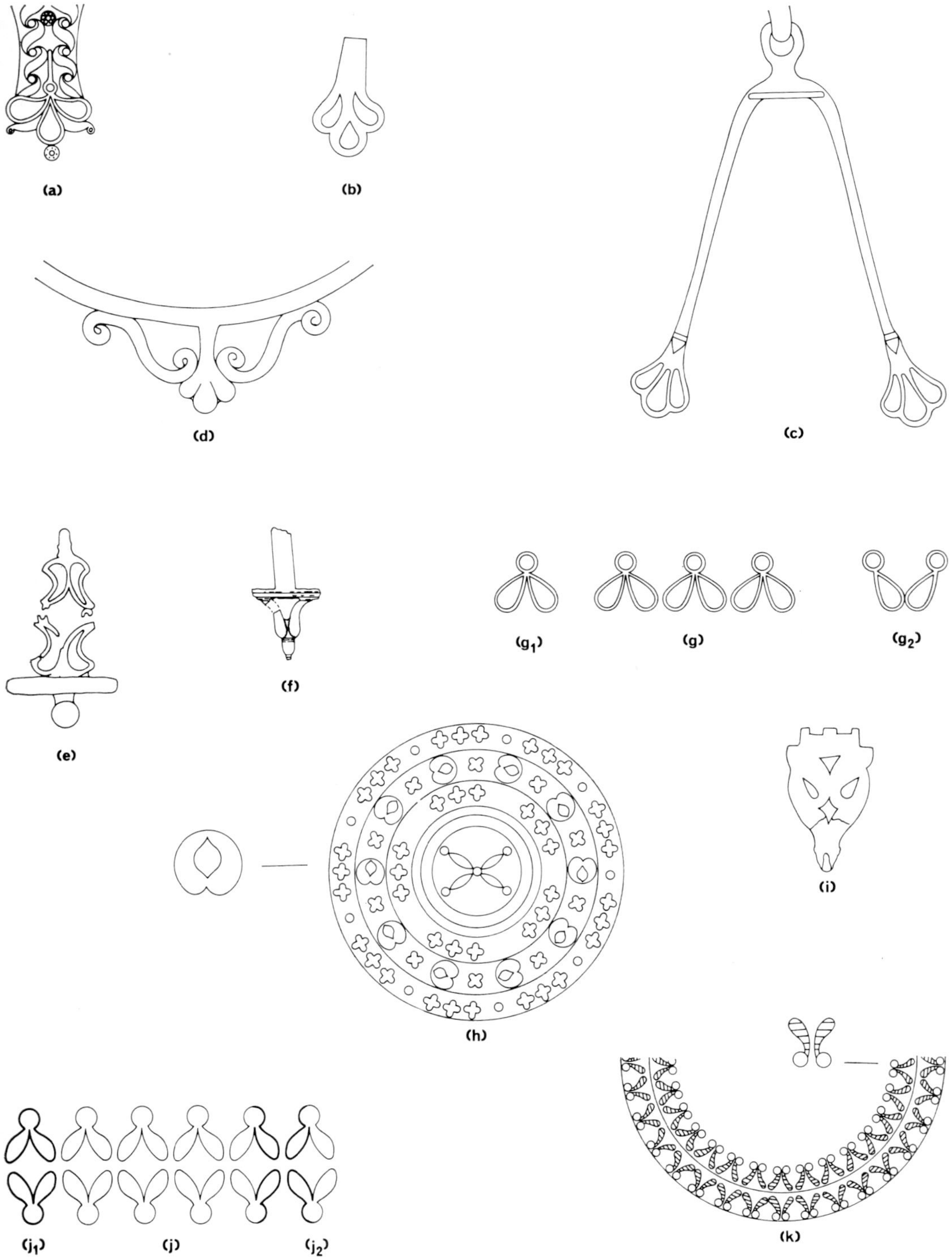

Fig. 13. Motifs végétaux du "Premier style" occidental représentés sur pièces en métal (a–f et i) et céramiques (g–h et j–k) de l'Est: (a, d et i) Dürrnberg (Autriche)[53, 55 et 58]; (b) Velem-Szentvid (Hongrie)[52]; (c) Sedlec-Hůrka (Bohême)[51]; (e) Liebau (Saxe)[57]; (f et j) Nynice (Bohême)[49 et 56]; (g) Richterskeller (Bavière)[60]; (h) Velká Turná (Bohême)[62]; (k) Stehelčeves (Bohême)[48].

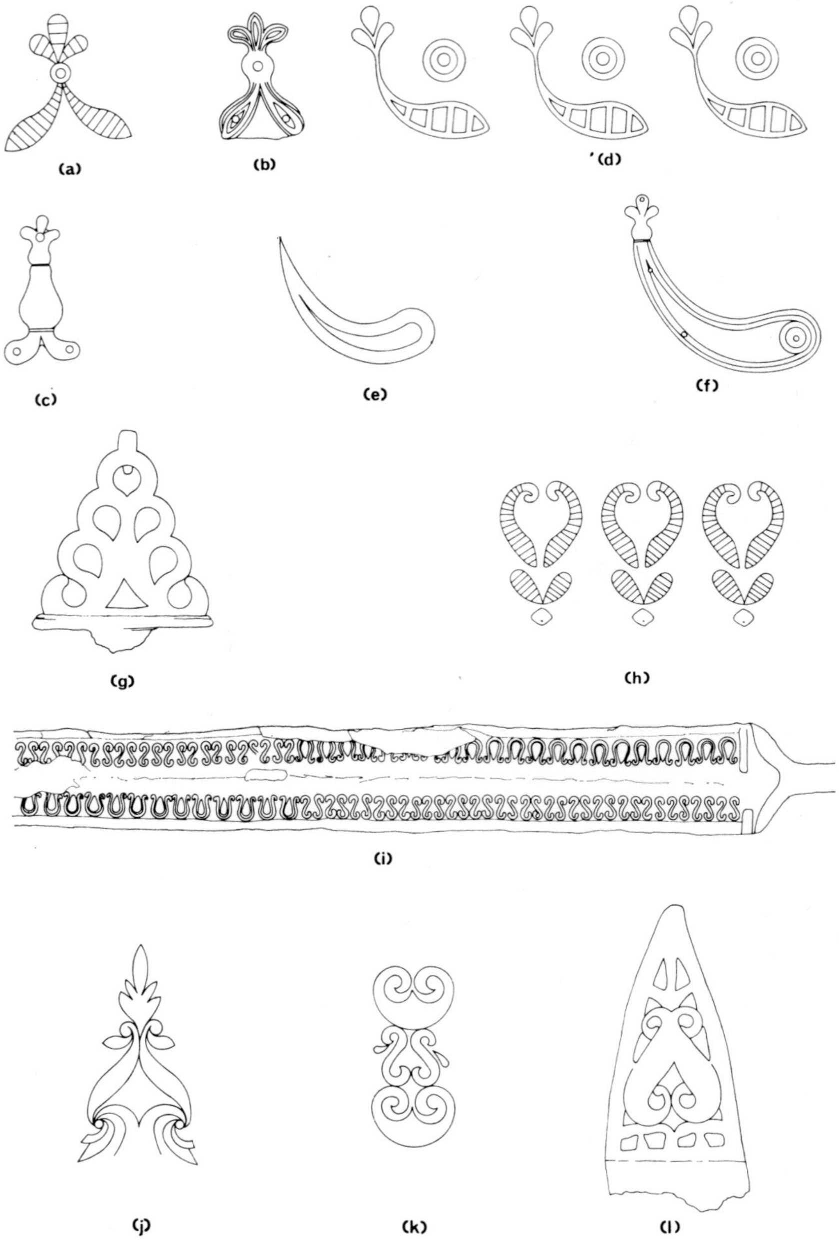

FIG. 14. Motifs végétaux du "Premier style" occidental représentés sur objets en métal (b–c, f–g, i–l) et céramiques (a, d–e, h) de l'Est: (a) Lobodice (Moravie)[63]; (b, c) (f) et (l) Dürrnberg (Autriche)[64, 66 et 79]; (d) Kallmünz (Bavière)[65]; (e) Libkovice (Bohême)[67]; (g) Gotha-Seebergen (Thuringe)[68]; (h) Poleňka (Bohême)[69]; (i) Jenišův Ujezd (Bohême)[82]; (j) Hallstatt (Autriche: complétée)[81]; (k) Liebau (Saxe)[78].

FIG. 15. Thèmes décoratifs du "Premier style" végétal dans la zone occidentale: parallélismes pour les motifs Figs 12–14[72].

petites cellules, semblables par leur contour à la feuille qui les entoure. Celle-ci, s'incurvant en élément isolé, motif si typique de l'art décoratif du "Premier style" occidental, se trouve sur un bol d'argile de Libkovice (Bohême: Figs. 14, e; 25, h)[67]. Une agrafe de ceinturon ajourée de Gotha-Seebergen (Thuringe)[68] comporte une décoration caractéristique faite de deux demi-palmettes (Fig. 14, g). Le motif estampé d'éléments floraux hachurés (Figs. 14, h; 25, d) sur un tesson de Poleňka (Bohême)[69] a aussi été inspiré par une tradition du "Premier style" occidental (Fig. 15, l–m)[70].

Tous les motifs floraux représentés sur les pièces de La Tène A orientale examinées jusqu'ici peuvent être rapportés sans aucune difficulté à des modèles celtiques occidentaux. Pour chaque motif, on trouve d'étroites correspondances dans la région du Rhin et de la Marne[71]. Et, en général, les motifs floraux que l'on rencontre à l'Est sont simplement des variations sur des thèmes décoratifs occidentaux bien connus. Il suffit donc ici de citer un ou deux de ces parallélismes typiques (Fig. 15), d'autres exemples de rapports stylistiques pouvant être facilement trouvés dans la "Grammaire" de Jacobsthal[72].

Un des motifs floraux les plus ornés que nous ayons reçus de l'Est est gravé sur le fourreau d'épée en bronze de Dražičky (Bohême)[73]. Ce décor (Figs. 16, c; 26, e) est en étroite relation avec le motif des deux lyres disposées verticalement l'une au dessus de l'autre (Fig. 16, b) mais nous n'avons conservé que les enroulements de la base des lyres. Ceux-ci ont des rejetons en spirale, se développant latéralement, qui leur donnent un caractère plus vivant et plus floral. Une palmette, dans un traitement raide très peu classique, pend entre les enroulements, qui se ramifient à partir de la lyre inférieure. La palmette est entourée de points, tandis que l'intérieur des vrilles qui la couronnent est constitué de pointillés gravés.

Sur le fourreau de Dražičky, le motif floral est pur, sans aucun accessoire géométrique du "Premier style" oriental. Sur un fragment en bronze de Chlum (Bohême)[74], un motif semblable à ce motif floral, encore que d'exécution plus simple, peut être relevé, mais il est mis en contraste avec une frise à arcs. La décoration de la "corne de char" de La Bouvandeau (Marne)[75] lui est comparable, pour l'essentiel (Fig. 16, a). La composition de Dražičky est évidemment en relation très étroite avec la tradition artistique occidentale. Le détail d'un ouvrage ajouré en bronze venant lui aussi de la tombe de La Bouvandeau (Fig. 16, b)[76] et d'autres pièces occidentales[77] peuvent aussi être étudiés à titre de comparaison.

Proche de la gravure de l'épée de Dražičky se trouve le décor floral du fourreau d'épée provenant de la tombe du guerrier de Liebau[78], déjà citée (Fig. 14, k). Des lyres, isolées aussi, se retrouvent sur les agrafes de ceintures du Dürrnberg (Fig. 14, l)[79] et de Loretto (Autriche)[80]: la lyre de Liebau comporte de petites feuilles pendant latéralement à partir des enroulements supérieurs de la lyre (Fig. 14, k); celle du Dürrnberg pouvait être couronnée d'une palmette (Fig. 14, e). On pourrait aussi se référer à un détail de la décoration du fourreau d'épée de Hallstatt[81]. Cependant, c'est seulement la moitié d'un motif à lyre qui apparait ici; pour une meilleure intelligence de la composition, le décor a été complété sur la Fig. 14, j. Des bandes de lyres alternant avec des rangées de lotus sur le fourreau d'épée de Jenišův Ujezd (Bohême)[82] doivent aussi être mentionnées ici (Fig. 14, i)[83].

FIG. 16. Décor (c) sur le fourreau d'épée de Dražičky (Bohême)[73] et comparaisons (a–b) de La Bouvandeau (Marne)[75–76].

Sur les objets estampés de l'Est, le motif de la lyre du "Premier style" occidental peut être trouvé dans quelques cas[84], bien que sous une forme stylisée et comme ceux de l'épée de Jenišův Ujezd (Fig. 14, i)—sans accessoires nettement floraux. Cependant, dans l'état actuel de notre information, ces pots décorés avec des lyres apparaissent pour la première fois dans la période La Tène B[85]. En fait, on peut également observer sur de nombreuses autres pièces de poterie et aussi de métal que des éléments de l'art décoratif du "Premier style" étaient encore très communs pendant la deuxième "phase" stylistique de l'art celtique selon Jacobsthal, et même postérieurement à l'époque de ce qu'il est convenu d'appeler le "style de Waldalgesheim"[86]; qu'on se réfère, par exemple, au fragment d'un *Hohlbuckelring* de Záboří, en Bohême (Fig. 17)[87]. Néanmoins, ce fait négligé par Jacobsthal ne sera pas examiné ici, mais étudié ailleurs[88].

Des ressemblances étroites avec les décors à lyres, constatées sur des objets découverts à l'Est, sont relevées dans les Figs 1, 19[89]. Pour d'autres comparaisons, il convient de consulter la "Grammaire" de Jacobsthal[90]. U. Osterhaus a mis en rapport l'épée de Jenišův Ujezd (Fig. 14, i) avec une pièce trouvée à Bavilliers (Territoire de Belfort)[91]. Un contact direct avec les motifs floraux occidentaux du "Premier style" est aussi apparent sur le décor d'une "Graphitton-Situla" du Dürrnberg[92] (Fig. 25, j) ; un essai de restituer ce décor très beau et très orné, constitué au moins de sept empreintes différentes, est présentée sur la Fig. 18, e. Si l'on se réfère aux gravures de l'oenochoé à bec tubulaire de Waldalgesheim (Fig. 19, e)[93] ou du tamis de Hoppstädten (Fig. 19, d)[94], on peut reconnaître le thème principal de la décoration de la situle du Dürrnberg. Mais la frise de la poterie estampée reprend aussi des éléments du disque bien connu d'Auvers-sur-Oise (Val d'Oise), par exemple (Fig. 19, c)[95]. Dans ce contexte, il faut mentionner une autre pièce de poterie de l'Est avec des caractères décoratifs semblables (Fig. 18, d); elle a été trouvée à Dobříčany (Bohême)[96]. Cependant, une analyse plus exacte de ce décor ne peut pas être proposée en raison de la préservation trop fragmentaire de la pièce.

Fig. 17. Pièce d'un "Hohlbuckelring" en bronze de Záboří (Bohême) (voir *n.87*).

La flore orientale propre au "Premier style", comparée avec celle de la zone celtique occidentale, est extrêmement pauvre. Très remarquable cependant, comme la frise du Dürrnberg (Fig. 18, e), est le décor des tessons de Rataje (Bohême); quelques uns de ceux-ci furent publiés pour la première fois par J. K. Hraše en 1900[97]; ceux dont nous disposons aujourd'hui n'ont été présentés que récemment par A. Beneš[98]. Le décor (Fig. 18, a) consiste en feuilles gonflées, dessinées à la main et avec cercles estampés (Fig. 26, c). La composition, comme une vrille à vague intermittente, présente des feuilles séparées roulant l'une vers l'autre. Sur la bordure supérieure, les feuilles sortent simplement entre deux estampes circulaires, tandis qu'en bas de la frise elles sont reliées par deux feuilles pendantes plus petites. Le fond du décor de Rataje étant en pointillé, l'artiste a mis l'accent sur le motif floral dominant.

La ressemblance entre ce décor de Bohême et ceux (Fig. 19, a–b) qui sont gravés sur l'oenochoé à bec tubulaire de Reinheim (Sarre)[99] est évidente, et je pense donc qu'il faut supposer là une influence directe. Cependant, dans ce contexte, il est aussi intéressant de comparer ces décors à deux lames d'or de l'Est, l'une trouvée dans la tombe princière 44/2 du Dürrnberg (Fig. 18, b)[100], l'autre (Fig. 18, c) venant de la riche sépulture de Chlum (Bohême)[101]; les deux pièces comportent des versions réduites des thèmes décoratifs de Rataje et Reinheim.

H. P. Uenze[102] a récemment étudié deux tessons décorés, venant des fouilles de Mintraching et Kreuzhof (district de Regensburg, Bavière). Selon lui, ces fragments devraient être considérés comme les bases de récipients en argile décorés à l'extérieur. Cependant, un examen plus attentif de la pièce de Mintraching (Fig. 20, b) peut révéler qu'il

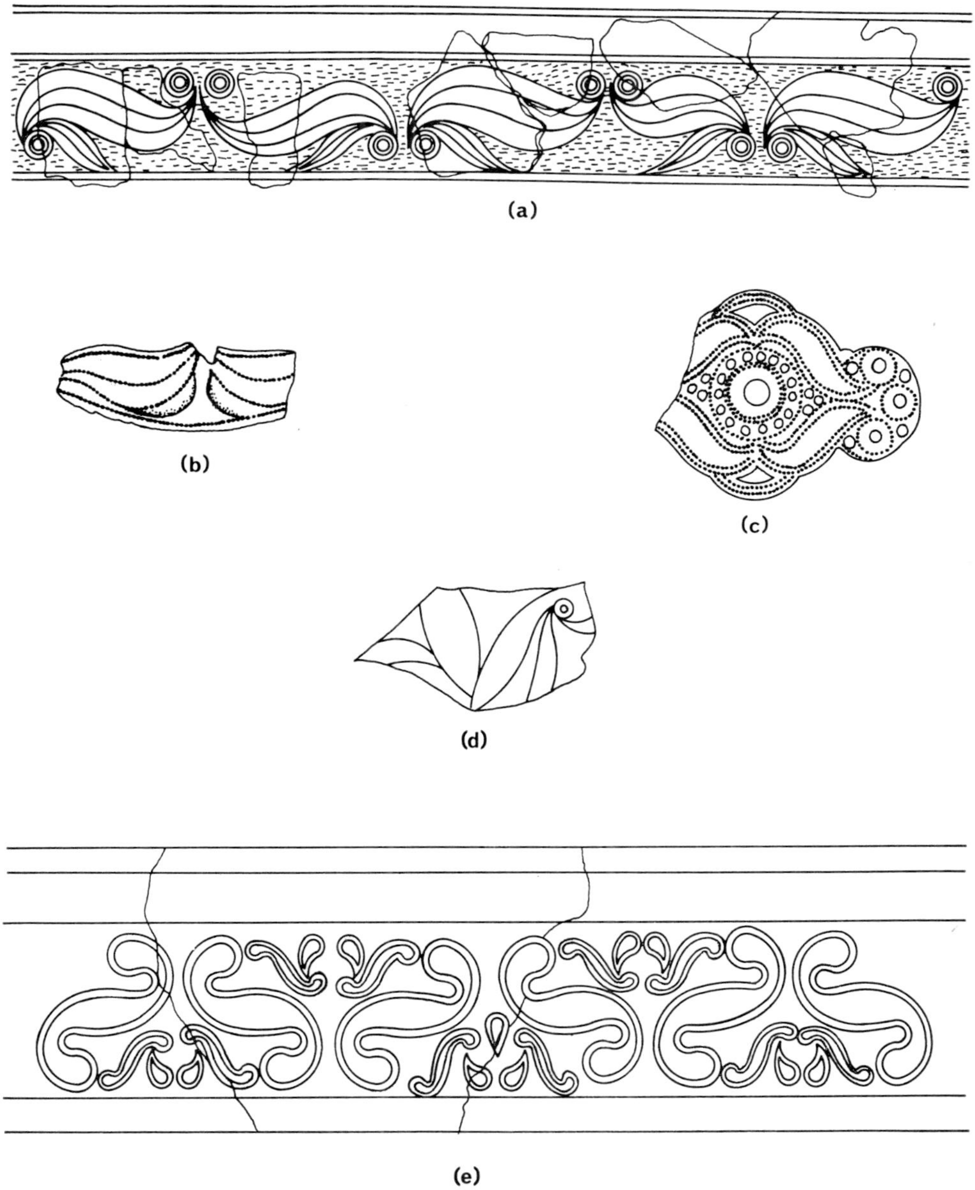

Fig. 18. Objets en or (b–c) et céramiques de Bohême et Autriche: (a) Rataje[97–98]; (b) et (e) Dürrnberg[92 et 100]; (c) Chlum [101]; (d) Dobříčany[96]. Pour parallélismes occidentaux voir Fig. 19.

appartient certainement à une coupe ("Braubacher Schale") à décoration *interne*. Cette hypothèse est confirmée par d'autres pièces de Bavière, de Kallmünz (Fig. 20, a)[103] par exemple et plus spécialement de Straubing (Fig. 20, c)[104]. Le motif en étoile estampé de cette dernière pièce (un bol) est cependant caractéristique du "Premier style" de l'Est. Contrastant avec celui-ci, les motifs à tourbillons des coupes de Kallmünz et Mintraching et du tesson de Kreuzhof reflètent nettement des modèles occidentaux (Fig. 21, a–f; Fig. 25, g)[105].

Le fragment de tasse de Straubing (Fig. 20, c) permet de savoir comment le motif du médaillon central était entouré par un cercle décoratif extérieur. Cette disposition apparaît sur le bol de bronze des Saulces-Champenoises (Ardennes) (Fig. 20, d)[106]. Mais ce ne sont pas seulement les motifs en tourbillons (Fig. 21) de l'ensemble du décor en général qui reflètent nettement une influence occidentale: celle-ci se retrouve aussi dans la constitution fondamentale des coupes qui, dans chaque cas, comprend un anneau en relief encadrant le motif central (Fig. 20, a–b). Là encore, le bol de bronze offre le parallèle le plus proche (Fig. 20, d).

Comme Jacobsthal l'a déjà souligné[107], il n'est pas rare que des tourbillons soient, dans l'art celtique ancien, accompagnés de décors végétaux. Les quelques exemples de ce motif relevés à l'Est suggèrent qu'il était lui aussi emprunté au répertoire ornemental occidental, et cela en connection avec des éléments floraux. Si l'on considère des pièces comme celles de Bavière citées plus haut (Fig. 20–21), une telle hypothèse paraît fondée. Sur un tesson de Leitzerdorf (Autriche)[108], les triscèles estampés ont été retirés d'une composition fermée et sont répétés, avec la même orientation, en une bande continue (Fig. 21, j). Le rapport avec l'art celtique occidental est là encore évident, lorsqu'on se réfère aux motifs semblables du bassin des Saulces-Champenoises (Fig. 21, i) ou aux pièces découvertes à La Gorge-Meillet et à Ecury-sur-Coole (Marne) (Fig. 21, k)[109]; quelques appliques de bronze en forme de triscèles de la sépulture princière 44/2 du Dürrnberg en sont aussi étroitement parentes (Fig. 21, g–h)[110]; sur un tesson estampé trouvé à Milovice (Moravie)[111], un triscèle est également accompagné d'éléments à feuilles accouplées, cette fois dans un traitement plus abstrait (Fig. 25, i). La base d'un flacon récemment trouvé par E. Soudská[112] au cimetière de Manětín-Hrádek (Bohême) comporte, comme décoration, un tourbillon à quatre branches. Une comparaison avec le décor incisé de l'oenochoé du musée de Besançon (Fig. 22, e)[113] peut aussi jeter de la lumière sur les liaisons fondamentales avec l'Ouest. Au vrai, l'habitude de décorer la base d'un récipient est un trait fort particulier, mais rarement enregistré, de l'art celtique ancien[114]. Un flacon estampé de Hidegség (Hongrie)[115] est aussi important à cet égard: comme le décor de sa base comporte, une fois de plus, un tourbillon à quatre branches, l'oenochoé de Besançon déjà mentionnée lui correspond de près (Fig. 22, a, e). Cependant, les rapports sont encore plus étroits. Des chaînes d'esses gonflées entourant

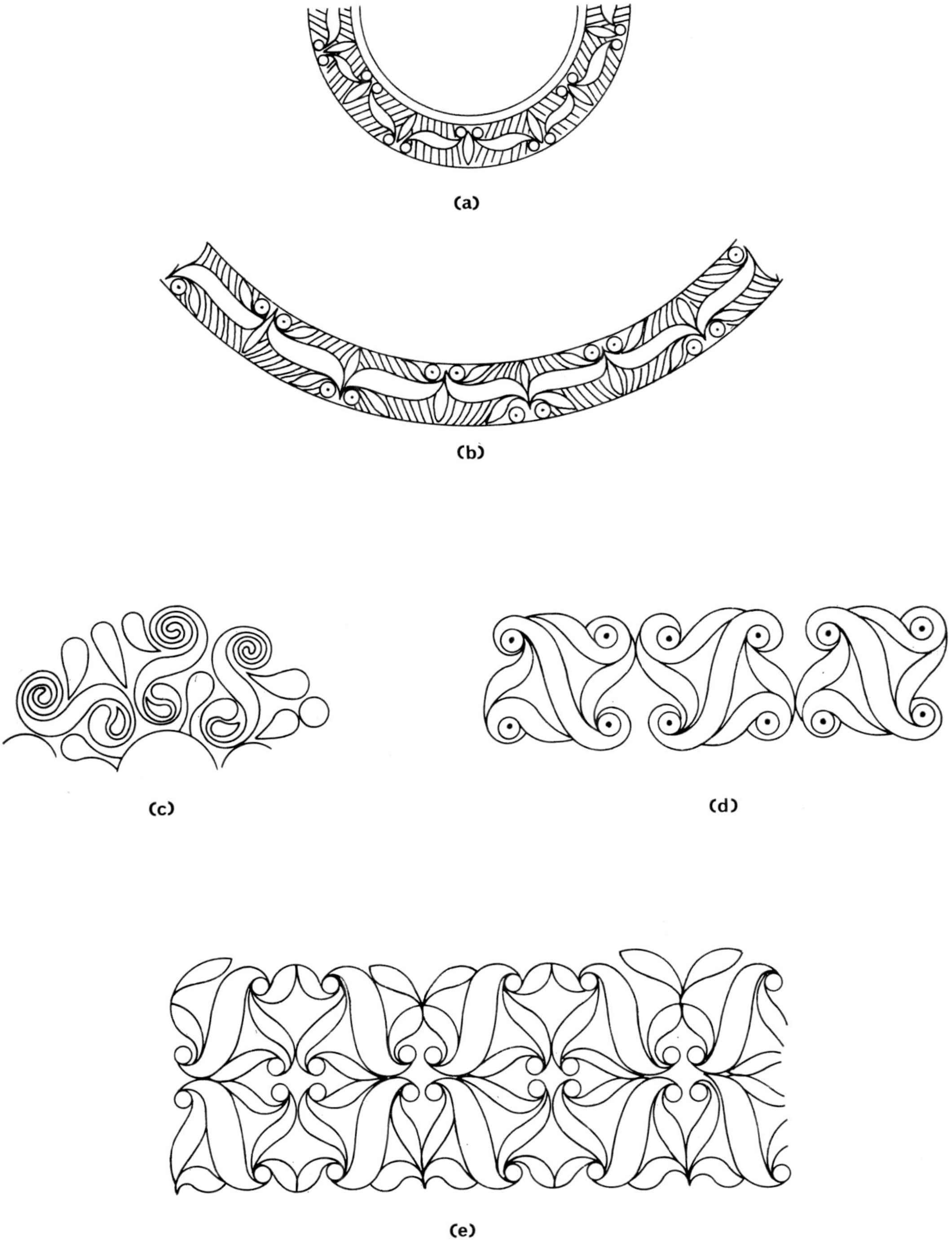

FIG. 19. Thèmes décoratifs (a–b) de l'oenochoé de Reinheim (Sarre)[99], (c) du disque d'Auvers-sur-Oise (Val d'Oise)[95], (d) du tamis de Hoppstädten (Palatinat-Rhénan)[94] et (e) de l'oenochoé de Waldalgesheim (Palatinat-Rhénan)[93].

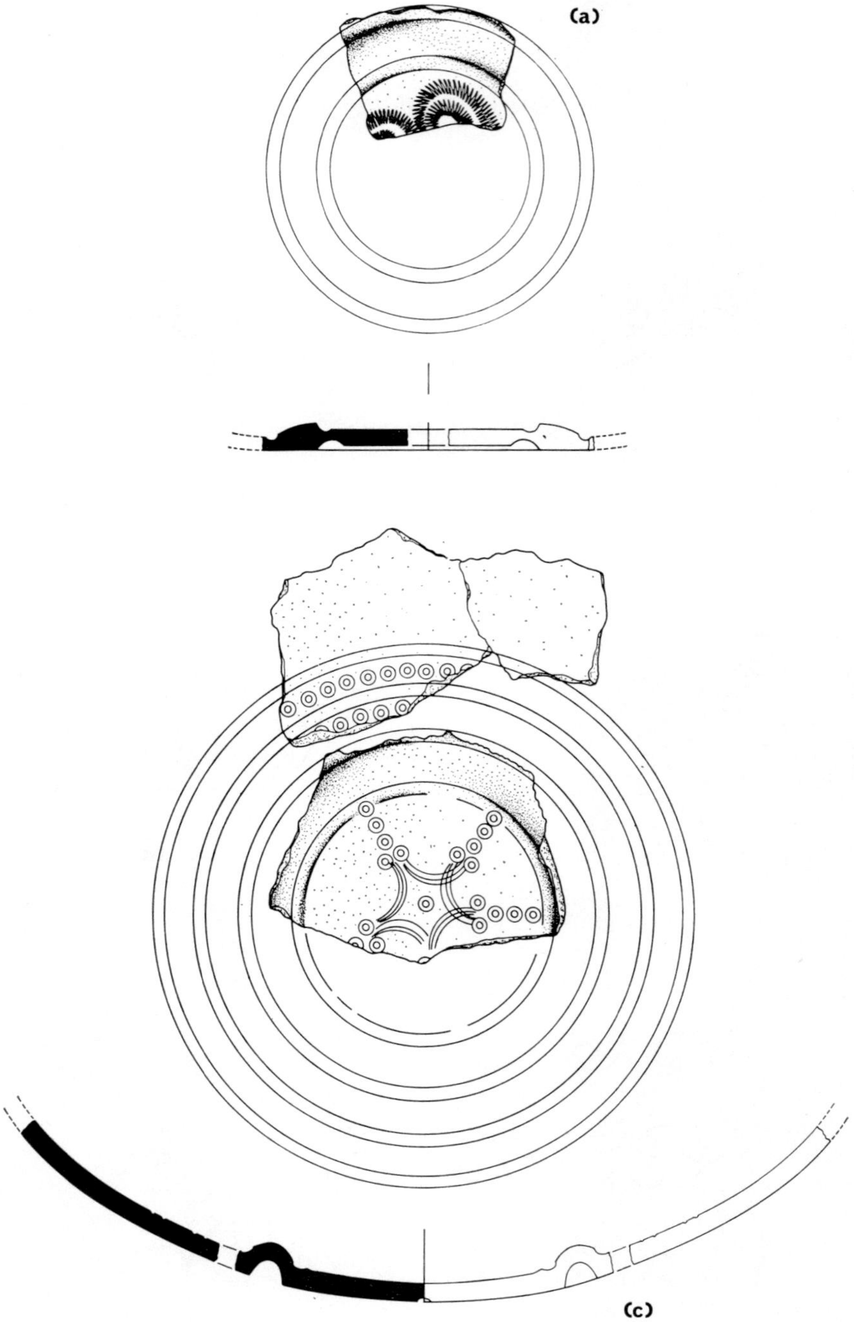

FIG. 20. Coupes en argile (a–c) et bol de bronze (d) à décoration interne: (a) Kallmünz (Bavière)[103]; (c) Straubing (Bavière)[104];

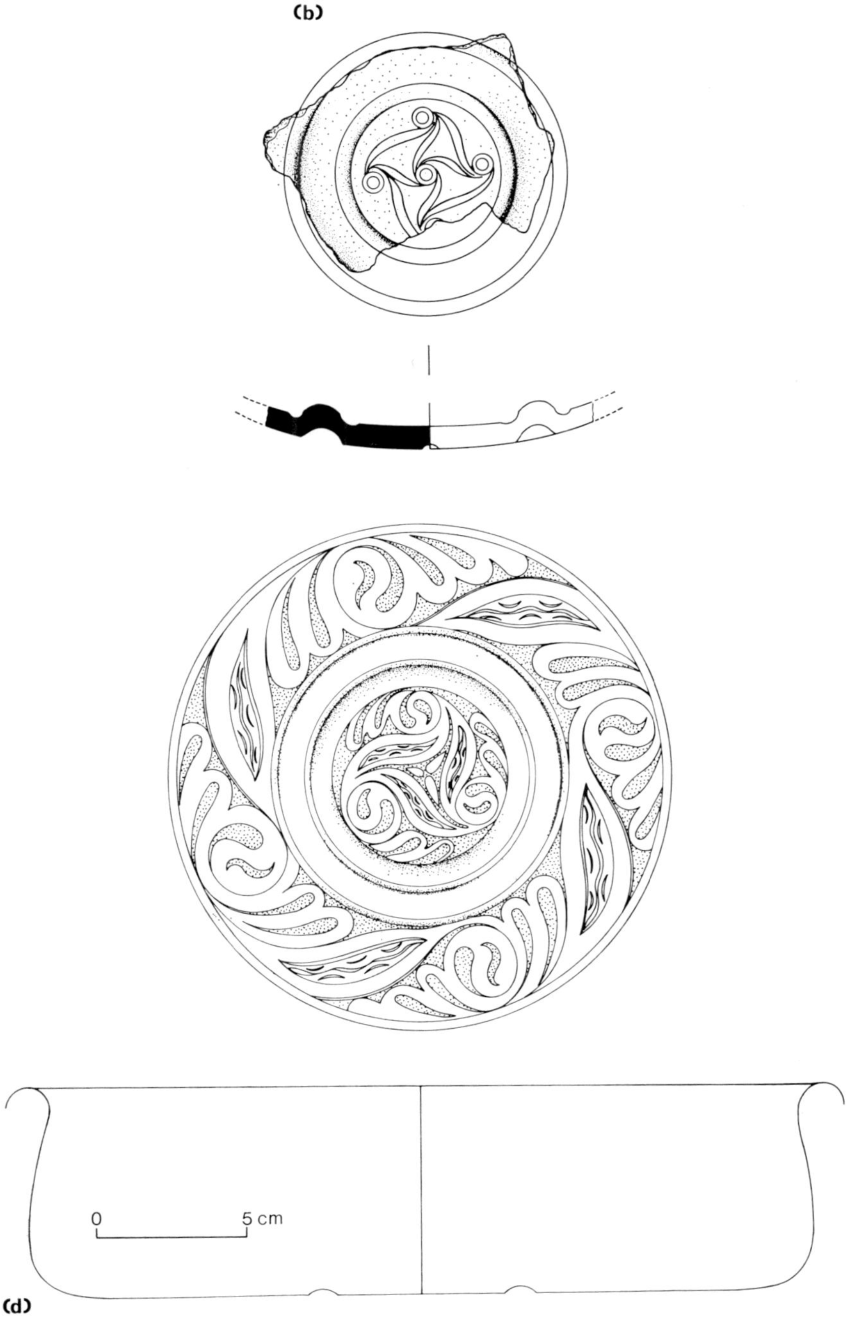

(Fig.20). (b) Mintraching (Bavière)[102]; (d) Les Saulces-Champenoises (Ardennes)[106].

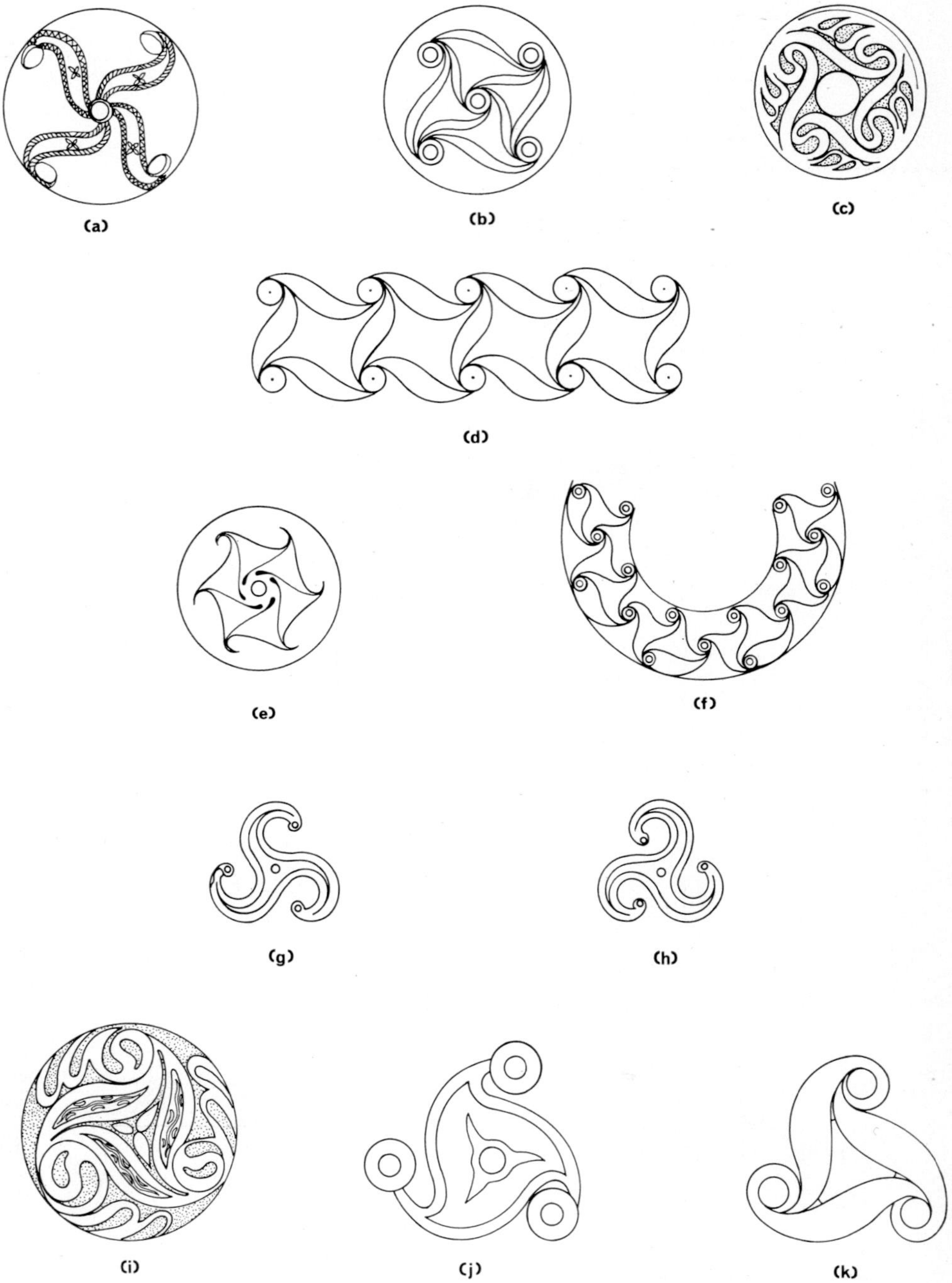

FIG. 21. Motifs en tourbillons : (a) du tamis de Hoppstädten (Rhénanie-Palatinat)[25], (b) de la coupe de Mintraching (Bavière)[102], (c) de l'oenochoé du Musée de Besançon[113], (d) du fourreau d'épée de Bavilliers (Terr. de Belfort)[91], (e) d'une céramique de Kreuzhof (Bavière)[102], (f) de la coupe de Schwarzenbach (Sarre)[28], (g, h) d'une oenochoé du Dürrnberg (Autriche)[110], (i) du bol des Saulces-Champenoises (Ardennes)[106], (j) d'un tesson de Leitzersdorf (Autriche)[108] et (k) d'un objet de La Gorge-Meillet (Marne)[109].

le flacon (Fig. 22, b) nous rappellent celui que nous venons de citer (Fig. 22, d). A plusieurs reprises, sur la pièce hongroise, des empreintes circulaires, dans une composition triangulaire, sont placées au dessus et au dessous des bandes de rouleaux en esse reliés de façon assez lâche les uns aux autres. Cela rappelle certainement les frises florales, où des palmettes poussent à partir des vrilles (Fig. 22, c; 13, d). Il est caractéristique d'un artiste de la zone orientale de La Tène de remplacer les palmettes par les motifs circulaires abstraits qui étaient si volontiers

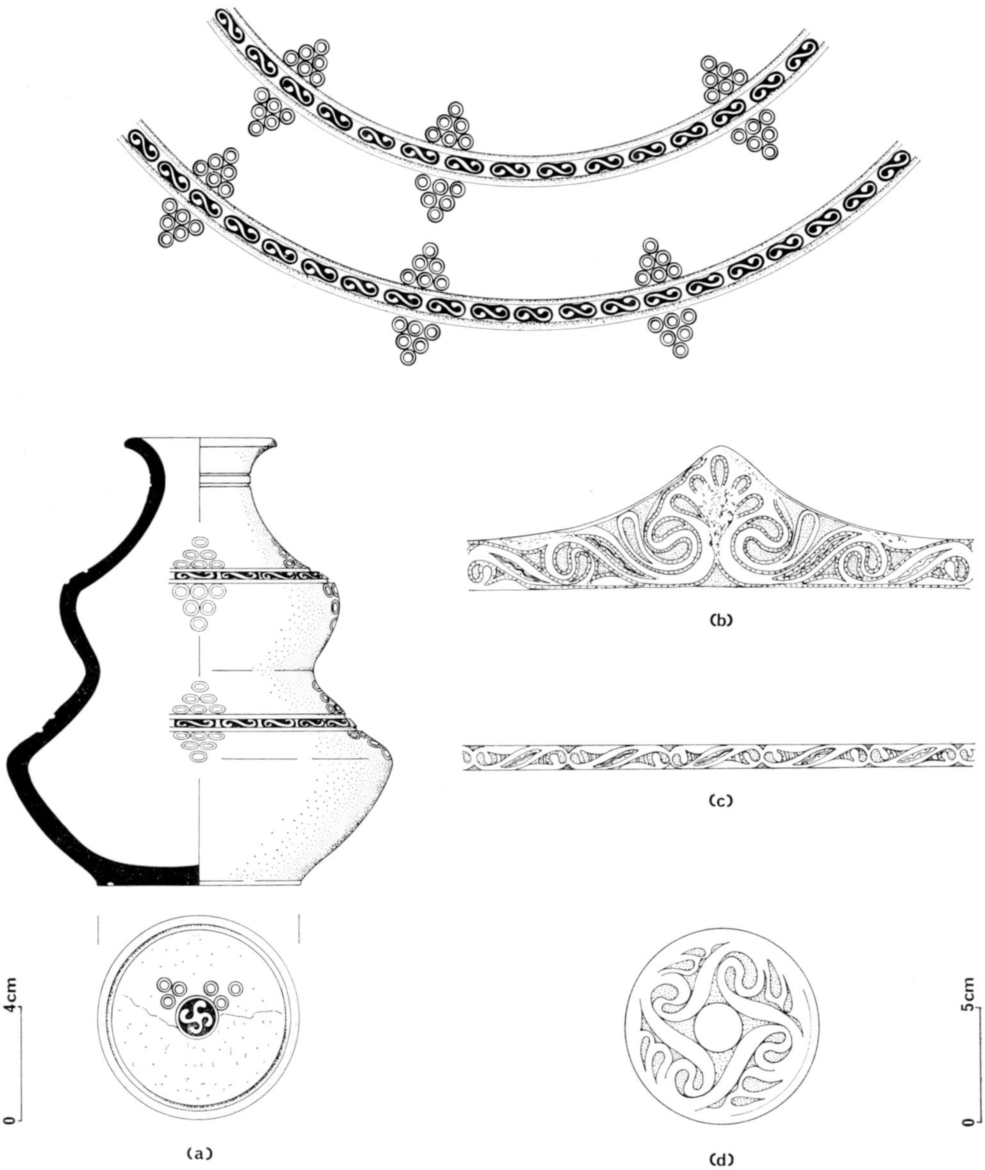

Fig. 22. (a, b) Flacon estampé de Hidegség (Hongrie)[115] et (c–d) motifs décoratifs de l'oenochoé du Musée de Besançon[113].

Fig. 23. (a) Décor du tamis de bronze découvert dans la région de la Marne[117] et (b), p. 93, frise de l'intérieur d'un bol d'argile de Thalmässing (Bavière)[116].

utilisés par les ateliers orientaux. Néanmoins, cette combinaison ornementale singulière devrait être dans son ensemble interprétée comme une nouvelle présomption en faveur de l'origine occidentale du motif de Hidegség. Et, dans ce contexte, rappelons également la coupe de Lobodice, avec ses motifs à feuilles poussant à partir d'une chaîne de rouleaux en esses (Fig. 25, e) décrits plus haut.

La frise décorée de l'intérieur d'un bol d'argile de Thalmässing (Bavière)[116], en partie estampée, mais surtout exécutée à l'aide d'une roue dentée de potier, est aussi une pièce d'un intérêt particulier (Fig. 23, b). La décoration consiste en un motif central à tourbillon (sur l'omphalos) ; tout autour, nous trouvons le motif d'un tourbillon très élaboré. Les branches du tourbillon se prolongent en vrilles. De cette décoration remarquable, il n'existe qu'un autre exemple très proche, le tamis de bronze découvert dans la région de la Marne (Fig. 23, a)[117]. Jacobsthal a déjà fait ce rapprochement[118]. En outre, on pourrait citer à titre de comparaison d'autres pièces de céramique de La Tène ancienne trouvées

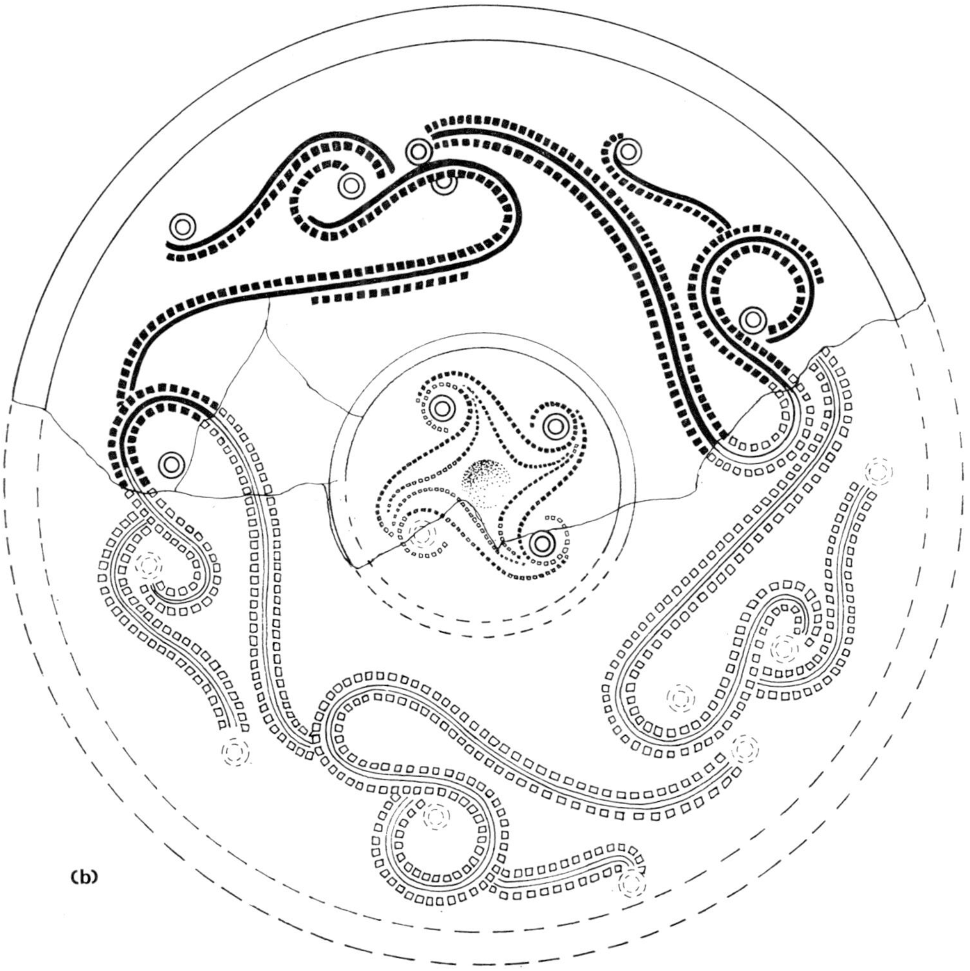

en Bavière, par exemple la coupe de Kallmünz (Fig. 20, a)[119]. Sur ces pièces, les motifs à tourbillons sont dessinés d'une manière semblable, encore que moins raffinée, puisque les vrilles font défaut.

Toutefois, il importe de remarquer que la décoration du tamis de la Marne (Fig. 23, a) doit être rattachée au "style de Waldalgesheim", plutôt qu'au "Premier style". Ce fait permettrait de donner aussi une date avancée (IVème siècle) à notre coupe bavaroise. J'ai déjà parlé des empreintes à lyre, appartenant incontestablement à la tradition du "Premier style" et apparaissant sur des récipients d'argile des périodes de La Tène B et C de la zone orientale[120]. En outre, le flacon de Hidegség, que nous avons rapproché de l'oenochoé du musée de Besançon (Fig. 22), date sans aucun doute du début de La Tène B (B1)[121]. Tout cela démontre que les influences de la région Marne-Rhin atteignant la zone orientale de La Tène ne se limitèrent pas à une courte période déterminée—c'est-à-dire la phase la plus ancienne de la culture de La Tène—mais persistèrent pendant les IVème et IIIème siècles avant J–C.

Enfin, on doit insister une fois de plus sur le fait que, contrairement à l'hypothèse de Jacobsthal, le "Premier style" ("Early Style") n'a pas de caractère uniforme dans toute la zone où on le trouve ("*Fürstengräberkreis*", région des tombes princières de La Tène A)[122]. Au contraire, *deux* tendances stylistiques principales, en genéral indépendantes l'une de l'autre, centrées sur *deux* zones différentes, doivent être distinguées. La zone occidentale du "Premier style" comprend principalement les régions du Rhin moyen et le Centre de la France; ici, nous pouvons constater une nette préférence pour des motifs *floraux* (Fig. 4). De l'autre côté, dans la zone *orientale* du "Premier style" (Fig. 5), en Bavière, Allemagne Centrale, Autriche, Bohême et Moravie, les artisans affectionnaient surtout des motifs curvilignes abstraits.

A l'Est, l'origine de cette prédilection pour les décors curvilignes peut être attribuée sans aucune difficulté à la période de Hallstatt, où elle est profondément enracinée[123]. A l'Ouest, au contraire, il n'existe pas de tradition aussi distincte et aussi nette. Nous pouvons supposer, dans cette région de la culture de La Tène, une nette "disposition" à prendre l'élément floral de l'art décoratif classique, en fait tellement étranger et nouveau dans l'art barbare au nord des Alpes.

Notre intention était de souligner, outre l'existence de deux provinces stylistiques distinctes avec des répertoires décoratifs différents, les relations qui existaient entre ces deux centres artistiques. Jusqu'à quel point cet échange—mutuel—des motifs décoratifs peut s'expliquer par des relations commerciales, ou bien dépendait d'artistes itinérants ou de groupes d'immigrants, cela doit dans chaque cas être examiné avec un soin particulier. Cependant, une analyse plus exacte de ce problème ne peut être proposée dans ce court essai[124].

Note additionnelle. Sur la Fig. 24, f–g, je montre le décor que porte la paire de bracelets de la sépulture de femme de Ciry-Salsogne (Aisne; H. Hubert, *Rev. arch.* 1902, **II**, p. 188, fig. 16), arcs tracés au compas, imbriqués à remplissage en pointillé: *voir* p. 109, Fig. 27 et le résumé en langue anglaise, avec renvois à mon article et à ceux de Hawkes (pp. 5–6) et de Kruta (p. 118).

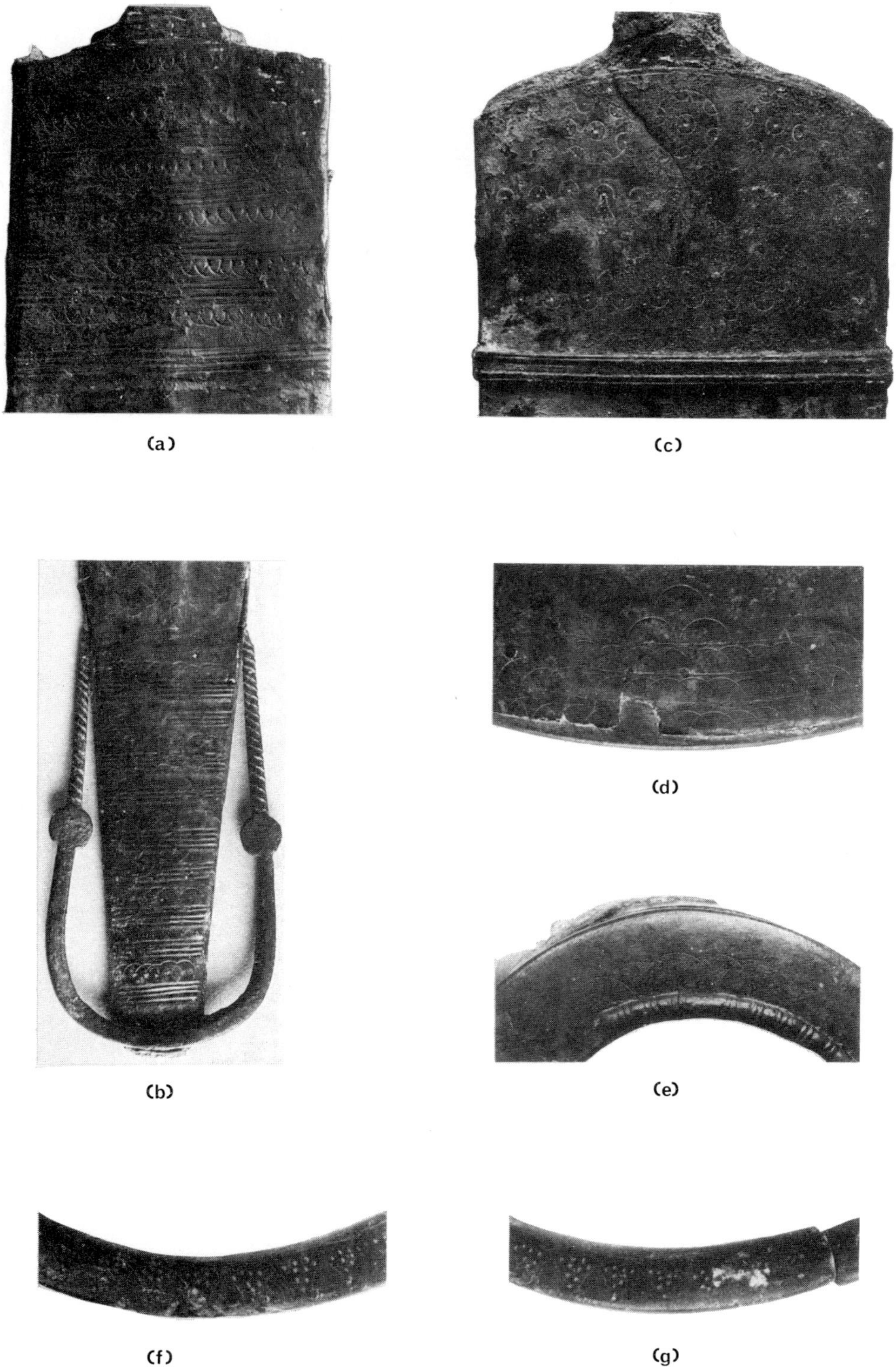

FIG. 24. (a–b) Châtillon (Marne); (c) Bussy-le-Château (Marne); (d) Bad Dürkheim (Palatinat-Rhénan); (e) Laumersheim (Palatinat-Rhénan); (f–g) Ciry-Salsogne (Aisne). (1/1)

FIG. 25. (a, f et j) Dürrnberg (Autriche) ; (d) Poleňka (Bohême) ; (c) Chlum (Bohême) ; (b) Chlum-Bezdědovice (Bohême) ; (c) Prague-Bubeneč ; (e) Lobodice (Moravie) ; (g) Kvenzhof (Bavière) ; (h) Libkovice (Bohême) ; (i) Milovice (Moravie). (1/1)

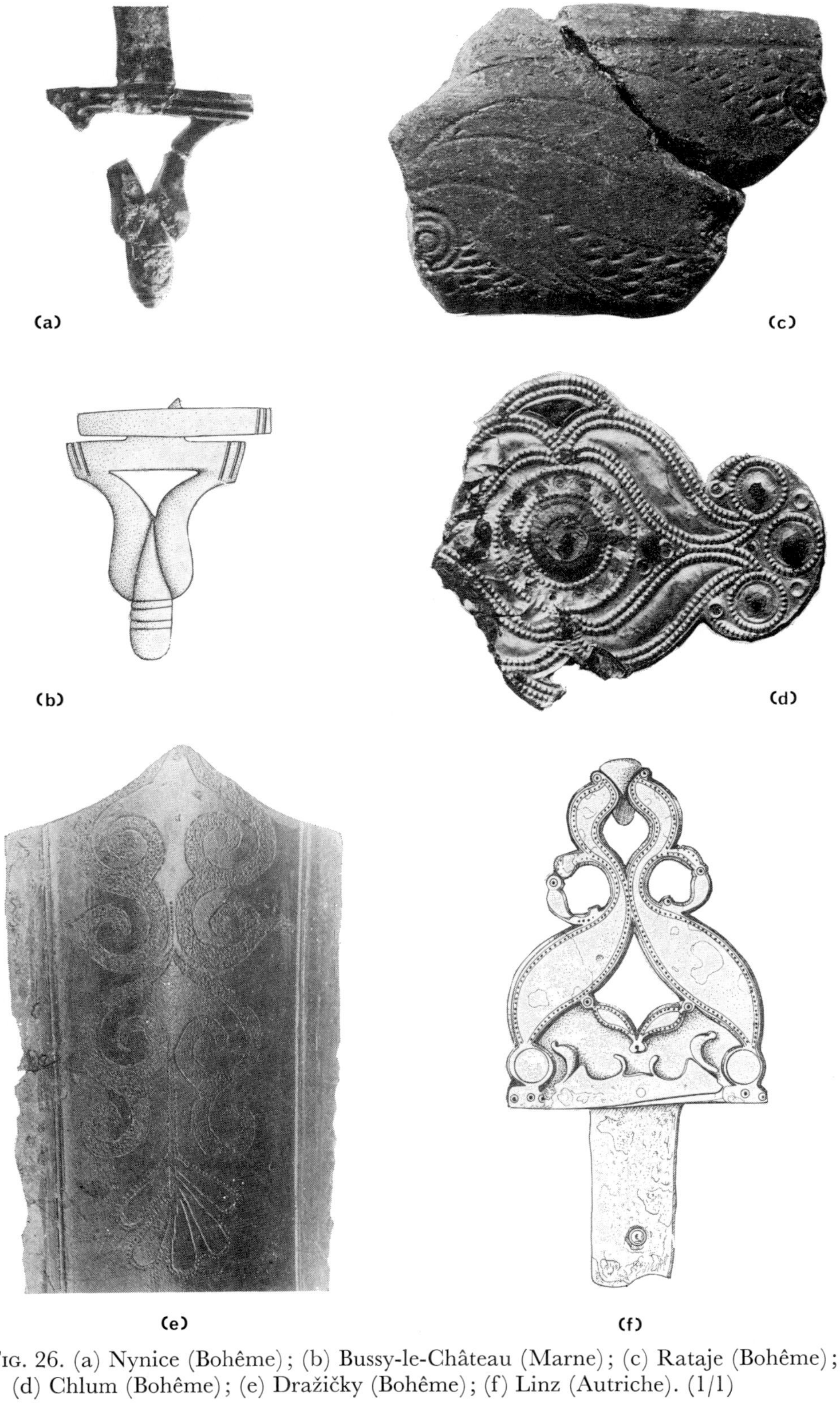

FIG. 26. (a) Nynice (Bohême); (b) Bussy-le-Château (Marne); (c) Rataje (Bohême); (d) Chlum (Bohême); (e) Dražičky (Bohême); (f) Linz (Autriche). (1/1)

Notes

(*Les renvois d'une note à une autre sont imprimés en caractères italiques gras*)

1. Jacobsthal, P. (1934). *Die Antike* **10,** p. 17 ss. *Idem* (1934). dans *Prähistorische Zeitschrift*, **25,** p. 62 ss. *Idem* (1935). dans *The Burlington Magazine for Connoisseurs* **67,** p. 112 ss. *Idem* (1944). *Early Celtic Art* (1944); 2ème ed. 1969.

2. Piggott, S. (1970). *Early Celtic Art*: Catalogue of the Exhibition at Edinburgh and London nos 113–18.

3. Keller, J. (1965). *Das keltische Fürstengrab von Reinheim.* **1.**

4. Penninger, E. (1972). *Der Dürrnberg bei Hallein.* **1.**

5. Jacobsthal, P. (1944). ***(n. 1)*** p. 60 ss.

6. *Idem*, (1944). ***(n. 1)*** p. 60 ss et PLANCHE 261 ss.

7. *Idem*, (1944). ***(n. 1)*** p. 221 ss.

8. *Idem*, (1944). ***(n. 1)*** PLANCHE 274, no. 392.

9. *Idem*, (1944). ***(n. 1)*** PLANCHE 261, no. 11. Sur la frise estampée de Tajanov, Bohême (*Ibid* PLANCHE 261, no. 10), *voir* Schwappach, F. (1973). *Etudes Celtiques* **13,** p. 710 ss. Fig. 2.

10. Schwappach, F. (1973). *Etudes celtiques*, **13,** p. 710 ss.

11. Fig. 2: a Prague-Hloubětín; b Nevězice; c Kralovice; d Těšetice; e g–h Dürrnberg; f Hallstatt; i Pňovany; j Opolánky; k Kelinprüfening; 12 Tuchoměřice—Kněžívka.

12. Schwappach, F. (1969). *Die stempelverzierte Keramik der frühen Latènekultur*, Marburger Beiträge zur Archäologie der Kelten: Festschrift W. Dehn.
Idem, (voir ***n. 10***).
Idem, (1971). *Hamburger Beiträge zur Archäologie* **1,** p. 131 ss.
Idem, (1974). *Fundberichte aus Baden-Württemberg* **1,** p. 337 ss, Nos 16 et 36.
Frey, O. H. et Schwappach, F. (1973). *World Archaeology* **4,** p. 339 ss.

13. Dehn, W. (1966). *Sborník Národního muzea v Praze* **20,** p. 137 ss nos 4 et 6.
Schwappach, F. (1974). *Fundberichte aus Baden-Württemberg* **1,** Nos 12–15 et 25 également ***n. 12 et 37.***

14. Megaw, J. V. S. (1970). *Art of the European Iron Age* p. 74.

15. Megaw, (1970). *Ibid.* p. 74: Le vase en bronze du Dürrnberg.
Penninger, E. (1972). *Der Dürrnberg bei Hallein* **1,** PLANCHE C ss; 47.

16. Schwappach, F. (*voir* ***n. 10***) p. 710 ss, 722 Fig. 9.
Idem, (1974). *Fundberichte aus Baden-Württemberg* **1,** nos 1–52 etc.

17. Jacobsthal, P. (1944). ***(n. 1)*** p. 203 no. 397.
Schwappach, F. (*voir* ***n. 10***) p. 723 Fig. 10.
Idem, (1974). *Fundberichte aus Baden-Württemberg* **1,** no. 49.

18. Schwappach, F. (*voir* ***n. 10***) p. 724, Fig. 11.
Idem, Fundberichte aus Baden-Württemberg nos 51–52.
Voir aussi le disque ajouré de Cuperly (Marne):
Jacobsthal, P. (1944). (*voir* ***n. 1***) PLANCHE 116, no. 187 et la pièce en bronze:
Schwappach, F. (1974). *Fundberichte aus Baden-Württemberg* **1,** Fig. 23, 3.

19. Kimmig, W. (1944–50). *Germania* **28,** p. 41 Fig. 1.
Schwappach, F. (*voir* ***n. 10***) p. 725, Fig. 12.
Idem, (1974). *Fundberichte aus Baden-Württemberg* **1,** no. 50.

20. Jacobsthal, P. (1944). (*voir* ***n. 1***) p. 84 ss.
Megaw, J. V. S. (1972). *World Archaeology* **3,** p. 276 ss.

21. Zürn, H. (1970). *Hallstattforschungen in Nordwürttemberg* p. 73 ss. PLANCHE 48, D.
Schwappach, F. (1974). *Fundberichte aus Baden-Württemberg* **1**, no. 48.

22. Oenochoé de Reinheim, tamis de Hoppstädten, agrafe de ceinture de Schwabsburg et oenochoé de Waldalgesheim:
Schwappach, F. (1974). *Fundberichte aus Baden-Württemberg* **1,** p. 337 ss.

23. Jacobsthal, P. (1944). (*voir* ***n. 1***) p. 202, no. 387, PLANCHE 189 ss.
Schwappach, F. (1974). *Fundberichte aus Baden-Württemberg* **1,** no. 17.

24. Jacobsthal, P. (1944). (*voir* ***n. 1***) p. 179 no. 138; PLANCHE 77.

25. Kilian, L. (1956–58). *Trierer Zeitschrift* **59,** p. 24–6 ss.

26. Mariën, M.-E. (1962), *Latomus* **18**, p. 1113 ss. (Eigenbilzen et Hallein).

27. Frey, O. H. (1971). *Hamburger Beiträge zur Archäologie* **1,** p. 87, Fig. 2, 1.

28. Jacobsthal, P. (1944), (*voir* ***n. 1***) p. 167, no. 18, PLANCHE 18–19.
Frey, O. H. et Schwappach, F. (1973), *World Archaeology* **4,** p. 339 ss, Fig. 10, 3.

29. Cf. *n. 26* (Mariën) Fig. 9, d et f; Schwappach, F. *Marburger Beiträge zur Archäologie der Kelten* (Festschrift W. Dehn), PLANCHE 20, 1.

30. Schwappach, F. (1973). *Bonner Jahrbücher* **173**, p. 65, Fig. 11, 2–3; p. 103 ss., nos. 23, 27, 36; p. 66, n. 23.

31. Frey, O. H. et Schwappach, F. (1973). *World Archaeology* **4,** p. 349 ss.
Schwappach, F. (1974). *Fundberichte aus Baden-Württemberg* **1.**

32. Frey, O. H. (1971). *Hamburger Beiträge zur Archäologie* **1,** p. 95 ss, Fig. 12, 1.
Frey, O. H. et Schwappach, F. (1973). *World Archaeology* **4,** p. 349 ss. Fig. 22–23.

33. Jacobsthal, P. (1944). (*voir* ***n. 1***) PLANCHE 9 ss, no. 11; 14, no. 14; 18–19, no. 18; 29–30, no. 34; 21, no. 20; 62–63, no. 100; 167, no. 350; 22, no. 23; 23, no. 24; 24, no. 26; 34, no. 41; 35–36, no. 42; 43, no. 53; 47, no. 59; 52, no. 72; 58, no. 95; 59–60, no. 96; 77, nos 136 et 139; 100, no. 157; 100, no. 158; 105, no. 168; 108, no. 171; 117, no. 189; 120, no. 199; 121, no. 200; 159–60, no. 316; 161, no. 318; 167, no. 351; 168, no. 356; 169, no. 355 c; 230, b; 177, no. 379; 178 ss, no. 381; 184–85, no. 382; 249, b;
Haffner, A. (1972). *Archäologisches Korrespondenzblatt* **2,** p. 279 ss, PLANCHE 51.
Piggott, S. (1970). ***(n. 2)*** nos 113–117.
Keller, J. (1965). Reinheim **1,** PLANCHE 12–13; 21; 23.

34. Dehn, W. (1951). *Bonner Jahrbücher* **151,** p. 83 ss.
Schwappach, F. (1969). *Marburger Beiträge zur Archäologie der Kelten.* Festschrift W. Dehn p. 252 ss.
Idem, (1971). *Hamburger Beiträge zur Archäologie* **1,** p. 131 ss, 141 ss.
Idem, (1973). *Etudes celtiques* **13,** p. 710 ss.
Idem, (1974). *Fundberichte aus Baden-Württemberg* **1,** p. 337 ss.
Frey, O. H. et Schwappach, F. (1973). *World Archaeology* **4,** p. 343 ss.

35. Schwappach, F. (1969). *Die stempelverzierte Keramik der frühen Latènekultur,* Marburg.
Idem, (1974). *Fundberichte aus Baden-Württemberg* **1,** p. 337 ss.

36. Fig. 11: a Hostomice; b et p Chlum-Bezdědovice; c Vliněves; d Dürrnberg; e Láz; f et k Dobev; g Opolánky; h Pňovany; i Bollstadt; 10 Hořany; l Líně; m Podolí; n Fuchsstadt; o Poleňka; q Tuchoměřice-Kněžívka. (Cf. ***n. 34***); également Schwappach, F. (1973). *Bonner Jahrbücher* **173,** p. 53, Fig. 2 et 4.

37. Cf. ***n. 13***. Schwappach, F. (1973). *Etudes celtiques* **13,** p. 720, Fig. 7, 1.
Frey, O. H. et Schwappach, F. (1973). *World Archaeology* **4,** p. 344, Fig. 13, 1.
Schwappach, F. (1973). *Bonner Jahrbücher* **173,** p. 53 ss, Fig. 2, 1–2; 4, 1.5–6.

38. *Voir* ***n. 16*** ci-dessus.

39. *Voir* ***n. 10***.

40. Hell, M. (1929). *Mitteilungen der Anthropol. Gesellschaft Wien* **59,** p. 155 ss, Fig. 5, 3.
Klose, O. (1932). *Wiener Prähistorische Zeitschrift* **19,** p. 39 ss, Fig. 2; PLANCHE 1, 7;
Schwappach, F. (1973). *Etudes celtiques* **13,** p. 712, Fig. 1.
Idem, (1973). *Bonner Jahrbücher* **173,** p. 68 ss, Fig. 14, 1. La 3e pièce non publiée, au Musée de Hallein.

41. Penninger, E. (1972). Dürrnberg **1,** PLANCHE 34, 16.

42. Eisner, J. (1914). *Památky Arch.* **26,** p. 7, Fig. 4, 7.
Schwappach, F. (1973). *Bonner Jahrbücher* **173,** p. 68, 70, Figs. 14, 4; 16, 2.

43. Schwappach, F. (1973). *Bonner Jahrbücher* **173**, p. 70, Fig. 16, 3.

44. Rybová, A. et Soudský, B. (1962). *Libenice,* PLANCHE 35, 2;
Schwappach, F. (1973). *Fundberichte aus Baden-Württemberg* **1,** no. 17.

45. Engelmayer, R. (1963). *Arch. Austriaca* **33,** p. 37 ss, Fig. 4.

46. Filip, J. (1956). *Keltové* p. 177, Fig. 53; PLANCHE 14.
Schwappach, F. (1973). *Bonner Jahrbücher* **173,** p. 65, Fig. 11, 1.

47. Pour les correspondances dans l'Ouest cf. Fig. 15, et surtout les planches de Jacobsthal, P. (1944). (*voir* ***n. 1***).

48. Schwappach, F. (1973). *Bonner Jahrbücher* **173**, p. 107, Fig. 51.

49. Šaldová, V. (1971). *Památky Arch.* **62,** p. 37, Fig. 36, 5.
Schwappach, F. (1973). *Bonner Jahrbücher* **173,** p. 71, Fig. 17, 1.

50. Schwappach, F. (1973). *Bonner Jahrbücher* **173**, p. 110, Fig. 54.

51. Filip, J. (1956). *Keltové,* PLANCHE 9, 6.

52. Miske, K. von (1908). *Die prähistorische Ansiedelung Velem St. Vid* **1,** PLANCHE 46, 42.

53. Jacobsthal, P. (1944). (*voir* ***n. 1***) PLANCHE 185, no. 382.

54. Jacobsthal, P. (1944). *Ibid.* PLANCHE 60, no. 96; 275, 395.
Krieger und Salzherren: *Hallstattkultur im Ostalpenraum*; Ausstellungskatalog 4 des RGZM. (1970); PLANCHE 81.

55. Sépulture 71, 1; au Musée de Hallein. Dessin de L. Pauli, Munich.

56. Šaldová, V. (1971). *Památky Arch.* **62,** p. 38, Fig. 37, 7.

57. Coblenz, W. (1956). *Arbeits- und Forschungsberichte zur Sächsischen Bodendenkmalpflege* **5,** p. 297 ss, Figs. 28–31.

58. Penninger, E. (1972). Dürrnberg **1,** PLANCHE 11, 9.

59. Munich, Prähistorische Staatssammlung.—Cf. également l'agrafe de ceinture de Kuffarn (Autriche):
Dungel, A. (1907). *Jahrbuch für Altertumskunde* **1,** p. 93, Fig. 14.

60. Uenze, H. P. (1964). *Bayerische Vorgeschichtsblätter* **29,** p. 93, Fig. 8, 5; Schwappach, F. (1973). *Bonner Jahrbücher* **173**, p. 75, Fig. 21. (Richterskeller).
Hannersgrün au Musée de Regensburg.

61. Frey, O. H. et Schwappach, F. (1973). *World Archaeology* **4,** p. 339 ss.

62. Dubský, B. (1928–30). *Památky Arch.* **36,** p. 94 ss, Fig. 7, Planche 31. Empreintes similaires sur un tesson de Hostomice (Bohême) au Musée de Teplice.

63. Schwappach, F. (1973). *Bonner Jahrbücher* **173**, p. 74, Fig. 20, 1.

64. Klose, O. (1932). *Wiener Prähistorische Zeitschrift* **19,** p. 47, Planche 1, 11.
Penninger, E. (1963). *Mitteilungen der Gesellschaft für Salzburger Landeskunde* **103,** p. 26, Planche 1, 2.
Voir également l'applique Fig. 14, c:
Penninger, E. (1972). Dürrnberg **1,** Planche 48, 37.

65. Müller-Karpe, H. (1959). *Funde von bayerischen Höhensiedlungen*, Planche 11, 3; 18; Schwappach, F. (1973). *Bonner Jahrbücher* **173**, p. 74, Fig. 20, 3.

66. Penninger, E. (1972). Dürrnberg **1,** Planche 48, 40 et 44; 113, 1–2.

67. Zápotocký, M. (1962). *Arch. Rozhledy* **14,** p. 22 ss, Fig. 8, 1; 15; Schwappach, F. (1973). *Bonner Jahrbücher* **173**, p. 105, Fig. 49.

68. Jacobsthal, P. (1944). (*voir* ***n. 1***) Planche 168, no. 356.
Kaufmann, H. (1964). *Gothaer Museumshefte* p. 54; Fig. 27, 20.

69. Filip, J. (1956). *Keltové* p. 179, Fig. 54, 1; Planche 15, 2–4.

70. Jacobsthal, P. (1944). (*voir* ***n. 1***) Planche 18, no. 18; 271, 313 (*a*), 322–23.

71. *Voir* Jacobsthal, P. (1944). (*voir* ***n. 1***), Planche 9 ss.

72. Jacobsthal, P. (1944). *Ibid.* Planche 261 ss.
Fig. 15: a Eigenbilzen (*Ibid.* Planche 23, no. 24);
b Weisskirchen (*Ibid.* Planche 21, no. 20);
c La Gorge-Meillet (*Ibid.* Planche 120, no. 196);
d No loc., Mus. St. Germain (*Ibid.* Planche 169, no. 355 f);
e Zerf (*Ibid.* Planche 52, no. 73);
f Kärlich (*Ibid.* Planche 274, 385);
g Langenhain (*Ibid.*, Planche 114, no. 183);
h Schwarzenbach (*Ibid.* Planche 30, no. 34);
i Oenochoé au Musée de Besançon (cf. ***n. 113***);
j–l et 0 Schwarzenbach (*Ibid.* Planche 18, no. 18);
m La Motte-Saint-Valentin (*Ibid.* Planche 169, no. 355 c);

n Bavilliers: Frey, O. H. (1971). *Hamburger Beiträge zur Archäologie* **1,** p. 91, Fig. 7, 9.

73. Filip, J. (1956). *Keltové* p. 33, Fig. 6, 3; PLANCHE 10, 2–4.

74. Kruta, V. (1973). *Etudes celtiques* **13**, p. 651, Fig. 1, 3.

75. Jacobsthal, P. (1944). (*voir **n. 1***). PLANCHE 105, no. 168.

76. Jacobsthal, P. (1944). (*voir **n. 1***), PLANCHE 108, no. 171.

77. *Par exemple* Jacobsthal, P. (1944). (*voir **n. 1***), PLANCHE 58, no. 95;
aussi Ibid. PLANCHE 171, no. 363.

78. Coblenz, W. (1956). *Arbeits- und Forschungsberichte zur Sächsischen Bodendenkmalpflege* **5,** p. 297 ss, Figs. 50–51.

79. Sépulture 62, 2, au Musée de Hallein. Dessin de L. Pauli.

80. Au Musée de Eisenstadt.

81. Cf. ***n. 54*** ci-dessus.

82. Filip, J. (1956). *Keltové* p. 33, Fig. 6, 7; PLANCHE 26, 8–9.

83. Des lyres apparaissent sur des agrafes de ceinture de Hladná-Hosty (Bohême) et du Dürrnberg (Autriche), dans des compositions plus ornées;
Voir Filip, J. (1956). *Keltové* PLANCHE 8, 1;
Penninger, E. (1972). Dürrnberg **1,** PLANCHE 43, 6–8; 113, 7–8.

84. Schwappach, F. (1971). *Hamburger Beiträge zur Archäologie* **1,** p. 148 ss, Fig. 10, 4–5; 18; PLANCHE 9, 2.

85. Cf. ***n. 84*** ci-dessus.

86. Schwappach, F. (1971). *Hamburger Beiträge zur Archäologie* **1,** p. 131 ss.

87. Au Musée de Protivín; dessin par A. Beneš, Plzeň.
Cf., entre autres, Jacobsthal, P. (1944). *Early Celtic Art,* PLANCHE 177, no. 379.
Schaaff, U. (1971). *Archäologisches Korrespondenzblatt* **1**, 107 ss, PLANCHE 22, 1.

88. Schwappach, F. (1971). *Hamburger Beiträge zur Archäologie* **1,** p. 131 ss.
Frey, O. H. *ici,* p. 141 ss.

89. Cf. ***n. 84*** ci-dessus.

90. Jacobsthal, P. (1944). (*voir **n. 1***), p. 84 ss.

91. Osterhaus, U. (1969). *Marburger Beiträge zur Archäologie der Kelten, Festschrift W. Dehn* p. 134 ss, Fig. 2, 1;

Voir également Megaw, J. V. S. (1968). *Revue Arch. de l'Est et du Centre-Est* **19,** p. 129 ss.

92. Hell, M. (1955). *Germania* **33,** p. 410 ss, Fig. 1–2.

93. Jacobsthal, P. (1944). (***n. 1***). PLANCHE 189 ss, no. 387; 272, 335.

94. *Voir* ***n. 25***.

95. Jacobsthal, P. (1944). (***n. 1***). PLANCHE 19–20m no. 19; 272, 329–30.

96. Streit, C. (1938). *Saazer Latènefunde* p. 21, Fig. 9, 3.

97. Dans *Památky Arch.*, **18,** (1898–99) p. 117 ss.

98. Beneš, A. (1966). Muzeum Keramiky v Bechyni. *Zprávy Čs. Společnosti Arch. při ČSAV,* **1,** p. 7–8; PLANCHE 17, 6–11.

99. Keller, J. (1965). *Reinheim* **1,** PLANCHE 24.

100. Penninger, E. (1972). *Dürrnberg* **1,** PLANCHE 43, 1; 113, 5.

101. Filip, J. (1956). *Keltove* p. 259, Fig. 76, 6; PLANCHE 3, 5.

102. (1966). *Beiträge zur Oberpfalzforschung* **2,** p. 55 ss.

103. Munich, Prähistorische Staatssammlung.

104. Krämer, W. (1952). *Germania* **30,** p. 256 ss; PLANCHE 10, 4.
(1956). *Bayerische Vorgeschichtsblätter,* **21,** p. 248 ss; PLANCHE 33, 4.

105. Uenze, H. P. (1966). (cf. ***n. 102***).
Megaw, J. V. S. (1968). *Revue Arch. de l'Est et du Centre-Est,* **19,** p. 139. Fig. 21: a cf. ***n. 25***; b cf. ***n. 102***; c cf. ***n. 113***; d cf. ***n. 91***; e cf. ***n. 102***; f cf. ***n. 28***.

106. Jacobsthal, P. (***n. 1***). *Ibid.* PLANCHE 249 b.

107. Cf. *Early Celtic Art* p. 83 ss.
Voir aussi Frey, O. H. (1971). *Hamburger Beiträge zur Archäologie* **1,** p. 89 ss, Fig. 6 ss.
Cf. entre autres, les pièces de nos Fig. 20, d; 21, c et f; 23, a–b.
Egalement *Early Celtic Art,* PLANCHE 118, no. 192; 176, no. 376, et l'oenochoé de Reinheim (cf. ***n. 99***).

108. Schwappach, F. (1973). *Bonner Jahrbücher* **173**, p. 90, Fig. 38, 2.

109. Jacobsthal, P. (1944). PLANCHE 120, no. 199; 117, no. 189; 270, 289.

110. Penninger, E. (1972). *Dürrnberg* **1** PLANCHE 48, 43.

111. Šimek, E. (1958). *Poslední Keltové na Moravě* p. 291, Fig. 166; Schwappach, F. (1973). *Bonner Jahrbücher* 173, p. 90, Fig. 38, 1.

112. *Voir Arch. Rozhledy*, **24,** (1972) p. 295 ss, PLANCHE 2, 4 et 7.

113. Frey, O. H. (1955). "Eine etruskische Bronzeschnabelkanne". *Ann. Litt. de l'Univ. de Besançon*, 2e *sér.*, t. 2, fasc. 1.

114. Frey, O. H. *op. cit.* p. 15–16.
Schwappach, F. (1969). *Marburger Beiträge zur Archäologie der Kelten*, Festschrift W. Dehn, p. 258–59.

115. Schwappach, F. (1971). *Hamburger Beiträge zur Archäologie* **1,** 161, Fig. 16–17; PLANCHE 10.

116. Jacobsthal, P. (1944). (*voir **n. 1***) PLANCHE 206, no. 404.

117. Jacobsthal, P. (1944). (*voir **n. 1***) PLANCHE 202, no. 400.
Piggott, S. (1970). *op. cit.* (***n. 2***) no. 155.

118. *Voir* Early Celtic Art p. 76–77.

119. Cf. également le tesson: Müller-Karpe, H. (1959). *voir **n. 65*** PLANCHE 18.

120. Cf. ***n. 84.***

121. Cf. ***n. 115*** ci-dessus.

122. Sur le "Fürstengräberkreis"
voir surtout Dehn, W. (1951). *Bonner Jahrbücher*, **151,** p. 83 ss.
Idem, (1964). *Germania* **42,** p. 73 ss;
Idem, (1966). *Helvetia Antiqua, Festschrift E. Vogt* p. 137 ss.

123. Cf. Kossack, G. (1959). Südbayern während der Hallstattzeit *Röm.-Germ. Forschungen* **24**;
Kilian-Dirlmeier, I. (1969). *Bericht RGK.* **50,** p. 132 ss.
Kimmig, W. (1970-71). *Bericht RGK.* **51–52,** p. 147 ss; 166 ss, Fig. 7.
Voir aussi Šaldová, V. (1968). *Památky Arch.* ***59***, p. 297 ss.

124. Cf. l'exposé dans (1973) *Bonner Jahrbücher* **173,** p. 53 ss.

Remerciements

Je suis reconnaissant au regretté Jean Lequiller, Directeur de la Maison Française d'Oxford, pour la traduction française de mon texte. Les dessins ont été préparés avec grand soin par Ingeborg Litcoff et Rita Volbracht, Hamburg. M. Jiří Břeň, Národní museum, Prague, m'a très généreusement confié la photo de la pièce d'or de Chlum, Fig. 26, d.

Résumé

Early-Style Ornament of Western Origin in The Eastern Centres of La Tène

The work of Paul Jacobsthal in his *Early Celtic Art* (Oxford 1944, but based on his researches of the 1930s) has remained fundamental for La Tène art-history. Yet though subsequent work on the period has taken mainly other directions, there is now an enlarged material awaiting treatment by his methods. The Erstfeld gold treasure (Switzerland), the princely tomb of Reinheim (Saarland), and the great discoveries at the Dürrnberg (Hallein near Salzburg, Austria), are only three examples of this enlargement. In defining his "Early Style", he used material chiefly Western, from both sides of the Rhine, and from the region of the Marne. What he scarcely noticed was an Eastern zone, where his examples of likeness to the Western art (Figs. 12–14) are unusual, and where this art's principal features are less common altogether. These features, which his "grammar of Celtic ornament" picked out, are elements from Greek floral or vegetal decoration: palmettes, leaves, lotus-flowers, or "lyres" of paired plant-scrolls. The Eastern Celtic artists preferred geometric decoration, based chiefly on "abstract" arcs, circles, and S forms. Patterns formed of these (shown on metal and pottery in Figs. 2, 3, 5) are found widely within their zone, in the countries of Central and Eastern-central Europe.

Taking the characteristic motif of intersecting circles for example, and making a map (Fig. 5) of its really numerous occurrences, one finds it typical of Bavaria, Austria and Bohemia, rather than at all of the Early-Style centres of the Rhine and Marne. J. V. S. Megaw, through his not having recognized this, took the few examples he found in the East as imports there from the West: the Želkovice phalera (Fig. 3a), with a "probably Rhineland owner", or the pilgrim-flask from the Dürrnberg (Austria, Fig. 6k). It is in the West, where the Early Style had the floral elements dominant, that purely geometric and abstract ones are rare (Fig. 7): on the circular cover (?) from Durkheim and the scabbards from Bussy-le-Château and Châtillon, and in stamping on pottery extremely rare (Eppelsheim, Jacobsthal p. 54). The two styles stand in contrast on the Laumersheim mount (Fig. 8a): border of compass-work as in Fig. 8b, Mühlacker (Württemberg) girdle-hook; on the Waldalgesheim spout-flagon, where the broad floral bands (Fig. 19e) are the major feature, the "abstract" borders the minor (Fig. 8d); and on the helmet from Ecury-sur-Coole (Fig. 8c). On the Hoppstädten spouted strainer (Figs. 19d, 21a: cf. spout-flagon pieces from Eigenbilzen: Fig. 9, e, g, j, from Mariën cited note 26) the compass-drawn arcs and circles can either be Eastern-style geometric, or simplified floral; compare with Fig. 9a (on a vase from Etruscan Caere) that on

Figs. 1e, 15k from the Schwarzenbach bowl's gold openwork. The simplification of floral in the Eigenbilzen gold mount, recalls Greek "red-figure vase" techniques in compass-drawing (Figs. 1, i, 15a); on Eastern stamped pottery it is more like "black-figure vase" technique (exx. in Figs. 2, 6, 9), yet floral motifs geometricized can be Western. Compare Figs 12, 14, with 9, b–c and 15, and the openwork of the Cuperly disc (Fig. 10) and Jacobsthal Pls. 118–19, Somme-Bionne, etc. Thus the map Fig. 4 of Celtic Early-style motifs that use the palmette shows their abundance in the Western art, their rarity in the Eastern.

The East's abundant repertory of geometric curved motifs, to be understood through compass-work and forming an "arc style" (*Bogenstil*), is in part new Celtic creation, doubtless in part from Hallstatt tradition, and even partly of Mediterranean origin. Map, Fig. 5; varieties shown Figs. 2, 3, 6. The extremities of the arc motifs are usually marked by circlets, and only quite seldom by plant or floral elements (Fig. 2, c, d, h); also Fig. 12c from Prague-Bubeneč, and perhaps in the cup from Prague-Hloubětín (Fig. 12, d), though the lotus-flower is there less explicit. On a vase from Ratzersdorf in Austria, also, geometric pattern has leaves in it, with punctuation given by stamped circlets (12g); but however it may be best described, with its mixture of compass and free-hand drawing, such a frieze is rare in the East (compare Fig. 12f, on a pottery flask from Hlubyně, Bohemia). Besides such "floralized geometry", there are some cases more purely floral; those of a vase from Stehelčeves and one from Nynice (Fig. 13k, f, j) still resemble the Ratzersdorf vase, but Fig. 20f (girdle-hook from Linz) has a floral motif alone. Examples using palmettes are seen in Fig. 13c (Sedlec-Hůrka), Fig. 13b (Velem-Szentvid, on the western edge of Hungary), Fig. 13a (on the handle-base of the well-known Dürrnberg flagon), Fig. 14j (on the Hallstatt scabbard), and Fig. 13d (on a collar from the Dürrnberg). The girdle-hook from the Liebau grave (Fig. 14k, Saxony) has lotuses like the Prague-Bubeneč frieze (Fig. 12c); alone, they are seen in Fig. 25f (belt-mount from the Dürrnberg; also Höresham in Bavaria), and in rows with circlets (Fig. 13g) on vases from Richterskeller and Hannersgüm (both Bavaria; circlets here with pairs of leaves, as Figs. 9h, 14b).

The West too has such separation of elements. There are leaves conjoined in twos and fours on the Velká Turná bowl-sherds (Figs. 13h, 14a); combined with palmette and S motifs, on the base of a pottery cup from Lobodice (Fig. 25e, Moravia), and again (without the hatching) on the bronze figure from the Dürrnberg. From Kallmünz, Bavaria, come pieces with motifs both similar (Fig. 20a) and still more Western (Fig. 14d); the latter recurs on a cup from Libkovice (Fig. 14e). The double palmette on a girdle-hook from Gotha-Seebergen (Fig. 14g, Thuringia), and on the hatched floral design of the stamp on a sherd from Poleňka (Fig. 14h, Bohemia), also suggests the Early Style of the West.

The Western Celtic resemblances, as in Jacobsthal's "grammar" of ornament, of all these motifs on pieces in the East, can be seen in detail after detail. The Dražičky scabbard with its superimposed lyres (Fig. 16c, has a palmette and uses pointillé; the piece from Chlum (p. 114, c2), although with contrasting frieze of arcs (cf. Fig. 9), recalls the openwork from La Bouvandeau (Fig. 16a–b); floral again is the Liebau grave's scabbard decoration (Fig. 13e) in its lyre of similar scrolls, as on the Chlum gold leaf, and girdle-hook from Linz (Figs. 18d; 26d, f); the Dürrnberg girdle-hook Fig. 25f ends in a palmette. On the Hallstatt scabbard tip is a half-lyre, completed in Fig. 14j. On the Jenišův Ujezd scabbard (Fig. 13i) lyres appear alternately with lotuses, and in richer designs on girdle-hooks from Hosty and the Dürrnberg. But lyres stamped on pottery in the East seem late (La Tène B); there and on metal too (Fig. 13a) they reach the "Waldalgesheim" phase, and later (Fig. 17, fragment of hollow-bossed ring from Záboří, Bohemia). For East–West resemblances in lyres, see Figs. 14–18. Figure 21d from Bavilliers (Territory of Belfort, France) is compared by U. Osterhaus with the Jenišův-Ujezd scabbard. A graphited-clay situla from the Dürrnberg (Figs. 18e, 25j) has stamped decoration recalling the engraved designs of Figs. 19e and d (Waldalgesheim, Hoppstädten), and even of Fig. 19c (the Auvers disc). Fragments from Dobříčany (Fig. 18d) may suggest the like. Early-Style floral work that is proper to the East itself, altogether poor, has little remarkable to show us: sherds from Rataje (Fig. 18a, Bohemia) combine stamped circlets with freehand leaves, on a background of pointillé, which recall the Reinheim spout-flagon (Fig. 19a–b, and cf. Fig. 21). Yet on Fig. 18b, d, c, the sheet-gold leaves from princely graves at the Dürrnberg and Chlum, show the designs in Eastern versions much reduced.

Eastern derivatives of floral work from the West, in patterns including lyres, may be discerned e.g. by comparing with that on the spout of the Reinheim flagon (Fig. 19a–b), certain stamped designs (Fig. 18d Dobříčany; and Hatzenhofen, Bavaria) and also engraved (Fig. 18b, on a Dürrnberg shield-mount). Among the interior-stamped motifs seen on "Braubach bowls" from the East (Fig. 20b, e, Mintraching and Kreuzhof, Bavaria, mistakenly thought exterior-stamped by H. P. Uenze; also Figs. 20a, 20c, Kallmünz and Straubing), the whirligig forms seem Western; only the Straubing star is Eastern. Besides the whirligigs, too (Fig. 21), that of a circle-enclosed medallion shows clear Western influence, as in Fig. 20b, c (both Bavaria): compare the bronze bowl from Les Saulces-Champenoises (Fig. 20d). Floral accompaniments to whirligig motifs suggest the same thing: Fig. 21j (on sherds from Leitzersdorf, Austria) recalls the same bowl again, and designs from La Gorge-Meillet (Fig. 21k) and Écury-sur-Coole. Motifs using the triskele, as 21g–h from the Dürrnberg (bronze), Fig. 22a, and on Moravian pottery (Milovice), again suggest it. The four-legged whirligig stamped on the base of a pottery flask from the Manětín-Hradek cemetery (Bohemia) recalls the decoration of the bronze flagon of Besançon (Fig. 22c, d); still more does that on such a flask from Hidegség (Hungary), which also has bands of S stamps set between circular ones in the place of palmettes (Fig. 22a, b, and see Fig. 25e, Lobodice). A stamped and rouletted design using the whirligig and tendrils, inside a pottery bowl from Thalmässing (Fig. 23b, Bavaria) has a counterpart only in the bronze strainer from the Marne, Fig. 23a; this, however, is already "Waldalgesheim" in style, which puts the Bavarian bowl well on in the IVth century; the Hidegség flask belongs to its beginning.

Thus the Early Style is not uniform throughout its area, as Jacobsthal thought: it has an Eastern besides a Western zone, each with its own artistic character. This in the Eastern is "abstract", while the Western preferred the "floral"; one looks to Hallstatt, the other to Classical impulse. For the one to penetrate the other, there must have been trade, or with greater probability, movement of craftsmen, between princely patrons' courts.

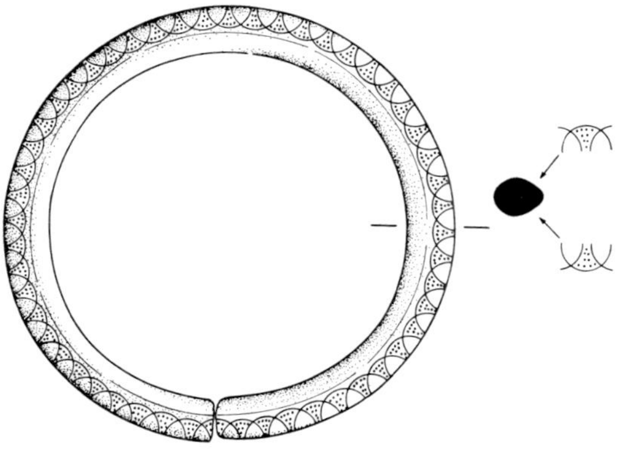

FIG. 27. Bronze bracelet, one of pair, Ciry-Salsogne (Aisne). (1/1). Mus. St. Germain. See note above, at foot of p. 94.

Discussion

Speakers:— Professors Jope, Klindt-Jensen, Hawkes, Dr Schwappach.

After brief remarks by the others, PROFESSOR JOPE advanced three matters. Praising the overall coherence of Schwappach's exposition, giving the "language" of his styles rather than recite mere "parts of speech", he reflected that Jacobsthal's famous term, the "Grammar of Celtic Ornament", was really a misnomer. It was a vocabulary, even an alphabet, or a catalogue of forms and elements; what Jacobsthal never attempted was the syntax. He would like to hear Schwappach now propound more syntax: to give his severely geometric archaic style more showing of inter-relationships, between its component parts; this would improve his demonstration. Secondly, Jacobsthal's holding away from the art in Central Europe was not a matter of sheer rejection; as he explained in his Introduction, he was unwilling to treat in detail anything he had not seen himself. All the more had Schwappach earned our thanks for redressing the balance so well. Thirdly, "Early Style" was a concept that now required to be analysed. Schwappach's distinction of eastern from western was just the beginning we needed. PROFESSOR KLINDT-JENSEN, endorsing the view of the eastern style as geometric, moved the discussion next towards the explaining of distributions. How should we explain the presence in the east of the western-looking designs?

DR SCHWAPPACH reminded him that eastern-looking designs could appear in the west: the process was mutual exchange between the regions. He therefore wished to explain it by personal movements of artisans. Not by invasive movements of tribes, conducted by warlike leaders; those indeed came later, to Bohemia and Moravia, Hungary, Transylvania, and so on, but the style diffused then was the Waldalgesheim, not the Early. PROFESSOR HAWKES, however, seeking the background for artisan mobility, found it difficult to believe that the great spread of flat-grave cemeteries, west into all those Danube lands and Bohemia besides, had not begun till after the Waldalgesheim style was formed. Such cemeteries, in regions new for them, should be consequent on movements. He was inclined to think that mobility of artisans, likewise, could be consequent on the establishing of princely courts by means of movements. The artisans might indeed migrate from one such court to another, and take service there to work in their accustomed styles. But the primary distribution of courts was a needful pre-condition; and he still wondered how it was brought about.

5

Le Premier Style laténien en Bohême

VENCESLAS KRUTA
Prague–Paris

LES PREMIÈRES manifestations d'un nouveau style artistique dans l'Europe celtique de la fin du Premier âge du fer sont considérées généralement par les protohistoriens comme les témoignages les plus évidents de la naissance d'une nouvelle civilisation: la civilisation laténienne. L'art de la période initiale, auquel est appliquée traditionnellement l'appellation un peu anonyme de Premier style[1] ou celle qu'on peut emprunter à l'art classique, de Style sévère[2], correspond à une période d'un peu moins d'un siècle, environ du début du troisième tiers du Vème siècle à la fin du second tiers du IVème siècle av. n. è. A la fin de cette période, la civilisation laténienne atteint déjà sa pleine maturité. C'est vraisemblablement la période la plus complètement étudiée de l'art laténien, mais aussi celle où le nombre relativement restreint d'objets a porté le plus les chercheurs à abandonner les études régionales au profit d'études portant sur l'ensemble du monde celtique. Les conséquences en sont, très souvent, la dissociation du milieu local et de ses problèmes spécifiques, et de grandes difficultés pour établir la relation avec l'évolution ultérieure. Il nous paraît donc intéressant de récapituler les problèmes de cette phase initiale en Bohême, province celtique qui devient par la suite un foyer artistique d'une importance fondamentale, fait généralement estompé par un intérêt trop exclusif porté à cette première période[3].

Le cadre géographique (voir la carte, Fig. 7, p. 120) est déterminé par l'occupation celtique antérieure, dont la limite nord est constituée par le cours de l'Elbe, en excluant pratiquement toutefois l'aire antérieure des riches sépultures princières de la civilisation de Bylany dans les plaines du Nord-Ouest et du Centre du pays. Deux régions semblent particulièrement privilégiées. La première est constituée par le bassin de la Vltava, en particulier sa partie centrale où les sables aurifères de son affluent l'Otava étaient exploités vraisemblablement dès l'âge du bronze[4]. La seconde région, avec une concentration encore plus importante, est le bassin adjacent de la Berounka avec la cuvette de Plzeň. La présence de gisements de minerai de fer, dont l'exploitation à cette époque n'est pas encore attestée, est peut-être, comme dans d'autres régions[5], associée à ce phénomène. Ces deux régions sont reliées directement à la vallée du Danube par des passages relativement faciles. Une troisième région reste un peu à l'écart au début mais elle joue un rôle décisif pour l'évolution ultérieure. C'est la riche plaine sous les Monts Métallifères aux abondantes ressources en minerais divers, dont l'étain présente pour la protohistoire un intérêt particulier[6]. Cette région communique par la vallée de l'Ohře et du Main directement avec la Rhénanie. Voir la carte, p. 120.

Ainsi que l'avait remarqué Schránil il y a déjà un demi-siècle[7], les premiers éléments du nouveau style laténien apparaissent dans un milieu qui représente le prolongement direct de l'évolution locale du Premier âge du fer. Les quelques objets que nous attribuons à la phase initiale proviennent en majorité d'incinérations plates ou sous tumulus où ils ont comme contexte des poteries de traditions hallstattiennes (qui sont les premières à attester l'emploi du tour), des sabres-coutelas et quelques importations d'origine étrusque (oenochoés, bassins). Des objets nouveaux s'y ajoutent progressivement (premières épées laténiennes, nouvelles formes céramiques: par. ex. le flacon lenticulaire, etc.), jalonnant ainsi la lente transformation du milieu hallstattien. Un tournant décisif se manifeste après le milieu du IVème siècle, avec la prépondérance absolue des nécropoles plates à inhumation, du moins dans les riches régions agricoles du Centre et du Nord-Ouest. C'est dans ce milieu qu'apparaissent en Bohême les derniers objets pouvant être rattachés directement au Premier style.

Le seul groupe d'objets caractérisant à notre avis la phase initiale du Premier style en Bohême est constitué par des fibules, généralement à ressort rapporté, dont le pied a la forme d'une tête d'oiseau (carte: no. 1). Ce sont les fibules de *Cítoliby* (Fig. 1 a), *Hořín* (Fig. 1 d), *Kralovice*[8] et *Hradiště* (sépulture no. 3)[9]. L'origine locale de ces fibules n'est pas improbable, mais il est impossible d'en décider sans faire l'étude générale des fibules à tête d'oiseau, dont la riche typologie comprend aussi bien des séries encore hallstattiennes que des séries relativement tardives. Les fibules à tête d'oiseau faites d'une seule pièce de *Tajanov-Husín* (Fig. 1 b) et de *Hradiště* (sépulture no. 8)[10] sont d'une inspiration différente de celle des précédentes et sont sans doute aussi quelque peu plus récentes.

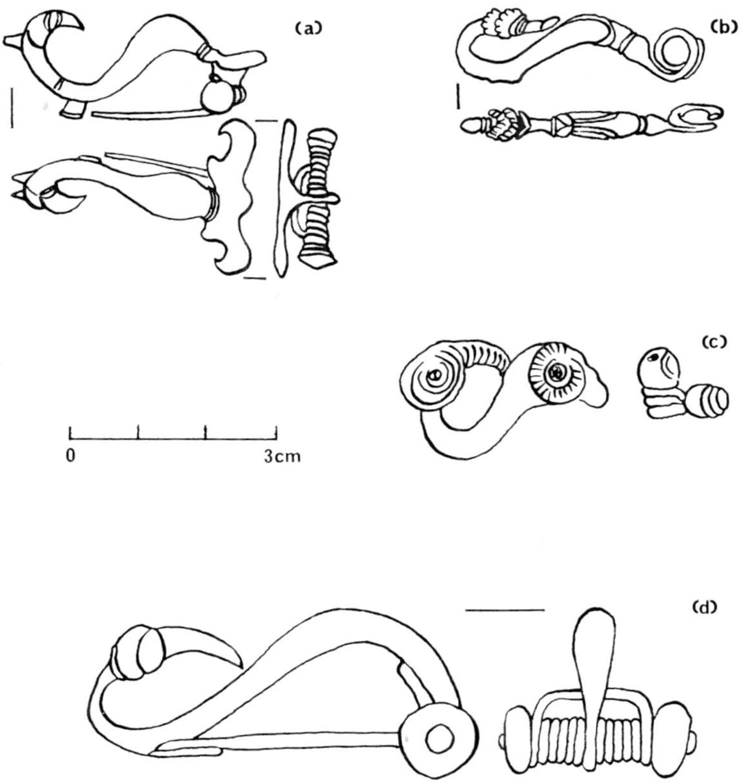

Fig. 1 (a) Cítoliby (distr. Louny): fibule à tête d'oiseau (d'après Schránil 1922). (b) Tajanov (distr. Klatovy): fibule à tête d'oiseau. (c) Bylany (distr. Kolín); fibule à masques (d'après Schránil 1922). (d) Hořín (distr. Mělník): fibule à tête d'oiseau (d'après Schránil 1922).

De par sa facture archaïque (incrustation d'ambre en rainures transversales et pastilles), la fibule de *Manětín-Hrádek*[11] semblerait devoir être rattachée à la phase initiale, mais il s'agit d'un objet tellement exceptionnel que nous croyons prématuré de se prononcer à ce sujet. L'origine locale semble de toute façon à peu près exclue, la parenté de cet objet avec les fibules à masques classiques est très lointaine, cette fibule anthropomorphe est par sa conception beaucoup plus proche des fibules zoomorphes trouvées à l'Ouest de la Bohême[12].

La fibule fragmentaire de *Kšice* (Fig. 8, 3), au pied figurant une tête humaine, et celle de *Bylany* (Fig. 1 c), qui présente d'étroites affinités avec les fibules à tête d'oiseau du premier groupe, annoncent la magnifique série des fibules à masques classiques du groupe oriental: celles de *Kyšice*[13], *Nová Huť* (Fig. 9, 11) et *Chýnov*[14]. Le nombre limité de ces fibules et des exemplaires de comparaison, ainsi que l'incertitude du contexte, rendent pour le moment trop hypothétique toute tentative de discerner un probable échelonnement chronologique dans le cadre de la première moitié du IVème siècle et de résoudre d'une façon plus précise le problème de la localisation des ateliers[15].

FIG. 2—CHLUM (distr. Rokycany) : (a) développement du décor gravé de l'embout en bronze (d'après Píč 1904/5) ; (b) schéma du décor de la plaque en or; (c) plaque en bronze à décor gravé (c i: schéma de la composition).

Un cas particulier est constitué par la fibule de *Panenský Týnec* (Fig. 9, 2 a–c)[16], considérée généralement comme une des plus anciennes de ce groupe. Le caractère hybride de cet objet associant des éléments disparates mais déjà très élaborés avec la forme rigoureusement observée d'une fibule de type Certosa évoluée[17], ainsi que le mode de fixation du ressort unilatéral rapporté, nous incitent à y voir un écho marginal des fibules à masques et zoomorphes classiques. Sa parenté avec les objets du trésor d'Erstfeld, plus particulièrement les torques,[18] est de ce point de vue tout à fait significative. Ces observations ne permettent certes

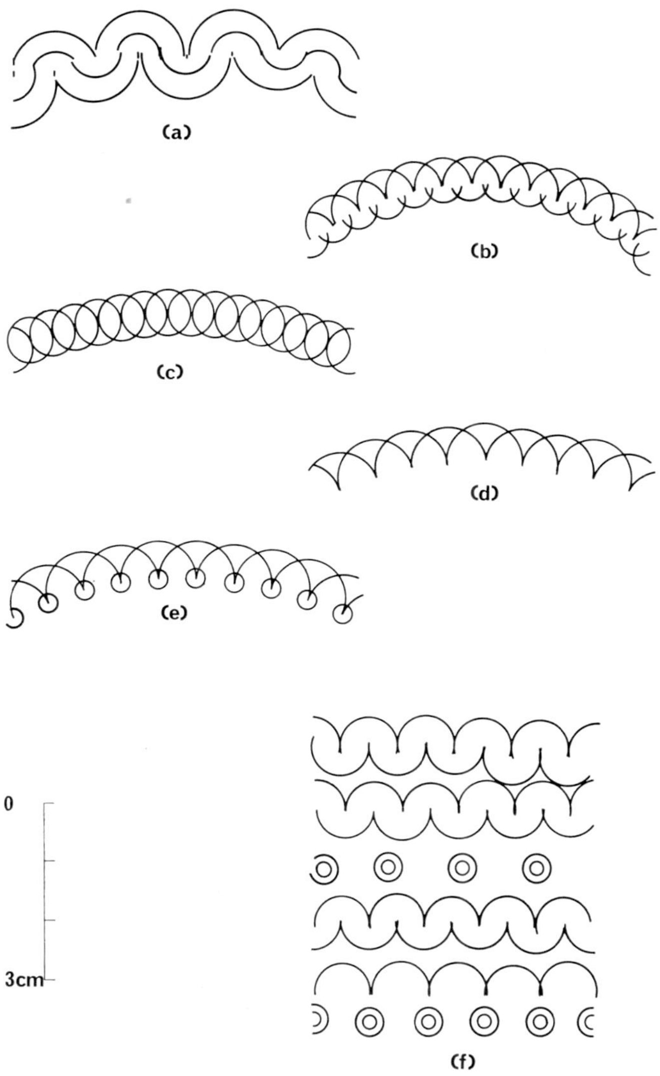

FIG. 3 (a–e) NEVĚZICE (distr. Písek) : décors des phalères en bronze (les décors c–e sont agrandis d'après Woldřich 1886; leurs dimensions sont donc approximatives). (f) PRAHA-PODBABA (Praha 6) : décor estampé d'un fragment de poterie.

pas une datation plus précise de l'objet, mais suggèrent à notre avis l'opportunité de réviser la date proposée dans le sens d'un abaissement peut-être assez sensible.

Nous connaissons de Bohême un second objet de la même veine et très probablement de la même origine. La bague en or du Musée National de Prague, provenant selon les indications du vendeur de la *région de Hořovice* (donc du voisinage des sites de Želkovice et Chlum), présente, disposées selon une symétrie rigoureuse, les mêmes volutes hélicoïdales et bandes de vannerie que la fibule de *Panenský Týnec* avec en plus, sur l'anneau, une double frise en miniature d'esses enchaînées (Fig. 8, 2).

L'agrafe de ceinturon de *Želkovice*[19] montre dans le traitement du masque ornant le crochet une étroite parenté avec les fibules à masques classiques, notamment celle de *Nová Huť*. Néanmoins, ainsi que pour la plaque-agrafe de *Stupava*[20], une parenté non moins étroite existe avec le groupe d'agrafes de ce type découvertes en Rhénanie[21]. La plaque-agrafe de *Želkovice* ne fait pas exception à l'éclectisme stylistique de ce groupe d'objets, où des motifs reproduisant encore fidèlement des proto-

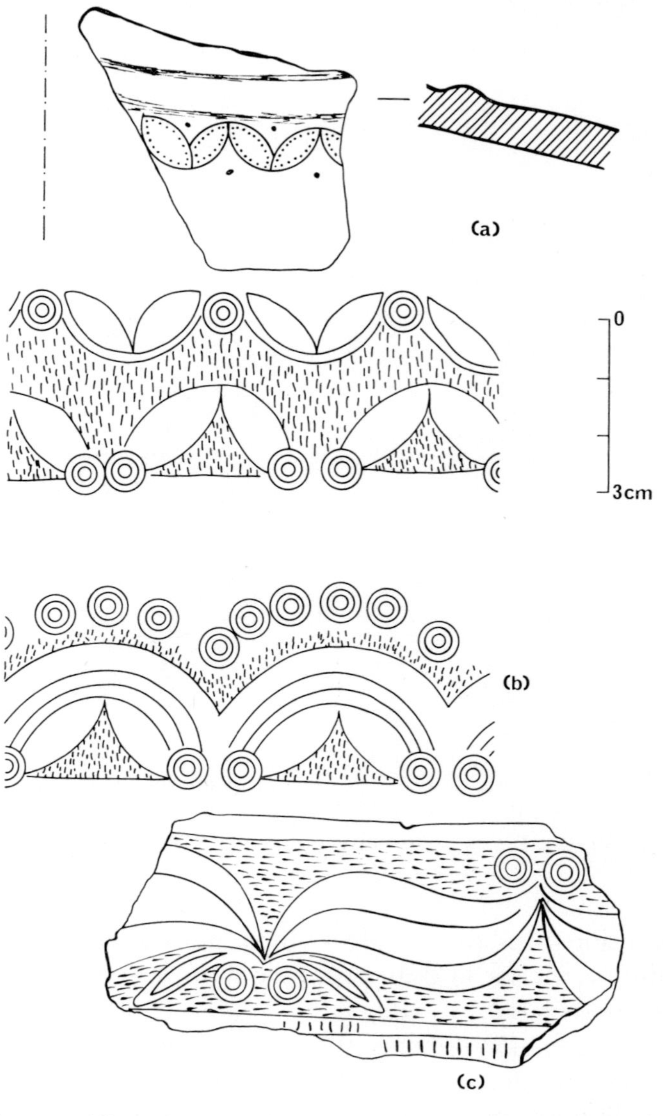

FIG. 4 (a) POČERADY (distr. Louny): fragment d'un flacon lenticulaire en poterie au décor gravé au compas. (b) HLUBYNĚ (distr. Příbram): décor gravé et estampé d'un flacon lenticulaire en poterie. (c) RATAJE (distr. Tábor): fragment de poterie à décor gravé et estampé (d'après Hraše 1898/9).

types de l'art orientalisant ou archaïques côtoient des motifs déjà assimilés appartenant à différentes écoles. Dans notre cas, le géométrisme encore hallstattien du décor, gravé au traçoir balancé[22], de la plaque contraste avec le masque vigoureux et équilibré, expression d'un nouveau style déjà en pleine possession de ses moyens.

La seconde agrafe de ceinturon du Premier style trouvée en Bohême, celle de *Hosty* (Fig. 6, a)[23], avec des lyres superposées aux volutes bifides bordées d'esses enchaînées, se rattache à un groupe d'objets au décor ajouré fondé sur la lyre et ses associations, dont la localisation est nettement occidentale et plus particulièrement marnienne[24].

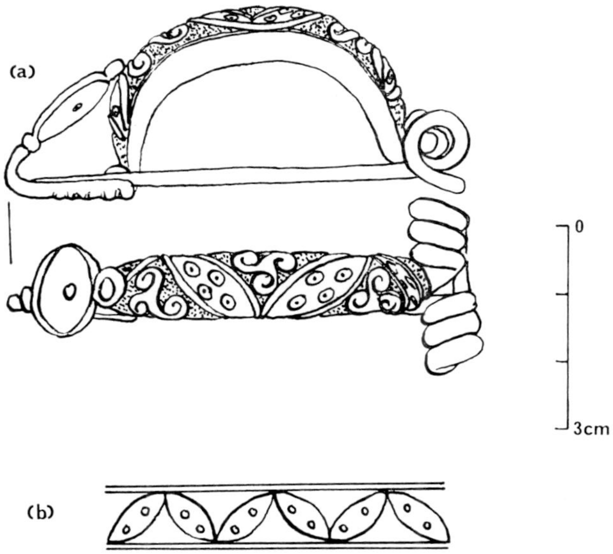

FIG. 5 (a) TOUŽETÍN (distr. Louny) : fibule en bronze à pied discoïdal au décor en léger relief. (b) LETKY (distr. Praha-zàpad) : développement du décor en relief de la bague en bronze avec cercles estampés.

Quelques objets dont l'origine occidentale (rhénane ?) est presque certaine relèvent d'une technique particulière, où une mince feuille d'or ou de bronze décorée par estampage au repoussé est appliquée sur une âme en fer ou en bronze. Sur les phalères de *Hořovičky* (Fig. 8, 1)[25], des masques humains, d'un style tout différent de ceux des fibules du groupe oriental, disposés en registres concentriques, alternent avec des éléments géométriques (cercles concentriques, grènetis). Sur la plaque en or et bronze de *Chlum* (Fig. 2, b ; Fig. 8, 4), le décor, rehaussé à l'origine par des cabochons de matière organique (corail ?), est dessiné par un double grènetis exécuté au repoussé. Partant du cabochon central, deux fleurs de lotus ouvertes constituent un motif d'une symétrie rigoureuse, évoquant deux lyres accolées par la base. L'origine de ce motif se trouve dans le répertoire de l'héritage orientalisant et le double grènetis est peut-être une lointaine imitation de la granulation des orfèvres étrusques. Les phalères de *Hořovičky*, la plaque de *Chlum*, celles de *Weisskirchen*[26], de *Schwabsburg*[27] et *du Klein Aspergle*[28], présentent de telles affinités qu'il faut considérer comme possible leur attribution au même atelier[29].

Deux objets, provenant comme la plaque discutée ci-dessus de la sépulture sous tumulus de *Chlum*, portent un décor exécuté à l'aide d'une technique qui semble avoir été utilisée d'une façon assez générale, la gravure, à main levée ou plus souvent encore au compas. Le décor principal de la plaque en bronze (Fig. 2, c) est fondé sur trois lyres enchaînées le chef vers le bas, l'inférieure étant inscrite dans une pelte et la supérieure surmontée d'une petite palmette trifoliée. L'ensemble de la composition évoque certaines agrafes marniennes[30], mais avec un raffinement très éloigné de la simplicité de ces dernières. La partie supérieure de ce décor est entourée d'une bordure constituée par un zig-zag de feuilles exécuté au compas. Nous retrouvons ce motif sur la seconde pièce, un embout en bronze: il y est utilisé de nouveau en bordure, de chaque côté d'une frise de demi-ondes imbriquées (Fig. 2, a); un pointillé souligne, comme sur la pièce précédente, certaines des lignes gravées.

Les six phalères décorées de *Nevězice* (Fig. 3, a–e)[31], dont on ne peut douter qu'elles proviennent du même atelier, sont une brillante démonstration des possibilités offertes par la gravure au compas: cercles entrecroisés (Fig. 3, c), demi-cercles imbriqués enfermant une onde (Fig. 3, a), demi-cercles entrecroisés simples (Fig. 3, d), agrémentés de petits cercles soulignant les centres (Fig. 3, e) ou encore avec des demi-cercles plus petits se chevauchant et imbriqués dans les premiers (Fig. 3, b). Sur la phalère de *Želkovice*[32], les triangles incurvés obtenus par l'entrecroisement des demi-cercles sont remplis par un pointillé, produisant ainsi en effet de contraste des surfaces, plus frappant que la simple gravure linéaire.

La grande vogue et l'anonymat de la technique de gravure au compas rendent à notre avis très difficile la détermination des provenances. Les arguments apportés récemment[33] en faveur de sa localisation dans le domaine oriental, dont elle serait une des caractéristiques, ne sont pas convaincants car ils sont fondés sur la fréquence des imitations sur céramique, qui n'impliquent aucunement la provenance locale des prototypes de métal. On ne connaît d'ailleurs en Bohême que neuf de ces derniers, donc proportionnellement très peu, moins que d'importations étrusques et provenant seulement de trois trouvailles. Il nous paraît, par contre, aussi peu fondé pour le moment de considérer ces objets comme caractéristiques du domaine occidental[34].

Le décor gravé du fourreau d'épée de *Dražičky* (Fig. 9, 3)[35] est de nouveau une oeuvre isolée en Bohême, excepté peut-être une vague parenté avec le motif central de la plaque en bronze de *Chlum*, dû surtout à la technique employée. Deux paires superposées de rinceaux divergents disposés en lyre servent de base à une palmette pédonculée à cinq feuilles. La présence du rinceau incite à attribuer à cet objet une date assez avancée dans le IVème siècle et même à envisager son rattachement au nouveau style végétal de la phase de transition marquant la fin du Premier style.

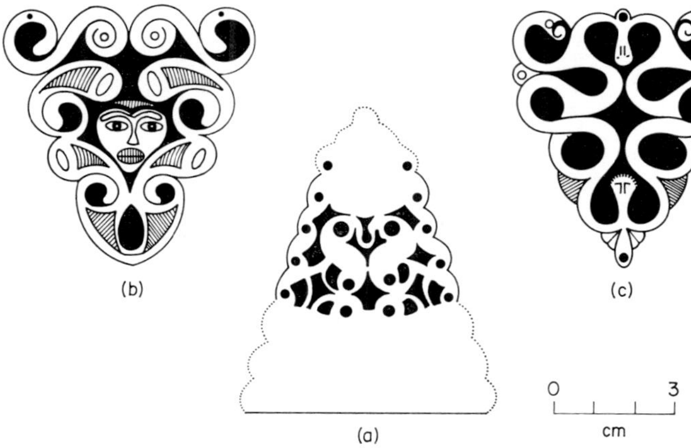

Fig. 6 (a) Hosty (distr. České Budějovice): reconstitution partielle de l'agrafe de ceinturon ajourée en fer. (b–c) Čížkovice (distr. Litoměřice): développement des garnitures ajourées en bronze.

Le cadre de cette phase de transition est tout différent de celui dans lequel apparaissent les objets exclusifs discutés précédemment. Ce ne sont plus les riches sépultures de seigneurs détenant le privilège de lointains échanges, mais les nécropoles plates à inhumation d'une population rurale dispersée de guerriers et fermiers, dont une partie de plus en plus importante prend goût aux parures décorées dans le nouveau style, contrastant si vivement avec l'héritage du géométrisme hallstattien, qui constitue encore la base du système décoratif appliqué sur les parures courantes[36]. C'est cette clientèle rustique, mais aisée, des plaines du Nord-Ouest, du Centre et plus tard du Nord-Est de la Bohême, qui est à la base du remarquable essor des artisans locaux dans les périodes ultérieures.

Les objets pouvant être rattachés à cette phase de transition, correspondant chronologiquement à l'horizon de la trouvaille de *Duchcov*, se concentrent très nettement dans le Nord-Ouest du pays et sont sans doute, au moins en partie, le produit d'ateliers locaux. Deux sources stylistiques principales peuvent y être distinguées. D'une part, des transpositions de compositions classiques du Premier style, ainsi que c'est le cas pour une des fibules de la trouvaille de *Duchcov*[37] et la parure annulaire de *Běšice*,[38] ou d'un élément isolé de ce style, tel le zig-zag de feuilles au compas de la période precédente, mais exécuté cette fois en léger relief à l'aide d'une technique différente. Sur l'arc de la fibule de

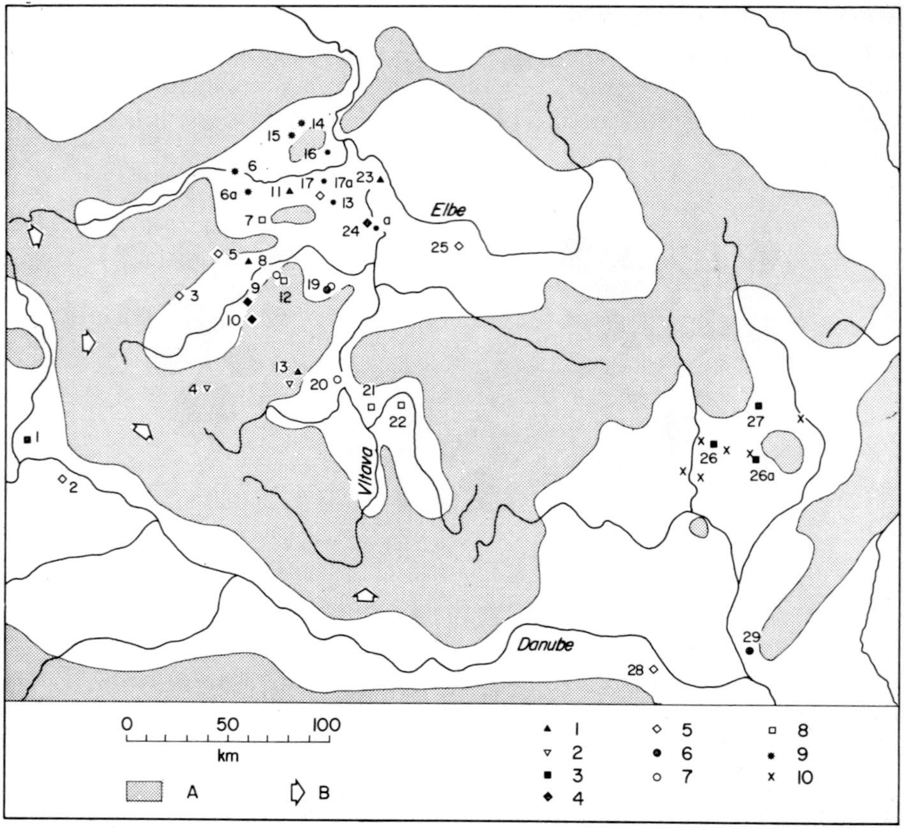

CARTE, FIG. 7:
Légende:
A: altitude supérieure à 500 m.
B: principales voies de pénétration en Bohême.
1: fibules à tête d'oiseau du groupe ancien (8, 11, 13, 23).
2: fibules à tête d'oiseau fabriquées d'une seule pièce (4, 13).
3: fibules à tête d'oiseau—variantes diverses (1, 26, 26a, 27).
4: fibules à masques classiques du groupe oriental (9, 10, 24).
5: fibules à masques—variantes diverses (2, 3, 5, 17, 25, 28).
6: plaques-agrafes à décor gravé et masque en relief (19, 29).
7: objets de métal au décor gravé au compas (12, 19, 20).
8: objets de métal au décor exécuté par diverses techniques: repoussé, gravure à main libre, ajouré (7, 12, 21, 22).
9: objets de la période de transition: dernières composition se rattachant au Premier style et nouveau style végétal (6, 6a, 14, 15, 16, 17a, 18, 24a).
10: objets marquant probablement la première apparition du style végétal en Moravie (Blučina, Brno-Maloměřice, Bučovice, Holubice, Postoupky, Sobotovice).
Liste des sites:

1/Grabenhäuser, 2/Riekofen, 3/Kšice, 4/Tajanov, 5/Manětín, 6/Běšice, 6a/Oploty, 7/Hořovičky, 8/Kralovice, 9/Nová Huť, 10/Kyšice, 11/Cítoliby, 12/Chlum, 13/Hradiště, 14/Duchcov, 15/Jenišův Újezd, 16/Čížkovice, 17/Panenský Týnec, 17a/Toužetín, 18/Klobuky, 19/Želkovice, 20/Nevězice, 21/Hosty, 22/Dražičky, 23/Hořín, 24/Chýnov, 24a/Letky, 25/Bylany, 26/Podolí, 26a/Vícemilice, 27/Otaslavice, 28/Wien-Leopoldau, 29/Stupava.

Toužetín (Fig. 5, a)[39], il se trouve accompagné de triscèles, dont c'est la réapparition en Bohême, et de cercles estampés comme sur la bague de *Letky* (Fig. 5, b). Un autre cas est le fourreau de *Jenišův Ujezd*[40], avec son décor où alternent des lyres, des motifs en forme d'U et des cercles estampés au repoussé. Nous avons un parallèle frappant de cet objet dans le fourreau de Bussy-le-Château[41], très probablement de même origine, incertaine encore mais extérieure à la Bohême.

D'autre part, nous constatons l'apparition d'un nouveau style végétal, fruit de l'occupation du Nord de l'Italie par les Celtes, et apportant non seulement de nouveaux motifs (pelte, rinceau) mais surtout un nouveau mode d'assemblage en compositions *continues*. Son faciès, dit de Waldalgesheim, caractérisé plus particulièrement par la présence de l'entrelacs[42], est représenté en Bohême par la très belle paire de garnitures ajourées provenant de *Čížkovice* (Fig. 6, b–c). Ornant vraisemblablement le même objet et produites par le même atelier, sinon le même artiste, ces garnitures illustrent parfaitement par leurs ressemblances et dissemblances le caractère ambigu et éclectique de ce faciès stylistique. Il ne s'agit certainement pas d'une oeuvre locale et nous rechercherions volontiers son origine dans la sphère d'influence des ateliers celtiques de l'Italie septentrionale[43].

Les rapports avec le matériel italien sont encore plus sensibles sur l'objet exceptionnel qu'est le torque en or d'*Oploty*[44]. Le curieux motif principal, enveloppant sur les côtés dans ses boucles des volutes foliacées et au centre une palmette estampée, est déjà bien loin de son prototype, les deux rinceaux encadrant une palmette. La frise de feuilles du tampon, présente aussi sur le torque de Filottrano[45], est un motif bien caractéristique du milieu italien[46].

Les quelques objets se rattachant à un aspect plus général du nouveau style végétal sont déjà très vraisemblablement le produit des ateliers locaux de la Bohême du nord-ouest. Ce sont trois bracelets à tampons, celui de la trouvaille de *Duchcov*,[47] celui de *Jenišův Ujezd*[48] et celui de *Klobuky*[49], fabriqués presque certainement par le même atelier et décorés d'une chaîne de peltes; une fibule de la trouvaille de *Duchcov*[50] à l'arc orné d'une paire de rinceaux divergents; une autre fibule du même ensemble[51], à l'arc orné d'un simple rinceau stylisé. Le décor de tous ces objets est exécuté en léger relief.

Le remarquable parallélisme de l'évolution en Bohême du nord-ouest et sur le plateau suisse à cette période, les nombreux rapports directs qui peuvent être distingués entre ces deux régions, ainsi que l'existence de jalons intermédiaires, plus particulièrement dans le Würtemberg[52], définissent clairement la voie de pénétration du nouveau style végétal en Bohême.

Il convient encore de mentionner, au moins brièvement, le domaine du décor céramique, dont l'importance particulière pour les zones périphériques a été démontrée de nouveau récemment[53]. L'abondance

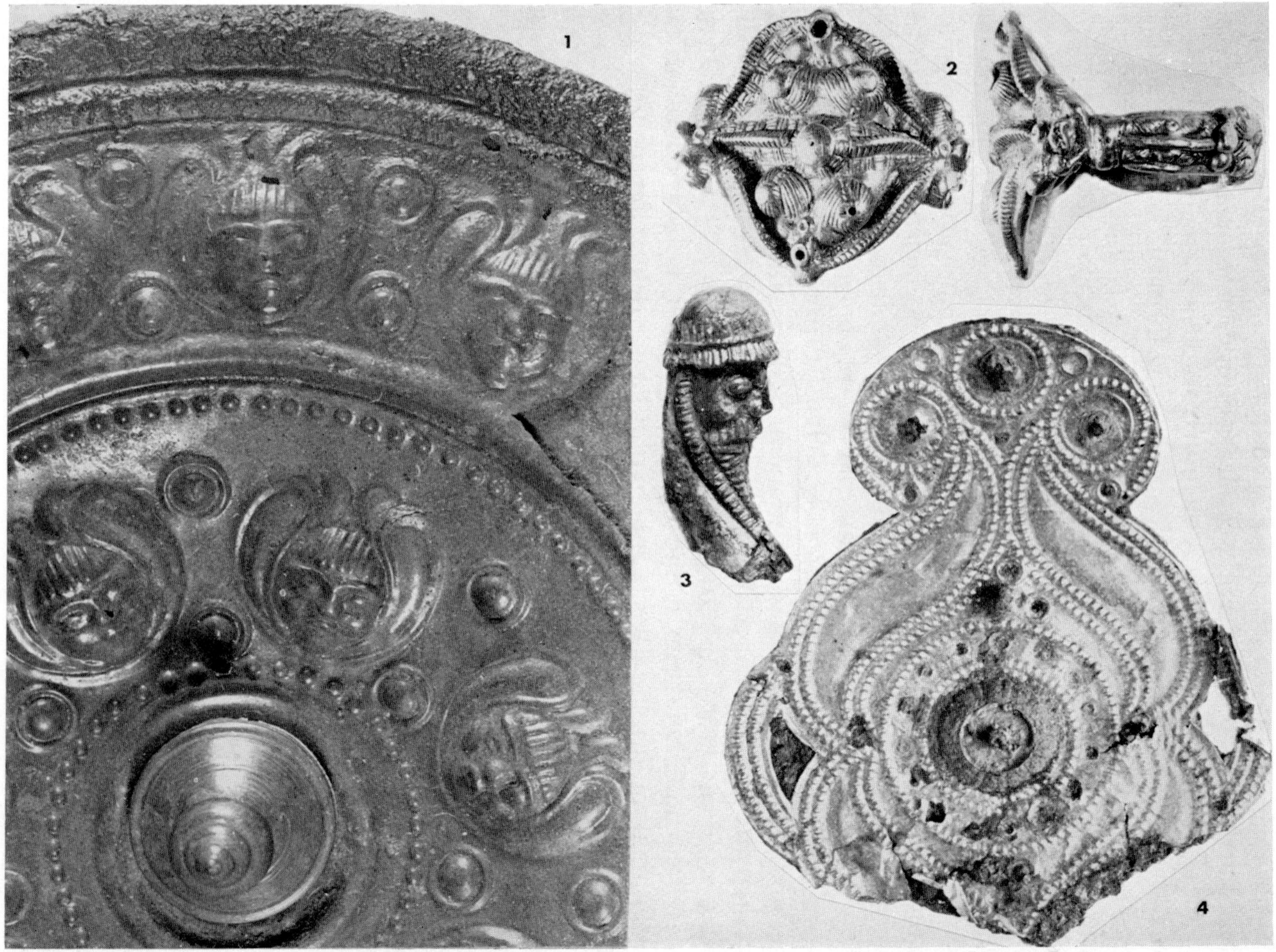

FIG. 8—1/ HOŘOVIČKY (distr. Rakovník): détail d'une des phalères en bronze (dimension réelle des têtes: ht. 17 mm, larg. 12 mm). 2/ Région de HOŘOVICE (distr. Beroun): bague en or vue de face et de côté (ht. réelle du chaton 25 mm). 3/ KŠICE (distr. Tachov): pied d'une fibule en bronze fragmentaire (ht. réelle 16 mm). 4/ CHLUM (distr. Rokycany): plaque en bronze recouvert d'une feuille d'or, décorée au repoussé (dimensions réelles: ht. 60 mm, larg. 52 mm).

et les caractères spécifiques (état généralement fragmentaire etc.) du matériel céramique rendent son étude assez difficile et sa synchronisation avec le matériel métallique est encore en Bohême à un stade embryonnaire. Un aspect positif de ce matériel est sa diffusion très limitée par rapport aux objets en métal, fait qui nous permet de caractériser une production locale ou plus largement régionale, mais ces caractéristiques ne peuvent, à notre avis, être reportées sur la production métallique sans un grand péril.

Nous croyons pouvoir distinguer à l'origine du décor céramique en Bohême deux impulsions stylistiques principales. Leurs rapports restent à préciser, mais il est clair qu'il n'y a pas de frontières bien nettes entre elles et que c'est leur fusion progressive avec l'adjonction d'éléments nouveaux ou transformés qui aboutit à ce que l'on pourrait appeler une *koinè* des provinces laténiennes à l'est du Rhin et qui est, avec le nouveau style végétal, une des manifestations les plus caractéristiques accompagnant l'expansion celtique dans les régions danubiennes.

La première impulsion se manifeste sur un groupe de céramique estampée où les mêmes estampilles (cercles, triangles, croix, esses etc.), alternées ou non mais toujours simplement juxtaposées et disposées généralement par registres, couvrent souvent presque toute la surface du vase ou, du moins, une partie importante. L'origine de ce type de céramique estampée, dont nous connaissons certains équivalents en Europe occidentale (Mont-Lassois), est peut-être à chercher dans la zone préalpine de l'Italie du nord, où une céramique estampée très semblable, prenant la relève de celle du foyer villanovien, connaît une vogue assez générale à la fin du Premier âge du fer. L'ensemble du tumulus de *Velká Turná*[54] est particulièrement intéressant à cet égard, car des céramiques portant ce type de décor y sont accompagnées d'un fragment de poterie sur lequel est reproduite très exactement la frise d'esses enchaînées décorant certains bassins étrusques. Il n'est donc pas improbable que ce type d'estampage ait suivi le même chemin que les bronzes étrusques importés et la technique du tournage, à laquelle il est généralement associé[55].

La seconde zone d'inspiration est le décor gravé et estampé de certains objets de métal, les vases en particulier, imité fidèlement à l'aide des mêmes techniques. Nous retrouvons donc le répertoire de la gravure au compas exécuté soit entièrement par estampage (Fig. 3, f)[56], ce qui connaîtra par la suite un développement et une vogue particuliers, soit par la technique originale (Fig. 4, a)[57], soit par la simple gravure à main levée (Fig. 4, b)[58], de même que des motifs du style végétal orientalisant, comme sur le tesson de *Rataje*[59] (Fig. 4, c) qui reproduit fidèlement l'un des motifs gravés sur le pied de l'oenochoé de Reinheim.[60] Fait digne d'attention, ces décors d'origine métallique semblent en Bohême liés plus particulièrement à une forme typiquement céramique, le flacon lenticulaire.

FIG. 9—1/ NOVÁ HUŤ (distr. Plzeň-sever): fibule à masques, a/ détail des masques (dimensions réelles de l'objet: long. 55 mm, ht. 24). 2/ PANENSKÝ TÝNEC (distr. Louny): fibule à masques, a/ détail du pied, b/ détail de l'oiseau couvrant le ressort, c/ détail de la fixation du ressort (dimensions réelles de l'objet: long. 102 mm, ht. 26 mm, envergure de l'oiseau 41 mm). 3/ DRAŽIČKY (distr. Tábor): décor gravé du fourreau d'épée en bronze (ht. réelle du décor 80 mm).

La synchronisation plus précise du matériel céramique avec le mobilier des sépultures, pour l'instant point crucial de l'étude comparative des habitats et des nécropoles, permettra sans doute de préciser cette rapide esquisse en modifiant peut-être ses données. Nous pouvons cependant constater dès aujourd'hui que l'aire de distribution de cette céramique décorée dépasse en Bohême largement celle des oeuvres métalliques du Premier style.

La première période de l'évolution du style laténien en Bohême se présente donc à l'image d'une mosaïque d'objets exclusifs, peu nombreux, d'origines diverses et ne présentant pas de réelle unité stylistique, couvrant principalement les bassins de la Berounka et de la Vltava. L'absence de styles régionaux est, d'ailleurs, une caractéristique générale de l'art du Premier style, art d'ateliers peu nombreux produisant des objets de luxe pour une clientèle restreinte et quelquefois assez lointaine. Déplacements des objets ou déplacements de leurs créateurs? Cette question nous paraît, pour l'instant, insoluble. De toute façon, la Bohême est pleinement intégrée dans les courants artistiques de l'Europe celtique archaïque, où l'art seigneurial du Premier style exprime l'assimilation et la transformation d'héritages hallstattiens différents dans une civilisation homogène. L'unité stylistique n'est réalisée en Bohême que plus tard, après une phase de transition apportant à une clientèle plus modeste les éléments déjà en partie transformés du Premier style, enrichis de nouvelles acquisitions. La Bohême du nord-ouest semble avoir joué dans ce processus un rôle décisif.

Le relatif conservatisme du Premier style, opposé au dynamisme de l'évolution ultérieure, reflète ainsi fidèlement la profonde mutation de la société celtique au cours du IVème siècle, transformation dont, incontestablement, l'une des causes principales fut l'impact de la civilisation méditerranéenne sur ce monde dit trop souvent barbare.

Notes

Les renvois d'une note à l'autre sont imprimés en charactères italiques gras

1. Equivalent français du terme "Early Style" introduit par P. Jacobsthal.
Cf. Jacobsthal, P. (1944). "Early Celtic Art" (réimpr. 1969), Oxford University Press, Oxford (=ECA).

2. Schefold, K. (1949–1950). Die Stilgeschichte der frühen keltischen Kunst, *Praehistorische Zeitschrift* **XXXIV/XXXV,** 11–17.
Duval, P.-M. (1964): L'art des Celtes et la Gaule, *Art de France* IV, 5–43.
Idem (1971): Les styles de l'art celtique occidental. Terminologie et chronologie, *Actes du VIIe Congrès International des sciences préhistoriques et protohistoriques,* (*Prague* 1966), 812–817.

3. Kruta, V. (1973): Débuts et développement du Style plastique en Bohême. Communication au *IVe congrès international d'études celtiques, Rennes 1971*; *Etudes celtiques* **XIII**/2, 644–661.

4. Kudrnáč, J. (1971): "Zlato v Pootaví," Písek.

5. C'est particulièrement le cas de la Rhénanie: Driehaus, J. (1965). "Fürstengräber" und Eisenerze zwischen Mittelrhein, Mosel und Saar, *Germania* **43,** 32–49.

6. Une carte des gisements de surface des minerais d'étain et de cuivre dans les Monts Métallifères est donnée dans: Pleinerová, I. (1966): Únětická kultura v oblasti Krušných hor a jejím sousedství, *Památky archeologické* **LVI,** 1–134; nous n'avons pour l'instant aucune preuve directe de leur exploitation au cours de la protohistoire.

7. Schránil, J. (1922): Kultura latènská a její vlivy na popelnicová pole v Čechách, *Obzor praehistorický* **I,** 15–24 (et pl. IV).

8. Filip, J. (1956): "Keltové ve Střední Evropě", Praha, (PLANCHE XII/1).

9. Siblík, J. (1906–1908): Žárové hroby u Hradiště, *Památky archeologické* **XXII,** 343–366. (Fig. 4/i).

10. Siblík, *Idem,* (Fig. 8/19).

11. Megaw, J. V. S. (1970): "Art of the European Iron Age: A study of the Elusive image", Bath (no. 31).

12. Telles les fibules de Langenlonsheim (Jacobsthal, ECA, no. 319), Reinheim (Keller, J. (1965): "Das keltische Fürstengrab von Reinheim" I, Mainz; Planche 26/26, 27/14),
et Dürrnberg (Hell, M. (1929): Neue Grabfunde der Hallstatt und Latènezeit von Dürrnberg, *Mitteilungen der Anthropologischen Gesellschaft in Wien* **LXIX,**

mais aussi les fibules en forme de chaussure à la poulaine de Hradiště (sépulture III, cf. appendice), Dürrnberg (Megaw, 1970, no. 32) et Wien-Leopoldau: Schwappach, F., 1967: Schnabelschuhe im östlichen Frülatènebereich, *Památky archeologické* **LVIII,** 320–324. Fig. 1/2).

13. Megaw, 1970, no. 68.

14. Megaw, 1970, no. 90.

15. Pour les données générales de cette question: cf. Kruta, V. (1970): Les fibules celtiques dites "à masques", *Annuaire de l'Ecole pratique des Hautes Etudes, IVe section*, 1969–1970, Paris 299–305. A compléter pour les fibules à double tête d'oiseau par: Dehn, W. (1966a): Die Doppelvogelkopffibel aus dem Val-de-Travers, *Helvetica Antiqua*, (Festschrift Vogt), 137–146.

16. Filip, 1956, (PLANCHE IV/3, V); décor développé de l'arc: Kruta (1973), *Idem*, (Fig. 1/1).

17. Les formes les plus proches sont les variantes longues et basses de l'Italie du Nord (Bologne, Spina, région atestine et Tessin): cf. Primas, M. (1967): Zur Verbreitung und Zeitstellung der Certosafibeln, *Jahrbuch des Römischgermanischen Zentralmuseum Mainz*, 99–133.

18. Megaw, 1970, no. 84.

19. Megaw, 1970, no. 71.

20. Megaw, 1970, no. 64: la nécropole de Stupava semble être le témoin le plus ancien de la pénétration celtique dans la zone karpatique: cf.
Benadík, B. (1971): Obraz doby laténskej na Slovensku, *Slovenská archeológia* **XLX,** 465–498.

21. Schwabsburg, Langenlonsheim, Hermeskeil etc.: cf. Franz, L. (1937–1938): Latènezeitliche Gürtelhaken, *Praehistorische Zeitschrift* **XXVIII–XXIX,** 406–411.

22. Cette technique, qui serait un héritage du hallstattien occidental, présente une assez longue persistance chronologique: Megaw, J. V. S. (1968): Une épée de La Tène I, avec fourreau décoré, *Rev. arch. de l'Est*, **19,** 129–144.

23. Filip, 1956, PLANCHE VIII/1.

24. Cf. en particulier les garnitures de La Bouvandeau (Jacobsthal, ECA, no. 171) et de La Gorge-Meillet (Jacobsthal, ECA, no. 196). L'agrafe en fer stylistiquement la plus proche est celle de Roseldorf (Basse Autriche), trouvée sur un site ayant fourni principalement du matériel de la fin de la période laténienne (Pittioni, R. 1938: "Österreichs Urzeit im Bilde"; Leipzig-Wien; PLANCHE 45/1). Une agrafe en bronze d'une composition très voisine provient aussi du Dürrnberg près de Hallein (Megaw, J. V. S.

1970a: Cheshire Cat and Mickey Mouse: Analysis, interpretation and the Art of the La Tène Iron Age; *Proceedings of the Prehistoric Society* **XXXVI**, PLANCHE XXXV).

25. Filip, 1956, PLANCHE VI.

26. Megaw, 1970. *ECA* (no. 46).

27. Jacobsthal, *ECA*, (no. 21).

28. Megaw, 1970, (no. 43).

29. Il nous parait difficile d'adopter la notion d'atelier de J. V. S. Megaw: Megaw, J. V. S. 1972: Style and style groupings in continental early La Tène art; *World archaeology* vol. 3 no. 3, 276–292 (PLANCHE 20–22), qui reste a mi-chemin entre l'usage de ce mot dans son sens propre et celui de faciés stylistique. Le résultat en est l'impression de choix arbitraire que l'on ressent en comparant les objets attribués à l'atelier de Schwarzenbach (Schwarzenbach workshop) à d'autres objets présentant les motifs qui devraient le caractériser.

30. Cf. en particulier: Jacobsthal, ECA, no. 355 a, c, et Bretz-Mahler, D. (1971): "La Civilisation de La Tène I en Champagne. Le faciès marnien". Paris (PLANCHE 81/14).

31. Dehn, W. (1966b): Eine böhmische Zierscheibe der Frühlatènezeit in Berlin, *Sborník Národního Muzea v Praze*, serie A, vol. XX (Fig. 9).

32. Dehn, W. (1966b) Fig. 11.

33. Schwappach, F. (1971): Floral decorations and Arc designs in the "Early Style". Communication au *IVe Congrès international d'études celtiques, Rennes* 1971; *Etudes celtiques* **XIII**/2, 710–732.

34. Megaw, 1970, p. 74.

35. Filip, 1956, Fig. 6/3.

36. Ce phénomène est particulièrement sensible sur le répertoire décoratif des fibules de la trouvaille de Duchcov: Cf. Kruta, V., 1971 (cit. ***n. 47***), PLANCHE 10–16; sa confrontation avec celui des fibules villanoviennes est un temoignage sans équivoque d'une filiation directe; nous sommes ici en présence de l'aboutissement d'une tradition de décor du bronze de l'Europe protohistorique, dont les premiers éléments suivent de peu l'apparition de ce métal en Europe centrale et dans les régions adjacentes.

37. Kruta, 1973 (***note 3***), Fig. 1/4.

38. Kruta, 1973 (***note 3***), Fig. 1/5.

39. Décor développé de l'arc: Kruta, 1973, (***note 3***), Fig. 3/6.

40. Filip, 1956, Fig. 6/7.

41. Jacobsthal, ECA, no. 92.

42. Jope, E. M. (1971). The Waldalgesheim Master, dans "The European Community. Studies in honour of C. F. C. Hawkes", London, 167–180, Fig. 21–26, 36–40.

43. Des confrontations particulièrement intéressantes peuvent être faites entre la garniture Fig. 66 et le décor de certain casques italiens: Canosa- type de peltes et facture générale: (Jacobsthal, ECA, no. 143). Casque d'Ombrie—masque pris dans une composition végétale (*Ibid*, no. 144).

44. Jacobsthal, ECA, no. 47.

45. Jacobsthal, ECA, no. 44.

46. Nous trouvons ces feuilles, associées à d'autres motifs adoptés à ce moment par l'art laténien (rinceau, postes) et à cet élément très voisin et bien caractéristique qu'est la frise de demi-oves (cf. les casques cités note 43), sur les remarquables flacons en bronze repoussé de Montefortino:
Brizio, E. (1899): "Il sepolcreto gallico di Montefortino presso Arcevia", Monumenti antichi della Academia dei Lincei 9, PLANCHE VIII/8.

47. Kruta, (1971), "Le trésor de Duchocv dans les collections tchécoslovaques," Ústi nad Labern: no. 247 (pl. 25/26).

48. Kruta, (1973), Fig. 3/3.

49. Píč, J. L. (1902): "Staržitnosti země české II sv. 1: Kostrové hroby s Kulturou marnskou čili latèneskou a Bojové v Čechách"; Praha (PLANCHE III/5).

50. Megaw (1970), no. 134.

51. Kruta, (1971), no. 561, pl. 15/132.

52. Krämer, W. (1964): "Das keltischen Gräberfeld von Nebringen (Kreis Böblingen"), Stuttgart.

53. Schwappach, F. (1969). Stempelverzierte Keramik von Armorica; Marburger Beitrage zur Archäologie der Kelten (Festschrift Dehn). *Fundberichte aus Hessen*: Beiheft I, Bonn (213–287).

54. Dubský, B. (1928–1930): Mohyla u Velké Turné; *Památky Archeologické* **XXXVI,** 94–96, Fig. 7, PLANCHE XXXI; Filip, 1956 Fig. 55/5–7.

55. Dehn, W. (1961–1963): Frühe Drehscheibenkeramik nördlich der Alpen; *Alt-Thuringen* VI (Neumannfestschrift), 372–382, Fig. 1–4, PLANCHE XXIX.

56. Praha 6-Podbaba: d'une fosse d'habitat (Musée de la ville de Prague no. T 172).

57. Počerady, distr. Louny: cabane 1/67: Koutecký, D. (1972). Sídliště z doby laténské a římské v Počeradech, o. Louny; *Archeologické rozhledy* **XXVV,** (Fig. 5).

58. Hlubyně, distr. Příbram: d'une sépulture à incinération?: Filip, 1956, Fig. 53, pl. XIV.

59. Rataje, distr. Tábor: d'une sépulture à incinération sous tumulus: Hraše, J. K. (1898–1899). Mohyla v Březovci u Rataj; *Památky archeologické* **XVIII.**

60. Keller, cité ***note 12***, PLANCHE 24.

Résumé

The Early Style of La Tène Art in Bohemia

The beginnings of La Tène art, at the end of the Hallstatt period, appear in what has been called the Early Style (Jacobsthal; or *Style sévère*, Duval), the "First Style" (*Premier style*) of the French title of the present study. In dated contexts, we know it from the years towards 430 B.C. to those around 350—just under a century. Its works, being relatively few, have been treated in wide comparative studies, rather than in regional ones which would make more clear its relation to ensuing developments. In Bohemia, we find it first in the basins of two chief rivers, the Vltava flowing from the south to Prague, and the Berounka from the west around Pilsen (Plzeň). There is stream-gold in the first region, iron ore in the second. The culture was one of continuance out of the previous Hallstattian, though excluding at first the areas of its rich princely tombs in the country's centre and on the north-west of this. The two river basin regions, wholly south and south-west of the Elbe (Labe), both have easy connection with the Danube. A third region, north of the second, along the foot of the Erzgebirge ("Ore Mountains"), shows little at first but becomes decisive later; it has a westward connection, by Eger and the Main, with the Rhineland. The continuance from local Hallstatt was a direct prolongation: pottery is hardly changed, though now showing signs of the potter's wheel; the graves, under barrows or flat, are still cremations. Datable imports are rare but Etruscan (beak-flagons, afterwards bowls, of bronze); La Tène types, of sword and pottery (necked lenticular flasks, etc.), come gradually in as the older culture's transformation proceeds. Then, in the mid-IVth century suddenly, come flat inhumation-grave cemeteries, spreading to a dominance (absolute in the third and in the central region) which at its outset gives us the last of our Early-Style objects.

The first of them, typical of our style's initial phase, are fibulas with the bird-head form of foot (map 1), as nos. 1 and 4 in Fig. 1 (Cítoliby; Hořín); future work might show they were locally made. They are anyhow a feature of the transition out of Hallstatt. Those as no. 2 in Fig. 1 (Tajanov-Husín), of one-piece construction and stylistically somewhat different, should be somewhat later in date. The distinctive Manětín fibula (Manětín-Hrádek) ought to be early, from its structure and its amber mountings, but its human form is exceptional, and places it probably with animal fibulas more from West Germany and Austria than Bohemia. Of such fibulas with human-mask foot, no. 3 in Fig. 8 (Kšice), probably still of the initial phase, leads us onward to the splendid classic group of our Eastern Celtic style, as Fig. 9, 1–1a (Nová Huť); their dates, wherever here made, should all be between

400 and 350. As for the Panenský Týnec fibula (Fig. 9, 2 a–c), despite its "Certosa" form of bow and its unilateral spring-coil, its highly elaborate detail (animal mask, bird, etc.) can connect it with the same group—and also with the Erstfeld gold torcs (Switzerland)— thus suggesting a lower date than has usually been thought. The gold finger-ring Fig. 9, 2 (reputed from district of Hořovice) is of the same style and probably same origin. The eclectic combination of elements archaic and fully-advanced, when appearing again in the girdle-hooks from Želkovice and Stupava, discloses affinities also with girdle-hooks from the Rhineland (Schwabsburg, Langenlonsheim, Hermeskeil, etc.). And our second early girdle-hook (Fig. 6, no. 1), from Hosty, uses the "lyre" and associated motifs in a manner that is quite distinctly Western, especially Marnian (openwork from La Gorge-Meillet and La Bouvandeau).

A Western (Rhine?) origin seems virtually certain in the technique of covering iron or cast bronze with a thin sheet, of gold or bronze decorated in repoussé or by stamping. The Hořovičky phaleras (Fig. 8, 1, detail) show it in their very un-Eastern human masks, concentrically disposed; so does the plaque from Chlum (Fig. 8, 4, and b in Fig. 2), with the lyre-like pair of lotus plants that spread from its central boss. Were both from the same workshops, somewhere in the West, as the Weisskirchen, Schwabsburg, and Klein Aspergle fittings? This barrow-grave at Chlum had also the plaque Fig. 2, c, of bronze with engraved decoration using lyre, pelta and palmette motifs, with a compass-drawn border of zigzag leaves, which appears again on Fig. 2, a; in these, there are Marnian likenesses, but the work is far more refined. The Nevězice phaleras (Fig. 3, a–e) give a brilliant demonstration of the range of compass drawing; a Želkovice phalera stresses the intersections by pointillé. To localize such work is difficult; and in spite of what Schwappach has published (citing local imitations on pottery), I remain here doubtful of the origin, Eastern or Western. Lastly the Dražičky scabbard (Fig. 9, no. 3) has again engraved decoration with palmette and lyre forms. But the lyres are formed of plant-scrolls, and these suggest a late date: perhaps already in transition from the Early to the following style.

Early-style work had been done to serve an exclusive class, which could command long-distance exchanges besides the products of local skill, with results shown its rich individual graves. But the transition from this to later work has a context wholly different: one of flat-grave cemeteries, distributed through the country, for inhuming a population bearing arms but living on the land. More and more of these people took to ornament made in the new style, still with the old as its base but no longer restrained by the old severity, which their graves in the country's north-western and central agricultural plains—soon, the north-eastern too—display as the start of what arose there afterwards. This new and transitional style—that of the well-known Dux or Duchcov find—has its major concentration, and doubtless workshops, in the north-west. It shows on the one hand the transpositions and developments of Early patterns, whether local or distant in source, with some advances in technique. In Fig. 5, the Toužetín fibula and Letky finger-ring illustrate this, as do other fibulas (Duchcov), ring-ornaments (Běšice) and sword-scabbards (Jenišův Ujezd). On the other hand it brings in plant-motif compositions, inspired by classical forms diffused from the Celtic invaders in Italy. New, besides motifs such as the plant-scroll and the pelta, is their composing in continuous spreads of pattern: more particularly, done in interlace, marking the art that is named Waldalgesheim. For its eclectic, ambiguous character, see in Fig. 6, b, c (from Čížkovice); this beautiful pair of openwork pieces is certainly not local, but should indicate the sphere of influence of North Italian Celtic workshops. Filottrano gives a comparison there for the gold torc from Oploty, and adoption of the style into local work may be seen in some notable bracelets, such as that from the Duchcov find, and amongst its fibulas. The route of passage for the style, up through Württemberg from Switzerland, is declared by numerous parallels there with north-west Bohemian finds.

Pottery is much more difficult, local or regional though it must be, and its relation in ornament to metalwork still awaits satisfactory study. A first decorative impulse that it shows is expressed in stamping, the small individual stamps being simply disposed most often in rows, and often over most or nearly all of the vessel's surface. I would see a North Italian source for this, by the foot of the Alps, where stamping could take its tradition from the Northern Villanovan. Amongst that from the barrow-grave of Velká Turná is a sherd with stamped imitation of the SSS frieze which can be found on Etruscan bronze bowls; stamping can thus have come in along with our imported Etruscan bronzes, and also with the craft of the potter's wheel, which is generally employed for this pottery. A second impulse is expressed in stamps and compass-drawing, taken from the like on metalwork now Celtic: Fig. 3, f, shows it all in stamps, and also Fig. 4, a, b, combined with compass and free-hand drawing, while Fig. 4, c (from Rataje) shows a motif amongst those on the foot of the bronze spout-flagon from Reinheim. This kind of ornament, with stamping in arcs or swags, appears especially on the necked lenticular flasks, although their form is itself ceramic and not metallic. As a whole, such pottery in Bohemia is distributed much more widely than is the Early Style metalwork. Their relation remains to be studied.

Thus the Early La Tène of Bohemia shows a patchwork distribution, at first mainly in the basins of the Berounka and Vltava, of high-quality works in metal for use by a ruling class; it shows neither local styles nor any entire stylistic unity, but affinities in part within the land itself, in part quite far outside it. This well-connected class presided over the change from Hallstatt legacies, here as elsewhere, towards a full La Tène culture. This itself, however, was only attained in the course of the IVth century, when a new demographic order appears in the inhumation cemeteries, and transition sets in (from an apparent north-westerly entry) towards stylistic unity at last, through the impulse of the Mediterranean South.

The Appendix gives a documented list for Bohemia, of work known in the Early and the ensuing Transitional Style.

Discussion

Speakers:— Drs Schwappach and Kruta, Professor Hawkes

More precise information was sought by DR SCHWAPPACH on Italian prototypes for Bohemian stamping on pottery. DR KRUTA repeated his argument from the Velká Turná sherd, with its imitation of a motive found on Etruscan bronze bowls, but Schwappach saw no direct connexion in stamped pottery between this in Bohemia and the Villanovan in Northern Italy. Kruta answered that the Villanovan had established the technique there; the Bohemian did not need more direct antecedents there than that, if the idea can have travelled in the current that brought the Etruscan bronzes. On Schwappach's objecting that Italy had none of the stamping in arcs or swags, he repeated that that was a different thing from the over-all kind of stamping. The pottery with this was of various forms; so were the stamps (crosses, triangles, circles, etc.), cut in simple line and arranged in rows; it used no arcs or swags, and although its vogue was probably short (since it appeared in less abundance than that with stamping in arcs or swags), but he believed none the less that the idea was one from Northern Italy. Though stamping was an older-established thing, with analogies also on metal, he still thought that that could explain its use in this over-all form. Schwappach however feared that there must be a chronological gap. Kruta observed that there were other transmissions, from Italy northwards, with gaps between; the wheel-made pottery appearing north of the Alps, as on the Rhine and also west of it, in the Hallstatt-La Tène transition, stemmed in Italy at Bologna from the Arnoaldi period, and if the transmission of that were proved, so he expected would be others. Among fibula types, for example, there were also cases of the kind.

PROFESSOR HAWKES enquired about the influence of the Certosa form of fibula. Kruta replied that the form's direct influence, which was clear on the Panenský Týnec fibula, on the Münsingen mask fibula, and on hardly more than one besides, should be distinguished from a possible prior one, from that form but indirectly affecting already the longer Late Hallstatt fibulas. Mask fibulas altogether, indeed, in the Eastern Celtic zone, appeared to him to require a Hallstatt background, where geometric ornament might suggest the mask's eyes. Hawkes thanked him for that opinion; and remarked that the bird-head form of fibula foot, though so changed in its style, should thus still represent the old water-bird of Hallstatt symbol-art.

Appendice

Objets du Premier style et de la phase de transition en Bohême

Běšice (commune Čachovice), distr. Chomutov (carte, no. 6) : *parure annulaire* fermée en bronze massif (Musée de Kadaň no. 512) ; provient d'une sépulture à inhumation découverte accidentellement en 1923 et contenant en plus 2 parures annulaires à tampons ornées de masques schématisés, un bracelet à tampons à côtes transversales et 3 fibules à pied discoïdal en bronze.
—Kruta 1973, Fig. 1/5.

Bylany (commune Chrášťany), distr. Kolín (carte, no. 25) : *fibule* fragmentaire en bronze dont le pied figure une tête d'oiseau et l'arc est orné d'une paire d'yeux stylisés (Musée National de Prague?) ; provient de la sépulture à incinération no. 15, qui à part l'urne en poterie comprenait encore les fragments d'une épingle (?) en fer.
—Píč, J. L. 1898/1899: "Archaeologický výzkum ve Středních Čechách: Pohřebiště u Bylan", *Památky archeologické* XVIII, p. 224, Planche XXIII/8, 10; Filip 1956, Fig. 78/5.

Chlum, distr. Rokycany (carte, no. 12) : *plaque* constituée d'une feuille d'or décorée au repoussé et recouvrant une plaque de bronze (Musée National de Prague, col. Píč no. 6714) ;
plaque en bronze au décor finement gravé (Musée de Rokycany no. 46–A) ;
embout en bronze à décor gravé (Musée National de Prague?) ; tous ces objets proviennent d'une sépulture (vraisemblablement à incinération) sous tumulus isolé, découverte en 1904 et contenant en outre une oenochoé et deux bassins en bronze, une épée, 2 pointes de lance, un couteau et une hache en fer, ainsi que 2 vases céramiques.
—Píč, J. L. 1904/1905: "Z archeologického bádáni 1904: Mohyla u Chlumu nad Berounkou", *Památky archeologické* XXI, 333–335, Planche XXIX. Filip 1956, Fig. 76.

Chýnov (commune Libčice nad Vltavou), distr. Praha-západ (carte, no. 24) : *fibule* à masques en bronze à l'arc incrusté de corail (Musée National de Prague, sans no.) ; découverte en 1901 avec un bracelet fermé en bronze à 6 nodosités dans la sépulture (incinération?) du tumulus no. 1.
—Felcman, J. 1902/1903: "Archaeologický výzkum v roku 1901; Mohyhy v háji u Chejnova", *Památy archeologické* XX, p. 42, Fig. 2/1–2; Filip 1956, III/16.

Cítoliby, distr. Louny (carte, no. 11) : *fibule* en bronze à tête de griffon (Musée National?) ; découverte en 1887 dans la sépulture à incinération no. XIII avec 2 poteries, 1 perle en verre bleu, les fragments d'une parure tubulaire en bronze à décor géométrique gravé, 1 anneau en bronze et 1 applique en fer avec anneau.
—Wiehl, A. 1908/1909: "Pohřebiště s popelnicemi n Cítolib", *Památky archeologické* XXIII p. 74, Planche XXV/8–15; Filip 1956, Fig. 78/6.

Čížkovice, distr. Litoměřice (carte, no. 16) : *deux garnitures* ajourées en bronze (Musée de Litoměřice : ancien fonds du Musée de Třebenice, sans no.) ; d'après les documents exploités par Filip, que nous n'avons pu retrouver, ces garnitures proviendraient d'une sépulture à inhumation contenant des parures annulaires, une chaînette et un objet tubulaire en bronze ainsi que des perles d'ambre ; le caractère assez hétérogène de l'ensemble nous incite à observer une certaine réserve quand à son authenticité.

—Filip 1956, p. 339, Fig. 13.

DRAŽIČKY, distr. Tábor (carte, no. 22): *fourreau* d'épée à face extérieure en tôle de bronze portant sur sa partie supérieure un décor gravé (Musée de Tábor no. Da 378); provient d'une sépulture, probablement à incinération, dans un tumulus exploré en 1939 et contenant en outre 4 poteries, un mors et une pointe de lance en fer.

—Archives de l'Institut d'Archéologie de Prague no. 162/45; Filip 1956, p. 161, Fig. 6/3, PLANCHE X/1–10.

DUCHCOV, *voir* Lahošť.

HOŘÍN, distr. Mělník (carte, no. 23): *fibule* à tête d'oiseau en bronze (Musée de Mělník no. Pr 2918); provient de la sépulture à incinération no. III découverte en 1895 et comprenant, en plus des poteries non conservées, l'urne de poterie travaillée au tour, un sabre-coutelas en fer, une épingle et un fragment de parure annulaire en bronze, ainsi que des fragments d'objets indéterminés en fer.

—Čermák, B. 1900/1901: "Předhistorické pohřebiště u Hořína", *Památky archeologické* XIX, p. 516–517, PLANCHE XLVIII/13–18; Filip 1956, Fig. 78/2; Sklenář, K. 1966: *Vlastivědně Muzeum v Mělníku: katalog pravěké sbírky* (Zprávy čs. společnosti archeologické, supplément 2, Praha), nos 2917, 2918, 2931, PLANCHE XX/750, 779.

HOŘOVICE (région de), distr. Beroun: *bague* en or (Musée National de Prague no. 18708); achetée en 1916 à un antiquaire duquel provient l'indication sur la provenance.

—Niederle, L. 1919: Archaeologické studie: I, Příspěvek k poznání časného Latènu v Čechách", *Památky archeologické* XXXI, 65–67, Fig. 4.

HOŘOVIČKY, distr. Rakovník (carte no. 7): *deux phalères* constituées par un disque de bronze entouré d'une moulure en fer, le tout couvert d'une mince feuille de bronze décorée au repoussé (Musée National de Prague nos 85028, 85029); proviennent d'une sépulture à char (vraisemblablement incinération) sous couverture rectangulaire de pierres fouillée en 1863 et 1864; le riche mobilier, aujourd'hui disparu en plus grande partie, comprenait en outre 10 autres phalères plus petites avec un seul registre de têtes, 4 parures tubulaires à tampons en forme de fer à cheval (vraisemblablement pièces de harnachement), 1 anneau en bronze avec pendeloque, les fragments d'un placage d'essieu (?) en tôle de bronze, 1 esse d'essieu (?) en fer à tête de bronze, 2 éléments cylindriques et 1 conique fixés à l'origine sur du bois (timon?), des anneaux en bronze, un sabre-coutelas en fer, un chenet, en fer à tête d'animal, une fibule (?) en bronze plaqué d'or, de petites appliques en feuille d'or, 2 bassins en bronze, des fragments de bandages de roues en fer et un grand nombre de tessons.

—Jičínský, K. 1863: "Zpráva o archaeologickém nálezu v Hořovicích u Peteršpurka v okrese Jesenickém v Čechách", *Památky archeologické* V, 368–371. Fodisch, J. E. 1865. "Fund bei Horzowitz in Böhmen", *Anzeiger für Kunde der deutschen Vorzeit*, N.F. 12, 183–185. Filip 1956, PLANCHE VI, XXII/1.

HOSTY, distr. České Budějovice (carte, no. 21): *agrafe* de ceinturon ajourée en fer (Musée de České Budějovice no. 185); provient d'une sépulture à incinération sous tumulus (cité aussi quelquefois sous le nom de la commune voisine de Hladná) qui contenait aussi une boucle ovale, un anneau, un couteau, un sabre-coutelas, une épée et une pointe de lance en fer.

—Filip 1956, Planche VIII/1–5.

Hradiště, distr. Plzeň-jih (carte, no. 13): *fibule* en bronze à tête d'oiseau de la riche sépulture à incinération no. III, qui contenait en plus 2 poteries, des perles en verre bleu, des parures annulaires et anneaux en bronze et en fer, un sabre-coutelas et une fibule fragmentaire en fer, 2 fibules exceptionnelles en bronze, dont une en forme de chaussure à la poulaine.

—Siblík 1906/1908, pp. 346–347, Fig. 4, 5/1, 6/12.

fibule en bronze à tête d'oiseau de la sépulture à incinération no. VIII, qui contenait aussi une fibule en fer, 2 appliques discoïdales et un anneau en fer, ainsi que les fragments d'une tige de fer constituant un objet indéterminé.

—Siblík 1906/1908, pp. 350–351, Fig. 8.

Jenišův Újezd, distr. Teplice (carte, no. 15): *bracelet* en bronze massif à tampons (Musée de Teplice no. K 8428); provient de la sépulture à inhumation no. 25, qui contenait en plus 2 fibules en bronze, 2 fibules en fer, 1 bracelet à tampons en bronze, 1 anneau en fer et 1 objet indéterminé de la même matière.

—Weinzierl, R., Ritter von. 1899: *Das La Tène-Grabfeld von Langugest bei Bilin in Böhmen* (Braunschweig), p. 41, Fig. 22–24, Planche V/22–29.

fourreau d'épée en bronze (Musée de Teplice sans no.); provient de la sépulture à inhumation no. 115 (fouilles 1909), ne contenant pas d'autre mobilier, excepté peut-être un anneau ou bague en bronze.

—Filip 1956, Fig. 6/7, Planche XXVI/8; Budinský, P. 1970: *Libkovice (Mariánské Radčice), Jenišův Ujezd, Hostomice: Významná naleziště doby laténské v Podkrušnohoří, II čàst, Jenišův Újezd* (Teplice), p. 21.

Klobuky, distr. Kladno (carte, no. 18): *bracelet* en bronze massif à tampons (Musée National de Prague no. 55811); fait partie d'une série de parures annulaires découvertes au siècle dernier à proximité de la gare et provenant vraisemblablement d'une nécropole.

—Píč 1902, p. 165, Planche III/4–11.

Kralovice, distr. Plzeň-sever (carte, no. 8): *fibule* en bronze au pied en forme de tête d'oiseau (Musée de Plzeň?); provient de la sépulture à inhumation (?) sous couverture de pierres no. 6, contenant en plus 2 vases céramiques, une épée, un sabre-coutelas et 3 anneaux en fer.

—Filip 1956, Planche XII/I, 6; Jansová, L. 1961: "Datování laténského pohřebiště v Kralovicích u Plzně", *Památky archeologické* LII, 268–273.

Kšice, distr. Tachov (carte, no. 3): *pied de fibule* en bronze représentant une tête humaine (Musée de Stříbro no. 148); provient de la sépulture à incinération du tumulus no. III, qui contenait en plus les 2 perles de bronze terminant l'axe du ressort de la fibule et de la céramique.

—Eichhorn, O. 1935: "Grabungen bei Mies", *Sudeta* XI, 33–47; Šaldová, V. 1971: "Pozdně halštatské ploché hroby v západních Čechách a jejich vztah k současným mohylám. Pohřebiště Nynice a Žákava-Svárec", *Památky archeologické* LXII, Fig. 68/5.

Kyšice, distr. Plzeň-sever (carte, no. 10): *fibule* à masques en bronze (Musée de Plzeň no. 9168); fait partie d'un lot d'objets provenant de la fouille ancienne de 6 tumulus du groupe I; une des sépultures fouillées avait une couverture de pierres d'environ 9m² et contenait une inhumation et une incinération; parmi les objets provenant du site, des flacons lenticulaires et une épée à poignée anthropomorphe correspondraient le mieux au probable milieu chronologique de la fibule.

—Křikava, F. 1883: "Mohyly v Čechách a jejich obsah: V. Mohyly v okolí řeky Klabavky", *Památky archeologické* XII p. 296–297, PLANCHE XVI (p. 371); Filip 1956, PLANCHE VIII/6, 10–13.

LAHOŠŤ, distr. Teplice (carte, no. 14): *bracelet* en bronze à tampons (Musée de Teplice no. 12451; Kruta 1971, cat. no. 247); *fibule* en bronze (Musée de Teplice no. 12289; Kruta 1971, cat. no. 561); *fibule* en bronze figurée par Š. Berger (1882, PLANCHE IV/48) et J. L. Píč (1902, PLANCHE de fibules après p. 16, no. 16), aujourd' hui disparue; *fibule* en bronze à pied annulaire du Musée de Teplice, actuellement disparue et figurée par J. Filip (1956, PLANCHE XXIII/5) et J. V. S. Megaw (1970, no. 134); tous ces objets proviennent de la trouvaille connue plus généralement sous le nom de trésor de Duchcov (Dux) et effectuée en 1882 dans la source thermale de Obří Pramen (Riesenquelle); cet ensemble comportait au minimum 1600 objets, dont 850 fibules, 650 bracelets et 100 bagues et objets divers.

—Berger, Š. 1882: "Bronzy duchcovské I", *Památky archeologické* XII, 71–78, 105–115, PLANCHE III/V; Kruta 1971.

LETKY (commune Libčice nad Vltavou), distr. Praha-západ (carte, no. 24a): *bague* en bronze massif (Musée National de Prague no. 55984); provient de la sépulture à inhumation no. 12 (fouilles de 1922; sépulture no. 30 de la numérotation de Filip), qui contenait aussi une épée, une pointe de lance et un brassard en fer, ainsi qu'un bracelet lisse en bronze.

—Vacek, J. 1925: "Laténské pohřebiště v Letkách", *Památky archeologické* XXXIV p. 322, PLANCHE XLVII/1–2, 12–13; Filip 1956, p. 358, PLANCHE XLIX/7.

MANĚTÍN-HRÁDEK, distr. Plzeň-sever (carte, no. 5): *fibule* anthropomorphe en bronze incrusté d'ambre (déposée actuellement à l'Institut d'Archéologie de Prague); provient de la sépulture no. 74 (fouilles de 1967), probablement à inhumation, qui contenait en plus 4 appliques discoïdales en bronze et 2 poteries, dont une terminée au tour.

—Soudská, E. 1968. "Hrob s maskovitou sponou Manětína-Hrádku", *Archeologické rozhledy* XX, 451–469, 567–570.

NEVĚZICE, distr. Písek (carte, no. 20): *six phalères* en bronze à décor gravé (Musée de Písek ?), d'un lot de 8 phalères provenant vraisemblablement d'une sépulture.

—Woldřich, J. N. 1886. "Beiträge zur Urgeschichte Böhmens: Bronzen aus Nevězic", *Mitteilungen der Anthropologischen Gesellschaft in Wien* 16, 92–93, PLANCHE IX, 12–17; Dehn, 1966b, p. 140, Fig. 9.

NOVÁ HUŤ (commune Dýšina), distr. Plzeň-sever (carte, no. 9): *fibule* à masques en bronze (Musée de Plzeň no. 8690); provient de l'un des 57 tumulus fouillés par Macháček entre 1907 et 1911.

—Eisner, J. 1911, "Latène v jihočeských mohylách", *Pravěk* VII, p. 108; Šaldová 1971, pp. pp. 68–69, 99.

OPLOTY (commune Kněžice), distr. Louny (carte, no. 6a): *torque* incomplet à tampons en or massif (Naturhistorisches Museum Wien no. 15015); trouvaille fortuite au cours du labourage d'un champ.

—*Památky archeologické* XIV, 1889, p. 606; Jacobsthal, *Early Celtic Art*, no. 47.

PANENSKÝ TÝNEC, distr. Louny (carte, no. 17): *fibule* à éléments zoomorphes en bronze (Musée National no. 64/37); provient d'une sépulture à inhumation sans autre mobilier connu.

—Píč 1902, p. 169, Fig. 8; Jacobsthal, *Early Celtic Art*, no. 318.

TAJANOV (commune Tupadly), distr. Klatovy (carte, no. 4) : *fibule* en bronze à tête d'oiseau (Musée de Klatovy no. 140) ; provient d'une sépulture à incinération du tumulus no. 11 (4e de la première série de K. Hostaš), contenant en plus des poteries, en majorité à décor estampé, 2 anneaux et 1 fragment d'épée en fer.

—Hostaš, K. 1887, "Mohyly na Husíně", *Památky archeologické* XIV, p. 6–7, PLANCHE I/2–10; Filip 1956, p. 185, Fig. 54/7, PLANCHE XI/4–7.

TOUŽETÍN, distr. Louny (carte, no. 17a) : *fibule* massive en bronze à pied discoïdal (Musée National de Prague no. 55818); provient d'un lot de matériel découvert dans une nécropole à inhumation.

—Filip 1956, p. 384, PLANCHE XL/9–11, LII/2–4.

ŽELKOVICE (commune Libomyšl), distr. Beroun (carte, no. 19) : *phalère* en bronze à décor gravé d'une série de 8 objets similaires, mais sans décor (Musée National de Prague no. 85001); fait partie d'un lot d'objets (mors en bronze, 2 sabres-coutelas et 1 couteau en fer, 2 garnitures en forme de U et 2 anneaux en bronze, les fragments de jantes de fer ainsi que d'anneaux de la même matière, de la céramique) découvert en 1900 et interprété généralement comme une sépulture à char sous tumulus.

—Felcman, J. 1900/1901; "Archaeologický nalez v Želkovicích", *Památky archeologické* XIX, 168–174, PLANCHE XXI; Filip 1956, p. 268; Fig. 75/1–3, PLANCHE VII/11–13, 17–18; Dehn 1966, p. 141, Fig. 11.

plaque-agrafe de ceinturon en bronze (Musée National no. 4/66); cette pièce, à l'origine dans une collection particulière, est généralement considérée comme provenant de la fouille, antérieure à la précédente, de l'un des autres tumulus.

—Franz 1937/1938; Filip 1956, p. 284, Fig. 79/1.

6

Du Premier style au Style de Waldalgesheim

Remarques sur l'évolution de l'art celtique ancien

Otto-Herman Frey
Hamburg

à Wolfgang Dehn

Dans son étude fondamentale, Paul Jacobsthal a classé l'art celtique ancien selon trois phases différentes: le Premier style, le Style de Waldalgesheim et le Style des Épées, avec le Style plastique—selon l'ordre chronologique[1]. Il considérait ces trois phases comme les éléments d'une seule évolution ayant commencé dans quelques centres, notamment dans la région rhénane. C'est là que les artisans travaillant dans les "cours" seigneuriales créèrent les premières oeuvres en suivant l'exemple de modèles grecs et étrusques. Selon Jacobsthal, les relations avec le monde classique étaient encore actives pendant la période de Waldalgesheim, même si la plupart des motifs étaient dus aux traditions celtiques, comme durant la période suivante.

Les opinions de Jacobsthal ont obtenu une adhésion très étendue et, malgré une série de nouvelles découvertes, il n'y a pas de raison de les modifier sensiblement. Il y a eu, naturellement, des tentatives pour différencier chronologiquement le Premier style[2] mais aucune n'a été pleinement convaincante. D'un autre côté, on a réussi à distinguer plusieurs ateliers[3]. En outre, Frank Schwappach, dans la communication qu'il a donnée à ce colloque, a pu démontrer que dans le Premier style, il y avait eu deux grands domaines, l'un plus occidental et l'autre oriental; ses conclusions sont fondées sur des documents nouveaux, principalement sur la poterie estampée, qui n'avait presque pas été utilisée par Jacobsthal. En raison de cette meilleure définition et classification du Premier style primitif, il convient d'examiner si nous pouvons encore parler d'une évolution homogène de l'art celtique ancien.

C'est ce problème que je désire étudier ici. Dans l'essentiel, nous traiterons des relations entre les manifestations complexes du Premier style et le Style de Waldalgesheim, qui est homogène dans de vastes régions. Nous négligerons de discuter le style récent, car les érudits sont d'accord pour penser que les différents groupes du Style des Épées et, en partie au moins, du Style plastique sont directement issus du Style de Waldalgesheim.

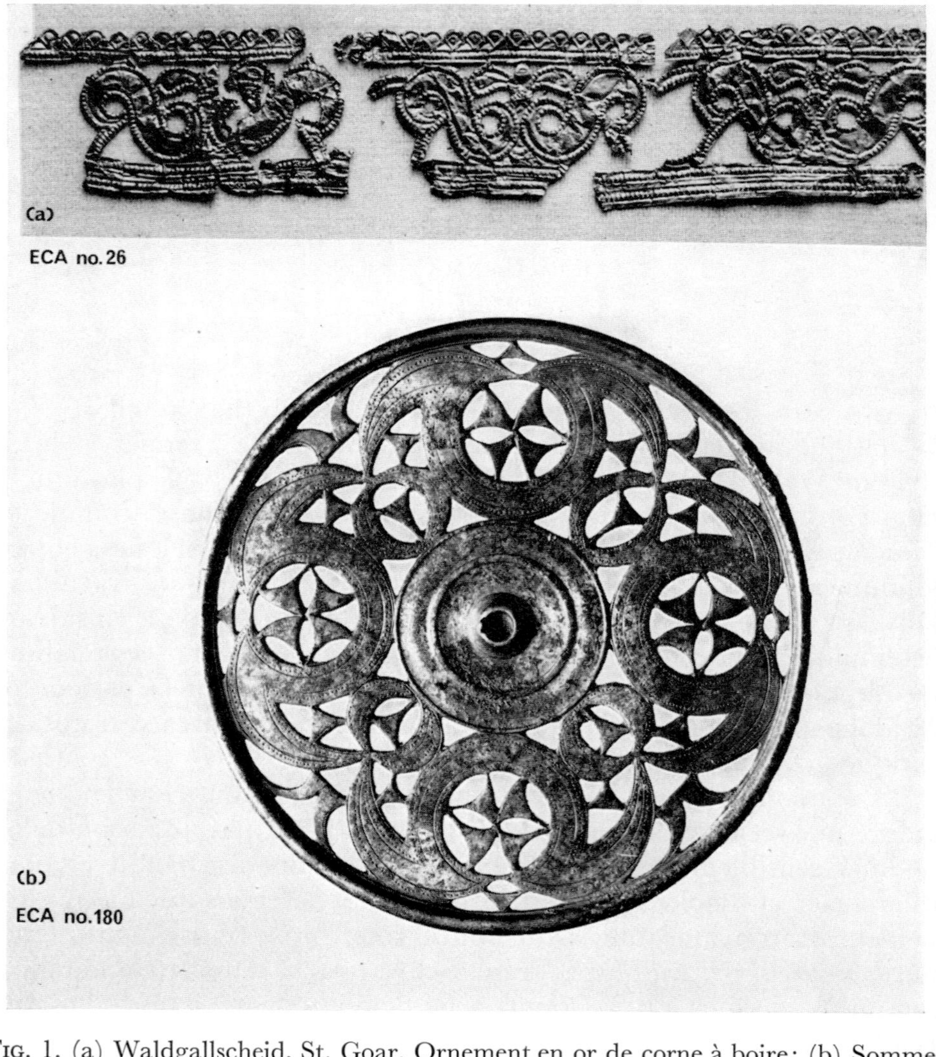

FIG. 1. (a) Waldgallscheid, St. Goar. Ornement en or de corne à boire; (b) Somme-Bionne, Marne. Disque en bronze (d'après Jacobsthal).

Dans sa définition du Premier style, Jacobsthal se référait principalement aux découvertes faites dans la zone du Rhin moyen. Un exemple caractéristique est l'ornement d'une corne à boire de Waldgallscheid, de St. Goar[4] (FIG. 1, a). L'influence du style décoratif grec ou étrusque est facile à discerner: les grandes formes en S remplacent les "vrilles" grecques; les palmettes sont réduites à trois feuilles. Dans le même sens, nous avons le droit de relier directement la frise de fleurs de lotus et de palmettes de l'ornement de la corne à boire d'Eigenbilzen (Fig. 2a–b)[5] à des prototypes méditerranéens. En outre, il y a des types d'exécution qui peuvent être mis en relation avec le flacon de Reinheim (St. Ingbert, Sarre), qui assemble, dans des compositions celtiques, des éléments isolés de la décoration florale grecque (Fig. 3)[6]. Pour les principes de l'ornementation, j'en ai traité, en collaboration avec Frank Schwappach,

FIG. 2. (a–b) Eigenbilzen, Limbourg belge. Ornement en or de corne à boire; (c–d) Etrurie: (c) Caere. Ornement d'une hydrie; (d) Tarquinia. Ornement d'un casque. (a–b) d'après Jacobsthal et Mariën).

dans un article de *World Archaeology* (sous presse au temps du Colloque)[6a]; je puis donc me dispenser de donner à ce propos plus de détails. Pour ce qui nous intéresse ici, l'important est de savoir que les éléments décoratifs isolés sont reliés simplement par la méthode accumulative; cela s'applique non seulement aux travaux sur métal mais aussi à la poterie estampée, où le processus technique trahit cette tendance.

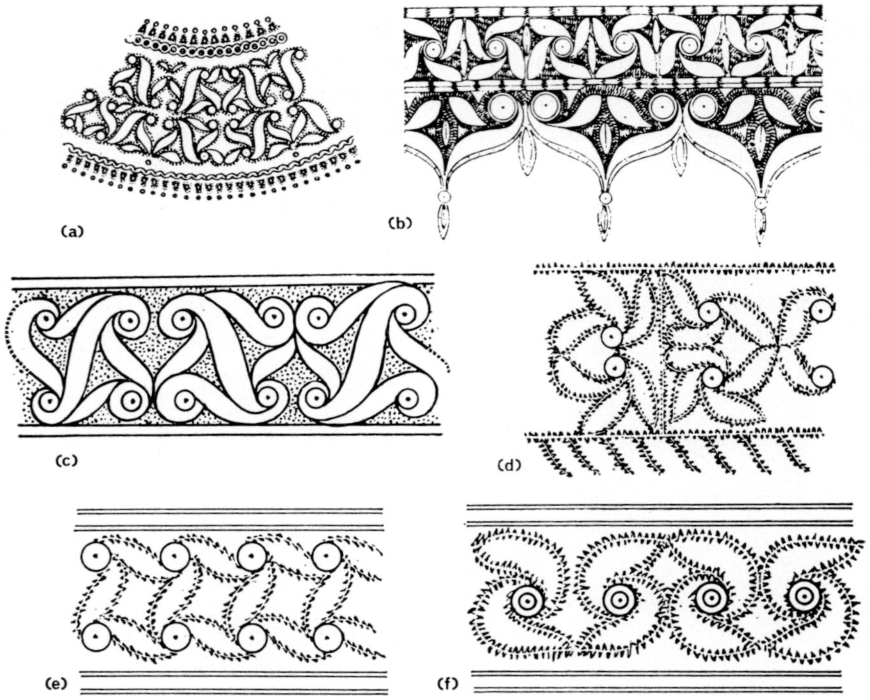

FIG. 3. (a) Waldalgesheim, Kreuznach. Gravure sur flacon en bronze; (b) Reinheim, St. Ingbert. Gravure sur flacon en bronze; (c) Hoppstädten, Birkenfeld. Gravure sur passoire en bronze; (d) Weitbruch, Haguenau. Gravure sur fourreau en bronze (d'après Megaw); (e, f) Bavilliers, Territoire de Belfort (d'après Megaw).

Des pièces semblables de style primitif ont été découvertes plus à l'ouest. Mentionnons le disque d'or d'Auvers-sur-Oise (Val d'Oise) et les montures de bronze d'Etrechy et de Mairy (Marne)[7]. Des pièces de cette nature apparaissent aussi à l'est; un exemple en est la feuille d'or de Chlum, en Bohême[8].

Dans sa communication à ce colloque, Frank Schwappach décrit les frises de cercles et d'arcs comme des décors caractéristiques du Premier style dans la région de La Tène. Un bon exemple à cet égard est la gourde de pèlerin du Dürrnberg (près de Hallein, Autriche) (Fig. 4a)[9]. Ces décors, qui étaient généralement tracés à l'aide de compas, appartiennent à la même période que la décoration florale de la région du Rhin, que nous avons déjà décrite; les relations étroites entre les découvertes des deux groupes suffisent à l'établir[10]. De même, une frise d'arcs, tracés au compas et entrecroisés (Fig. 4b), apparaît sur le versoir à tamis de Hoppstädten (Birkenfeld, Allemagne)[11] qui, en raison de sa décoration occidentale, doit être mis en relation avec des oeuvres comme le flacon de Reinheim (Fig. 3c avec b).

Dans l'article de *World Archaeology* cité plus haut, nous avons expliqué que les compositions circulaires largement espacées, telles qu'elles apparaissent par exemple sur le flacon d'Eigenbilzen (Fig. 4c)[12], se sont développées uniquement à l'ouest; l'exemple le plus beau de ce style est le grand disque orné à jour de Somme-Bionne (Marne) (Fig. 1b)[13]: ici aussi nous trouvons non pas des décors continus, mais des cercles et des lunes curieusement reliés les uns aux autres.

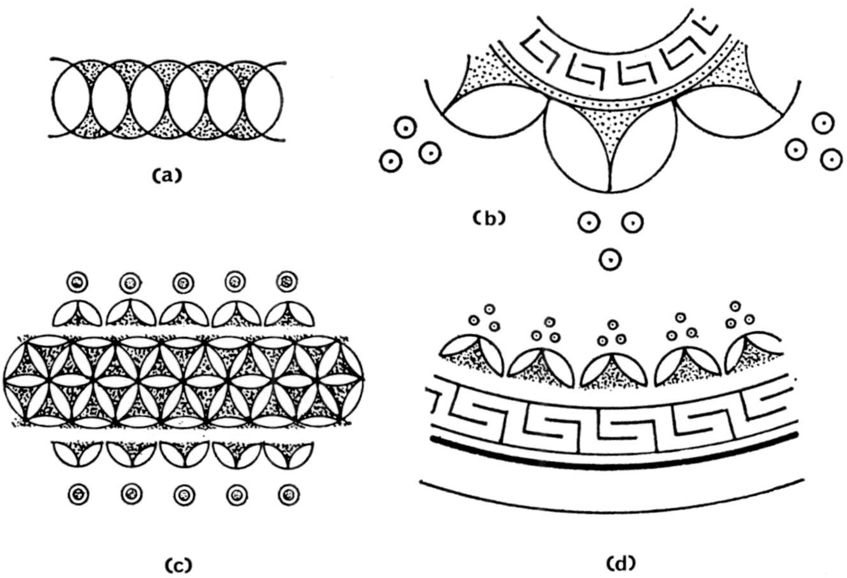

Fig. 4. (a) Dürrnberg près de Hallein. Gravure sur gourde de pèlerin en bronze; (b) Hoppstädten, Birkenfeld. Gravure sur passoire en bronze; (c–d) Eigenbilzen, Limbourg. Gravure sur flacon en bronze (d'après Megaw).

Dans cet exposé rapide sur le Premier style, considérons enfin les productions d'un atelier qui semble avoir existé principalement dans la région de la Marne. Un bon exemple est le casque de Berru, dont la décoration consiste en une vrille ondulante intermittente qui est surimposée sur des palmettes à trois feuilles entourées par des demi-cercles (Fig. 5a)[14]. Ici aussi, la vrille grecque est divisée en parties distinctes. Au contraire, les décors semblables du flacon de Besançon[15] (voir aussi le détail Fig. 5b) se présentent en un mouvement continu dont la raison est le fait que le fond lisse est encadré.

En dehors des oeuvres de La Tène à décors purement ornementaux, nous devons citer les pièces comportant des masques et des représentations d'animaux[16]; certaines d'entre elles dénotent des influences orientalisantes. Elles ne seront pas considérées ici.

Fig. 5. (a) Berru, Marne. Gravure du casque; (b) Oenochoé à bec, Mus. de Besançon. Détail de la gravure; (c) Brunn am Steinfeld, Wiener Neustadt. Monture bronze; (d–e) Waldalgesheim, près Kreuznach. Détails du torques en or et d'un bracelet en bronze; (f) Italie du Nord. Gravure sur monture en bronze; (g) Canosa, Apulie. Ornement du casque. (d–g d'après Jacobsthal).

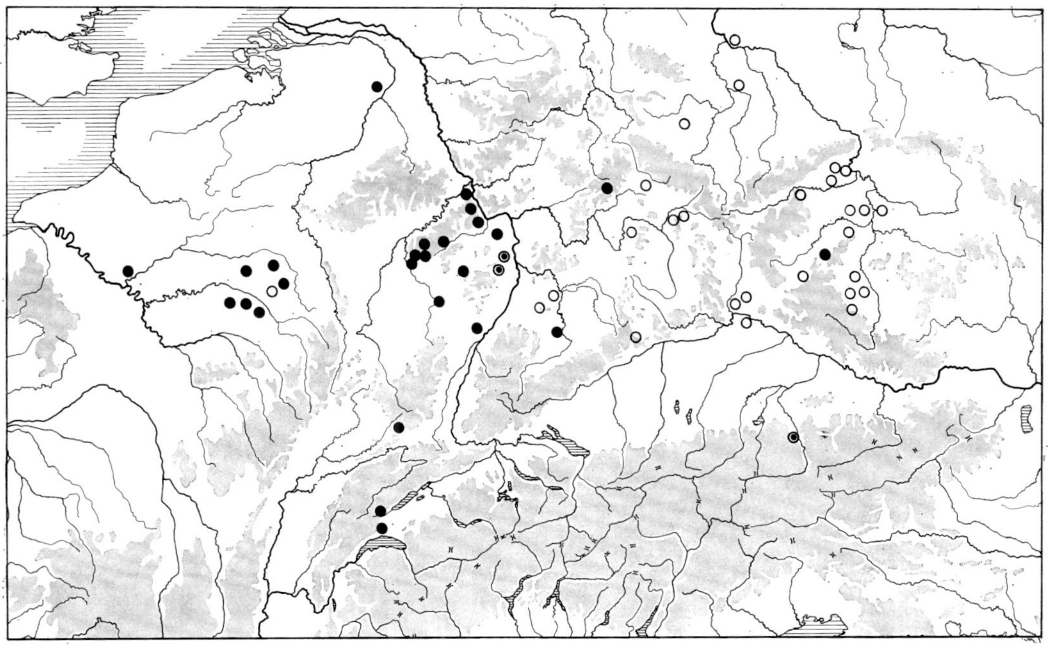

FIG. 6. Répartition continentale d'oeuvres caractéristiques du Premier style. ● Decoration occidentale, florale; ○ frises d'arcs, orientales (d'après Schwappach); ⊙ les deux ensemble.

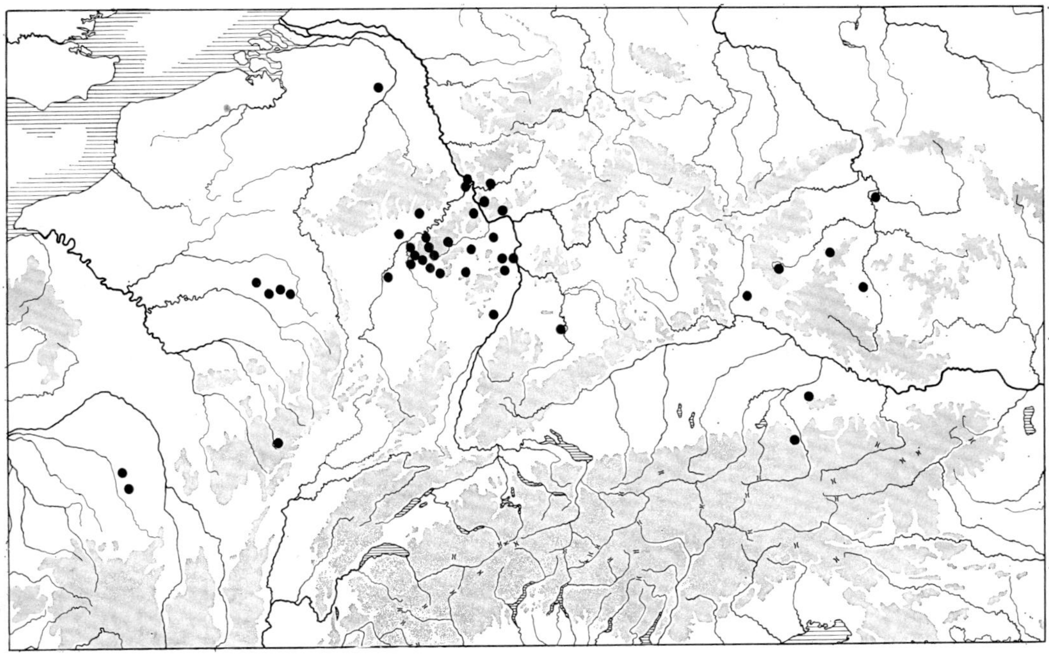

FIG. 7. Répartition des tombes princières de La Tène ancienne avec objets importés, grecs et étrusques.

Les pièces caractéristiques du Premier style se trouvent dans une région qui s'etend de la Champagne à travers le Rhin moyen jusqu'à la Bohême méridionale et à Salzbourg (Fig. 6)[17]. C'est la région des tombes princières, comme on les appelle, qui contiennent des importations grecques et étrusques (Fig. 7)[18]. Si l'on considère aussi la poterie comportant des décors semblables, la zone orientale s'étend à l'Allemagne moyenne et au Nord-Est de la Bavière[19] mais ces deux régions peuvent aussi être étroitement reliées (par exemple par les fibules à masques et à têtes animales) aux tombes princières[20]. De telles découvertes sont au contraire presque complètement absentes du Sud-Ouest de l'Allemagne, du Nord, de la Suisse et de l'Est de la France, où des centres également riches existaient à la période de Hallstatt[21]. Le Premier style, donc, est un phénomène strictement limité à une région.

Fig. 8. Waldalgesheim, Kreuznach. Décors des cornes et du passe-guide du char (d'après Jacobsthal).

Nettement différent est le Style de Waldalgesheim. J'utilise ce terme, encore que je sois d'accord avec E. M. Jope pour estimer qu'une expression plus neutre serait préférable[22]. Ni dans la région rhénane ni dans la zone orientale du Premier style de La Tène, on ne trouve de pièces qui démontreraient une transition graduelle et dont on pourrait se demander si elles appartiennent à un style ou à son successeur. Comme exemple, nous pouvons indiquer les décors des cornes et le passe-guide de Waldalgesheim (Kreuznach) même (Fig. 8)[23]. Ici, une vrille pénètre dans des tourbillons et des éventails; on ne peut pas séparer une forme de l'autre; aucun élément du décor ne pourrait être isolé. Ce contraste très net avec les décors accumulatifs du Premier style nous paraît particulièrement remarquable parce que la tombe de Waldalgesheim comporte aussi un flacon à bec décoré dans le pur Premier style (Fig. 3a)[24].

C'est seulement dans la région de la Marne qu'il existe des pièces décorées de telle façon qu'elles trahissent des rapports entre le Premier style et le Style de Waldalgesheim. Nous avons déjà indiqué le flacon à bec de Besançon[25]. La zone de l'épaule est ornée d'une vrille en vague intermittente, ses palmettes à trois feuilles sont fermées par un demicercle à fond lisse (Fig. 5b). Nous avons là un prototype précoce de l'éventail celtique, un des motifs les plus caractéristiques du style de Waldalgesheim (cf. Fig. 5c–g)[26]. En comparant toute la composition ornamentale du flacon avec, par exemple, celle du casque de Canosa en Apulie (Fig. 5g)[27], qui appartient nettement au style de Waldalgesheim, nous pouvons facilement établir entre ces objets des rapports directs. Les mêmes tendances sont évidentes dans d'autres pièces[28].

FIG. 9. Waldalgesheim, Kreuznach. Détail du décor du torque en or (d'après Jacobsthal).

Cependant, d'un autre côté, on hésite à parler du style ornemental dit de Waldalgesheim dans son ensemble comme issu d'un développement direct du style de la région de la Marne. Ce n'est là qu'une relation entre le Pemier style et le Style de Waldalgesheim. En outre, nous pouvons déceler, dans le décor de Waldalgesheim, des motifs grecs, comme Jacobsthal et plus tard E. M. Jope, en étudiant certains détails de la joaillerie de Waldalgesheim même, l'ont déjà souligné:[29] les petites rosettes en étoiles du torque (Fig. 9), par exemple, sont dérivées de la décoration de la situle de l'Italie méridionale qui a été trouvée avec lui (FIG. 12a)[30]. D'un autre côté, et en dehors de tels détails, nous tendons à faire dériver toutes les compositions en forme de lyre de la décoration de pièces grecques. Jusqu'ici, on avait conclu que l'intégration de ces motifs avait été l'oeuvre d'un artiste spécialement doué, et un cas isolé.[31] Une pointe de lance de Hongrie, récemment publiée, qui comporte aussi des fleurs étoilées (voir le détail de la Fig. 11k), démontre cependant que nous avons ici affaire à des motifs plus répandus[32]. Il y a même d'autres pièces comportant des rosettes semblables, en provenance de la Hongrie occidentale[33]. Nous pouvons encore déceler une influence grecque directe dans un groupe de fibules décorées de la Suisse (p. ex. Figs 10, 11 h)[34–35]. On peut donc constater, pour cette période, l'existence d'ateliers en différents endroits de la région de La Tène, qui utilisaient directement des thèmes méditerranéens.

FIG. 10. Münsingen, Berne. Décors de deux fibules (d'après Jacobsthal).

Il est quelque peu étonnant que, jusqu'ici, et de façon répetée, on ait rattaché seulement ces pièces remarquables aux principes décoratifs grecs, et non pas les simples vrilles de Waldalgesheim qui ne peuvent pas être mises en rapport avec les motifs cumulatifs du Premier style. Or, nous voyons en elles une répétition de la vrille continue grecque (Fig. 11a et c). Sans définir exactement l'origine de plusieurs motifs, il nous plaît d'illustrer les relations des décors de Waldalgesheim avec les motifs

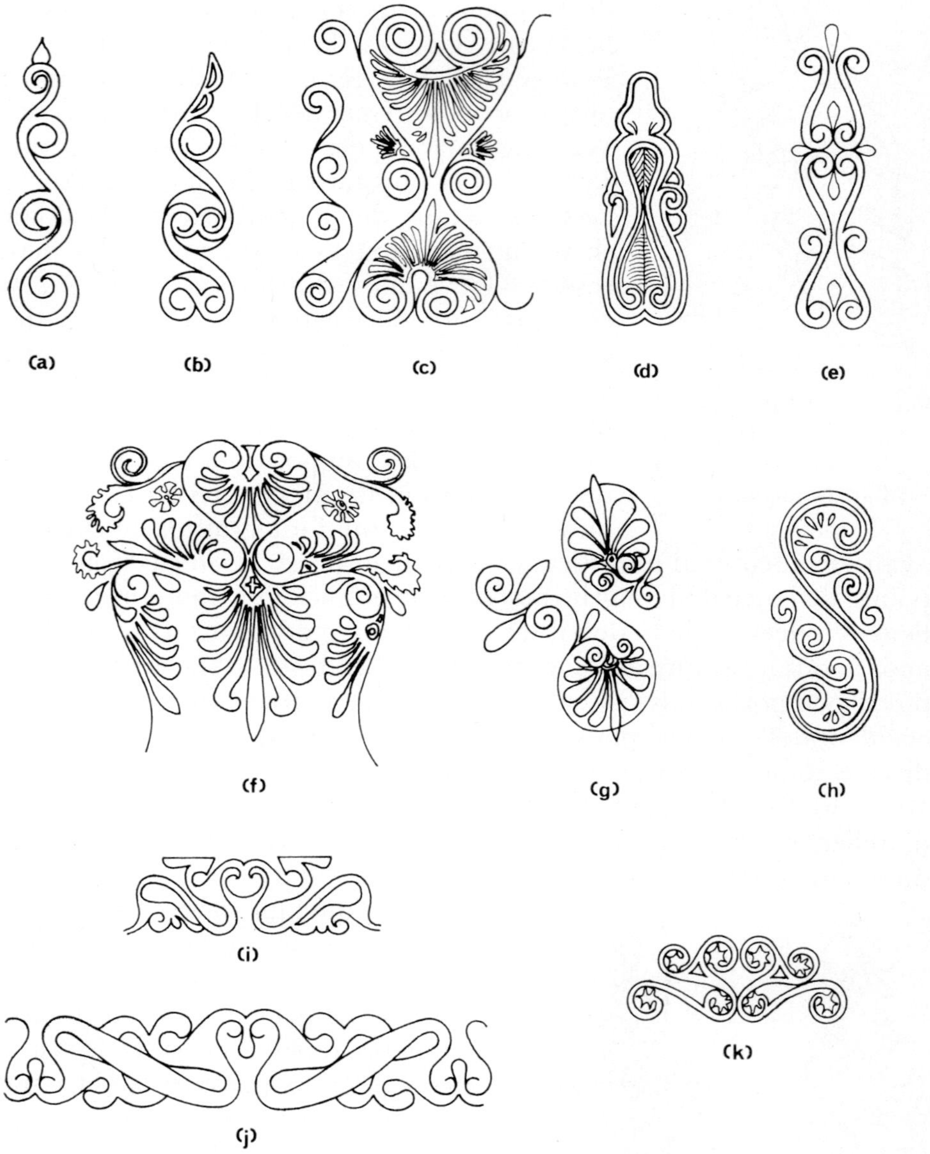

FIG. 11. Décors grecs (c, f–g, sur vases à figures rouges) et celtiques: (a) du Dammelberg, Gross-Geran; (b) Zibar, Bulgarie, sur bague en or; (d) Lisieux, Calvados; (e) sur un torques trouvé en France; (h) Schosshalden, Berne (fibule); (i) Waldalgesheim, Kreuznach (passe-guide); (j) Filottrano, Ancona (fourreau); (k) Hongrie (pointe de lance). D'après Jacobsthal et Szabó.

FIG. 12. (a) Waldalgesheim, Kreuznach. Détail de la situle en bronze de l'Italie méridionale; (b) Alabastron grec, British Museum; (c) Bussy-le-Château, Marne. Détail d'un torque en bronze (d'après Jacobsthal).

méditerranéens en les confrontant avec certaines compositions grecques communes (Figs 11 et 12b, c)[36].

Comme on l'a déjà indiqué, le style de Waldalgesheim est répandu de façon homogène à travers une vaste région qui a certainement été le théâtre d'un échange d'artisans. Jacobsthal comparait déjà le torque de Waldalgesheim avec celui de Filottrano, dans le *Picenum*[37]. Le motif d'un fourreau trouvé à Moscano di Fabriano—c'est à dire dans une région où les *Senones* s'établirent lorsqu'ils pénétrèrent en Italie—se retrouve sur une fibule de Rickenbach (Soleure, Suisse)[38]. Les spirales en vrilles d'un collier de la région de la Marne réapparaissent selon un motif identique sur différentes pièces de métal du Wurtemberg, de Suisse et de Basse-Autriche, et ont même été trouvées sur l'anneau d'or de Zibar en Bulgarie[39]. On pourrait multiplier aisément de tels rapprochements.

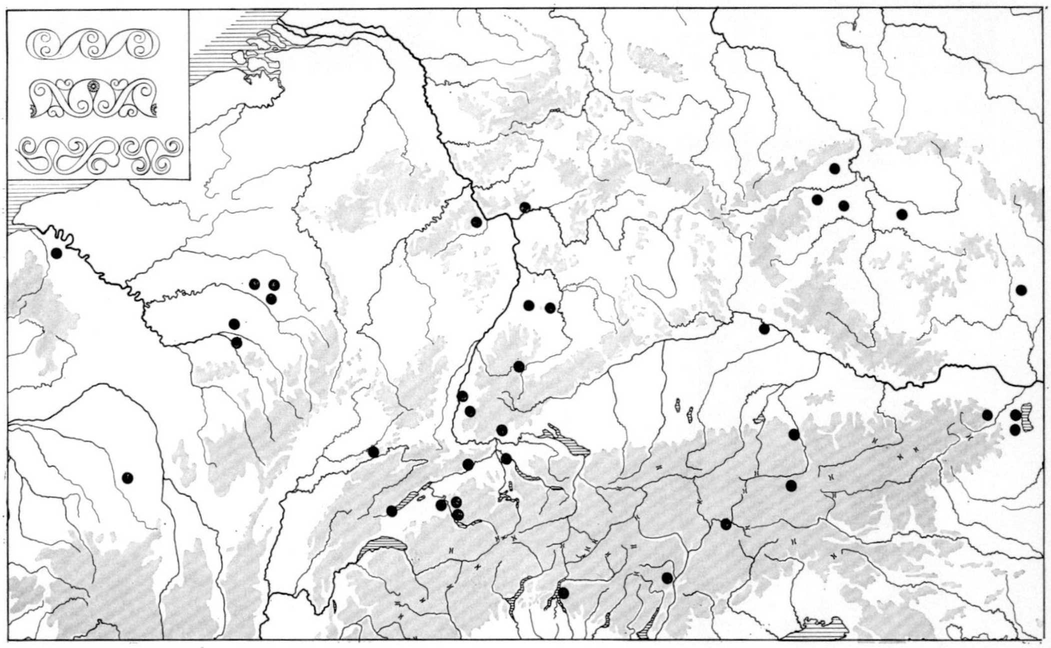

FIG. 13. Répartition d'oeuvres avec décors caractéristiques du style de Waldalgesheim en Europe centre-occidentale.

Mais, en dépit de cette répartition étendue, il n'existe pas, dans la zone du Premier style (en dehors de la région de la Marne), de pièces dont l'ornementation soit nettement du Style de Waldalgesheim (cf. Fig. 6). Au contraire, nous les trouvons dans la zone des tombes plates, c'est à dire entre la Suisse et la Bohême septentrionale (Fig. 13)[40]. Non seulement en raison des différences stylistiques, mais aussi en raison de ces différences de répartition, il est clair que le Premier style et le Style de Waldalgesheim ne sont pas les phases d'un seul développement, mais deux phénomènes distincts.

Wolfgang Dehn a souligné dans plusieurs articles que les deux phases primitives A et B de La Tène—selon la terminologie de Paul Reinecke—ne sont pas de simples étapes dans le temps mais correspondent à des groupes régionaux.[41] Nous voulions montrer ici que cette division, qui a été établie au moyen de types d'objets de parure, se retrouve aussi dans l'art celtique à travers ces deux provinces stylistiques. Il faut toutefois admettre que le Premier style et le Style de Waldalgesheim appartiennent à deux époques différentes. Je puis cependant me référer à une étude de Schwappach qui prouve clairement, au moyen de la poterie estampée, l'existence d'un chevauchement temporaire des deux styles[42].

Je m'abstiens de discuter les problèmes historiques qui pourraient se poser à partir de cette différenciation de groupes dans la région de La Tène ancienne. Je souhaite simplement provoquer une discussion sur le fait que l'art celtique primitif ne s'est pas développé selon un mouvement uniforme, mais s'est divisé en deux branches successives et différentes.

Notes

Les renvois d'une note à l'autre sont imprimés en caractères italiques gras

1. Jacobsthal, P. (1944; réimpression 1969). *Early Celtic Art* (=*ECA*).

2. *Voir* par exemple Schefold, K. (1953). *Prähist. Zeitschr.* **34/35** (for 1949/50), II, 11 ss.; Megaw, J. V. S. (1965/66). *Prähist. Zeitschr.* **43/44,** 96 ss.

3. *Voir* par exemple Megaw, J. V. S. (1971/72). *World Arch.* **3,** 276 ss.

4. cf. *ECA* no. 26;
Greifenhagen, A. (1970). *Schmuckarbeiten in Edelmetall,* 1: Fundgruppen. Staatl. Mus. Preuss. Kulturbesitz, Antikenabt. Berlin **86,** Taf. 65.

5. *ECA*. no. 24;
Mariën, M. E. (1962). *Hommages a Albert Grenier.* (Coll. Latomus **58**), 1113 ss.
Pour les deux ornements étrusques Fig. 2, c–d *voir:* P. E. Arias et M. Hirmer, *Tausend Jahre griechischer Vasenkunst* (1960) 57 Taf. 78–79; XXVII (Caeretan hydria, Louvre E 701).
et Neugebauer, K. A. (1943). *Jahrb. d. dt. Arch. Inst.* **58**, 248 Abb. 34 (applique d'un casque de Tarquinia).

6. Megaw, J. V. S. (1971/72). *World Arch.* **3,** 280 ss. Fig. 15.
6a. Frey, O.-H., et Schwappach, F. (1972–73). *World Arch.* **4,** 339 ss.

7. *ECA* nos 19; 376; 379. Megaw (*voir* **note *6***) 280 Fig. 13.

8. *ECA* Plate 274, P. 392; Megaw (*voir* **note *6***) 278 Fig. 11, 6.

9. Penninger, E. (1960). *Germania* **38,** 360 s. 45–46; le même, *Der Dürrnberg bei Hallein* 1. Katalog der Grabfunde aus der Hallstatt-und Latènezeit, erster Teil (Münchnr. Beitr. z. Vor- u. Frühgesch. **16**)**,** pl. 46, 34.
Voir aussi pour la Fig. 4, 1 et les numéros suivants: Megaw (cf. **note *6***) Fig. 14.

10. Par exemple la tombe du Dürrnberg qui contient la gourde de pèlerin contient aussi des montures en or avec des décors floraux caractéristiques, cf. Penninger, *Dürrnberg I* (*voir* **note *9***), 43, 1.

11. Kilian, L. (1956/58). *Trierer Zeitschr.* **24–26,** 62 ss., 86 ss., Taf. 19.

12. Mariën, (*voir* **note *5***).

13. *ECA* no. 180.
Frey, O. H. (1955). *Ann. Litt. de l'Université de Besançon 2. Sér* **2,** 1, 22 ss. Abb. 8–9.

14. Bertrand, A. (1889). *Archéologie Celtique et Gauloise* PLANCHES 11–12; *ECA* no. 136;
Frey (*wir* **note *13***) 12 ss. Abb. 5.

15. Frey (*voir* **note** ***13***) 4 ss. Taf. 1–8.

16. Jacobsthal, (1941). "Imagery in Early Celtic Art". *Proc. Brit. Acad.* **27,** 301 ss.; *ECA* passim.

17. Pour les pièces à décors floraux v. Megaw (*voir* **note** ***6***), et Frey (*voir* **note** ***13***).
Pour les oeuvres en métal avec frises d'arcs, cf. les références données par Schwappach, F. (*voir* **note** ***19*** *ci-dessous*).

18. Une liste de tombes de la fin du VIIème et du VIème siècles avec importations grecques et étrusques est donnée par Frey, O. H. (1960) dans *Mostra dell Etruria padana e della citta di Spina*, Bologna, II: Repertori 147 ss. Des références supplémentaires se trouvent dans Frey, O. H. (1969). *Die Entstehung der Situlenkunst,* Röm:-Germ. Forsch. **31,** 115 ss. et Schaaff, U. (1969) dans: *Marburger Beiträge zur Archäologie der Kelten: Festschr. W. Dehn. Fundber. aus Hessen,* Beih. **1,** 195 ss. La carte de la Fig. 7 n'indique que les découvertes datant nettement de la première période de La Tène.

19. Une liste d'ouvrages en métal et de poterie décorée de frises à arcs est donnée par Schwappach (1974) dans *Fundberichte aus Baden-Württemberg* 1; *voir* son article ci-dessus (renvois, 102 ss.), et cf. celui des *Etudes Celtiques,* 13, **11** (1973), 710–731.

20. Pour une carte de répartition des fibules à masques cf. Kollmann, J. (1937). *Sudeta* **13,** 33 ss. Abb. 1. Une nouvelle carte, par W. Dehn, est en préparation.

21. Cf. la carte de répartition des tombes princières de Hallstatt et des pièces en or de Hallstatt dans Kimmig W. et Hell, H. (1958). *Vorzeit am Rhein und Donau* 73, Fig. 82–83.

22. Jope, E. M. (1971). "The Waldalgesheim Master", en *The European Community in Later Prehistory: Studies in honour of C. F. C. Hawkes* 165–180.

23. Cf. *ECA*. no. 156 a-b.

24. *ECA* no. 387.

25. Frey (*voir* **note** ***13***) Taf. 1–8.

26. Jacobsthal, P. (1934). *Prähist. Zeitschr.* **25,** 62 ss;
Frey (*voir* **note** ***13***) 8 Abb. 3.

27. *ECA* no. 143.

28. *Voir* par exemple *ECA* nos 136; 168; 171; PLANCHE 249 b.

29. *ECA* 87 s; Jope (*voir* **note** ***22***).

30. *ECA*. no. 156 h.

31. Jope (*voir* **note** ***22***).

32. Szabó, M. (1971). *Auf den Spuren der Kelten in Ungarn*, Abb. 15, 4; Taf. 7. Edition en anglais, *The Celtic Heritage in Hungary*, Pl. 7 et pp. 48 (no. 4), 84 (154).

33. Schwappach (1972) *Hamburger Beitr. z. Arch.* **1,** 2 1971, 131 ss.

34. *ECA* 86 nos 332–333 (Munsingen).

35. *ECA* 92, 94, no. 331 (Schosshalden, en argent).

36. Références pour Fig. 11 : Jacobsthal, P. (1927). *Ornamente griechischer Vasen*, Taf. 108b; 122a; 103b. *ECA* nos 224; 46; 331; 156b; 103 et PLANCHE 273–274, p. 361; 363. Szabó (*voir* **note** ***32***).—pour Fig. 12, b–c. Jacobsthal, *Ornamente* Taf. 105c; et *ECA* no. 207.

37. *ECA* 153, nos 43–44.

38. Frey, O. H. (1972). *Hamburger Beitr. z. Arch.* **1,** 2, 173 ss.

39. *ECA* nos 228; 230; 337; 46.
Vogt, E. (1951). *Jahresber. Schweiz. Landesmus. Zürich* 60**, 57** Abb. 30; 32.

40. Les références pour la plupart des découvertes à décor de style nettement Waldalgesheim peuvent être trouvées dans *ECA*. Une liste complète sera donnée dans une étude spéciale sur le Style de Waldalgesheim, qui est en préparation. Une première carte de répartition des motifs de Waldalgesheim a été établie pour une communication de Mlle. Dibbern à Hambourg en 1971.

41. Dehn, W. (1951). *Bonner Jahrb.* **151,** 91; (1964), *Germania* **42,** 75 s.

42. Schwappach (*voir* **note** ***33***).

Résumé

From Early Style to Waldalgesheim Style

Paul Jacobsthal's three phases of Early Celtic Art, Early Style, Waldalgesheim Style, and the phase of the Sword Style and the Plastic Style, were conceived by him as parts of a single development. It had been started in a few centres, particularly around the Rhine, by artisans at the courts of chieftains, creating its first products by following Greek and Etruscan example. Its Waldalgesheim phase had connections with the Classical world still, even if most of its motifs had become (then and later) Celtic ones. Claims for chronological distinctions within the Early Style, and for workshops (the latter more convincingly) have been made since Jacobsthal wrote; and the present colloquy has heard the concept of a Western and an Eastern zone, notable through Schwappach's study of the stamped pottery. Can we still see the whole development, then, as single? We agree that the groups of the later styles stem mostly from the Waldalgesheim; what is crucial are thus the relations of this to the Early —which has now grown complex.

Jacobsthal's Greek or Etruscan derivations in the Early Style are familiar: the Waldgallscheid drinking-horn mount (Fig. 1a), or the Eigenbilzen gold openwork (Fig. 2, a–b: again from a drinking-horn), directly declare their prototypes. For Celtic compositions uniting Greek-derived single elements, we have works related to the Reinheim spout-flagon (Saarland: Fig. 3). For *World Archaeology* (1973, no. 4), with Schwappach, I have lately dealt with the principles: the conjunction method is *additive*, on both metal and stamped pottery (where the technique must have promoted its employment). The Auvers disc, in gold, and the mounts from Etrechy and Mairy, in bronze, show the like farther west, as in the east does the sheet-gold piece from Chlum. The decoration, by compasses usually, in circles or arcs, which is typically Eastern, as on the pilgrim-flask from the Dürrnberg (Fig. 4a: above Hallein, Salzburg) appears as early as the same period, as associations show; and we see it on the spouted strainer from the Western site of Hoppstätten (Fig. 4b) along with Western-style ornament (3c; cf. Fig. 3b, Reinheim). But more advanced circle-compositions, as on the Eigenbilzen spout-flagon body (Fig. 4c), were developed only in the West: seen best in the Somme-Bionne openwork disc, with its lunate arcs and circles (Fig. 1b). And since that is from the Marne, I would state that the famous old helmet of Berru has its ornament formed of an intermittent plant-scroll, superimposed on three-leaved palmettes enclosed in semi-circles (Fig. 5a), and was produced in a workshop chiefly represented in the Marne. Its division of the scroll into parts contrasts with the continuous movement seen on the flagon in Besançon (detail,

Fig. 5b). I omit here works using masks and portraying animals; the influences they show are in part orientalizing.

The Early Style, if we take the West and East together, is represented in the west from a little outside the Champagne, across both sides of the Middle Rhine, to south-west and middle Bohemia, and in Austria to Salzburg (Fig. 6). This is the territory where "chieftains' graves" have Greek and Etruscan imports (Fig. 7). If pottery similarly decorated is taken into account, it adds a part of Middle Germany and the north-east part of Bavaria; these areas are connected with the rest by fibulas too: those with mask and bird- or animal-head embellishment. Southern parts of West Germany, northern Switzerland and eastern France, all of them wealthy centres in the preceding Hallstatt period, are almost void of such finds; so the style is limited geographically. Contrast now the Waldalgesheim Style—a name that I here retain, though I agree with Jope in desiring one more neutral. Neither around the Rhine, nor again in the Eastern Early La Tène zone, have we works which show it issuing from a gradual inward transition, such that their placing in either style would be matter for doubt. From the grave of Waldalgesheim itself (4 km. west of the Rhine at Bingen), in spite of its spout-flagon (Fig. 3a) in pure Early Style, the fair-lead and horns etc. on which the new style is deployed (Fig. 8) show tendril penetrating whirls and fans so that nothing can be taken apart: a contrast to the Early additive patterns that is strikingly abrupt. In France alone, in works from the Marne and the Besançon flagon-decoration, do the Early and Waldalgesheim styles appear connected. On the shoulder zone of the flagon with its intermittent plant-scroll filling, the semi-circle closing its palmettes embraces a space of ground left smooth (Fig. 5b): an early prototype of the characteristic Waldalgesheim "Celtic fan" (Fig. 5c–f, and g which belongs to the helmet of Canosa in Apulia).

Yet this Marnian or French connection of the styles is the only instance of the kind. Waldalgesheim has palpably its own Greek patterns, as Jope, further to Jacobsthal, has pointed out. They go beyond the starflowers which on the grave's large torc of gold (Fig. 9) are taken from those on its bronze South-Italian bucket (Fig. 12). The lyre-constructed but intricate compositions on all its gold-work, transcending the details, should be Greek-derived themselves. And the deriving was not done only by one especially gifted artist. Nor was it confined to the West: Fig. 11k shows detail from a spearhead, again displaying the starflowers, found in Hungary. Pottery also from there has stamps with designs that include the like. In Switzerland certain fibulas, richly ornate, show direct Greek influence, remarked by Jacobsthal himself (Fig. 10: from the Münsingen cemetery, Bern); that from Schosshalde (Fig. 11h, Bern) is a precious example in silver. Mediterranean designs were thus attractive to Celts in quite widely various regions. It is surprising to find this observed, till now, on outstanding pieces only, disregarding the general primary element of plant-stem and tendril, used in a manner quite foreign to the Early additive patterns, and continuously composed on principles like the Greek. Figs. 11 and 12 afford comparison of Waldalgesheim design with some common Greek compositions; for the continuous tendril especially, see Figs. 11a and g.

The style's distribution, noted already, is homogeneous. We can no doubt explain it by movement of artisans. But it extends to Italy: notably down the Adriatic (Po to Picenum) where the Celtic invasion had established the Senones. To the torc from Filottrano there, resembling that from Waldalgesheim, we can add the sheath from Moscano di Fabriano, with exact parallels in ornament on a fibula in Switzerland (from Rickenback, Solothurn). And for the westward-eastward stretch we may cite the involuted-spiral design, identical in the Marne (on a neck-ring), Württemberg and Switzerland, Lower Austria and even the Danube bank in Bulgaria (on the Zibar gold rings). But apart from the Marne and vicinity, the lands of the Early Style (Fig. 6) have nothing with distinct Waldalgesheim ornamentation; for this, going east (Fig. 13), we have instead the regions of flat graves, from Switzerland to north Bohemia and down the Danube. In geography just as in style, the two are distinct. In Reinecke's formal archaeology of La Tène A and B, using mostly the various types of costume accessories, the phases so denominated are not chronological simply, but stand for regional groups, as Wolfgang Dehn has explained repeatedly.

My purpose has been to show them as two provinces of style: two different phenomena, not two phases of the same development. Each has its own chronological place, starting within respectively the Vth and the IVth century; the second overlaps the first in time, yet is differently grouped in space. Early Celtic art has grown in two successive and differing branches. Historical problems arise from this. But the whole invites discussion.

Discussion

Speakers:— Professors Jope, Frey, Duval, Hawkes, Doctors Schwappach and Kruta, Miss Sandars.

JOPE (*addressing Frey*): To open the discussion, I will ask you a question in two parts. First, would you accept that in its basic principles, the Waldalgesheim style was a creation of one man? as a springer, from which the whole development comes?

FREY: Not of one man: several workshops, though only few. Distribution of motifs and pieces shows there were artisans who travelled over the distances between these few centres.

JOPE: In my paper last year in the "Later Prehistory" volume written for Hawkes, I tried to show that there was a "Waldalgesheim master" who created the writhing strand, convoluted into the ornament but enabled to end outside it. Through that, I stressed his creating of his own particular style.

FREY: There may have been derivation from such centres as his, elsewhere. The Filottrano torc could suggest this: at least it has no priority. Do you think those Münsingen fibulas came from him, or were Swiss derivatives?

JOPE: I think they stand for a third stage, Filottrano standing for a second, in the attaining of general currency by what was his own style first.

FREY: Yet their ornament is itself so close to Greek patterns, that I cannot see Waldalgesheim coming between them. Might the use of Greek models in such centres have been direct, even if applied in a manner learnt from a first Waldalgesheim master?

JOPE: This might be so—though a stimulation is hard to state as a principle.

FREY: My geographic distinction of the new style from the Early, with its additive method, does I think point to dependence on Greek work within a widespread area. The compositions take various forms. But perhaps one man might just have started it.

JOPE: Yes; the compositions are various, while the style is as a whole coherent. The coherence is what is important. It gave the style what the Early Style had so often lacked: a logic of its own, and this was attained in what I call the second phase. Of the first, when it was started, the one example is Waldalgesheim. If others remain unknown, it would just show a contribution; but this coherence arises anyhow as new. Would you agree?

FREY: Maybe there is a Waldalgesheim master, yes—though I am not convinced that the style is the feat of any one man. But a starting-point, for me, is not so important as the area, showing direct dependence, unlike the Early Style's, on Greek patterns.

DUVAL (*giving his opinion that "Waldalgesheim Style", an expression he found exaggerated (only from one long note of Jacobsthal's), should be taken in a limited sense, and distinguished by its use of interlace*) : Je suis d'avis qu'on utilise trop largement l'expression "Style de Waldalgesheim", que Jacobsthal a indiqué presque incidemment dans une longue note de la fin de son livre, où il distingue plusiers styles par des dénominations hétérogènes. "Waldalgesheim" ne doit pas s'appliquer à toute une époque, et à toute une catégorie de décors: ce style est limité, spécial, et se distingue principalement, comme l'a dit justement M. Kruta, par l'emploi de l'entrelacs, qui ne se trouve presque pas ailleurs.

HAWKES: I think that what we see from Waldalgesheim itself is one original man's contribution to what was wider: a new Celtic style-movement, in a new historical setting. The Early Style's start, in the Vth century, has been in interaction of centres, creating from outside impulses and all north of the Alps. The IVth century's Celtic movements, going much more widely, Celtic mercenary service (from Dionysius of Syracuse onwards), made an ambience largely different; and the response was a new style-onset, to which the man at Waldalgesheim made a primary contribution. His place's name need not be applied to the whole resultant art: this would be a false extension of prehistory's naming cultures after type-sites. Bernhard Salin, for the art of the Germanic Migration Age, was certainly wiser with mere numbers, his Styles I and II. I agree with Duval: "Waldalgesheim Style" should be restricted. "Early Style" itself is a term that might be improved on. Anyhow we ought not to become prisoners of the terminology. A widespread whole, such as Frey has here demonstrated, merits naming more widely than from a single contributory place, original though the master at work in it was. We also need to remember survivals of Early Style elements. And lastly, also the story of Celtic art in the farther west, where Gaul and the British Isles start new relations within this period.

SCHWAPPACH: Early Style elements indeed persist, on stamped pottery; but where there was no such pottery of Early Style, and Waldalgesheim Style arises (in the regions where Frey has shown it), this does not get stamped on the pottery of its period. And the Eastern spread of flat graves does not bring it on to pottery either; I know only a single exception. The distinctness of the two styles is surely, I think, of historical importance.

KRUTA (*demurring to the confrontation of pottery and metalwork, and to the isolating of particular traits among stamped pottery in general, as found e.g. in Bohemia in settlement sites but not in graves*): J'estime qu'on ne devrait pas utiliser dans une même démonstration, ou sur une même carte de répartition, la poterie et le métal. D'autre part, il ne convient pas d'isoler une certaine poterie estampée de la poterie estampée en général—qui existe, par exemple, parfaitement bien en Bohême à La Tène B dans les habitats mais pas dans les sépultures, pas plus qu'à La Tène A car ce n'était pas l'usage. D'ailleurs, qu'est-ce que La Tène A en Bohême?

SCHWAPPACH (*the words here represent more detailed argument*): Je dois rappeler qu'il y a des poteries dans les sépultures en Moravie à La Tène B2.

KRUTA (*concluding the argument*): Il y en a aussi, et encore de l'estampée, en Bohême à la même époque, mais toujours pas dans les sépultures. Ce qu'on trouve à la période ancienne, c'est, dans les incinérations, de la poterie lisse de tradition hallstattienne (*plain coarse pottery*).

HAWKES: As the terms La Tène A and B (B1 and B2) have crept into the discussion, I may remark that they have come from the alphabet-chronological system of Paul Reinecke, which greatly irritated Jacobsthal. He found these periods artificial, and refused to correlate their dates with anything in his own system of art-styles. Thus at 400 B.C., when Reinecke began his B, Jacobsthal's Early Style was to continue unaffected; just as Reinecke's B ran on through the IVth century, unaffected by the start of Jacobsthal's Waldalgesheim Style in the course of it. The one was like a chest of drawers (*commode à tiroirs*, *Schubladen*), the other, artistically motivated, more like waves.

FREY: Beside both of those, I have tried to show the geography. The Early Style, complex as it is in its components, does occupy an area; and within this are the "chieftains' graves". Even in the Eastern Celtic zone, they appear connected with the famous Middle Rhine ones. So in culture and style and time and space, we have really here a unit. The area of the Waldalgesheim Style is quite a different one. Besides eastern France and the Marne, it extends to Switzerland and south-east Germany, enters Bohemia by its north-west corner, and stretches through Austria down the Danube. The creation and development of the style, I would admit, will have been due to a few masters; but working directly from Greek models, new to them, and not the same as had motivated the Early Style. It does not reflect a further growth, if anything at all, of that. Thus the art of the whole age has grown in two distinct branches, geographically divided, starting each at a different time.

MISS SANDARS: Does this mean that Jacobsthal's "Plastic Style" (or styles), following after, could have a connection of its own with the Early?

FREY: I would say that it did embody some Early Style traditions; but not that it is derived as whole from that. I think it took traditions from the Waldalgesheim Style as well. Jacobsthal's "Sword Style" has certainly a derivation from the Waldalgesheim Style. But the "Plastic" is more difficult to analyse.

DUVAL (*to show Plastic retaining Early elements in the Eastern zone*): Je voudrais dire un mot à propos du disque de Ciumeşti (Roumanie), qui est du style plastique en effet, et qui est très postérieur a l'époque du vrai Early Style. C'est une survivance, si vous voulez, du Early Style, dans une région orientale, et assez tardive. Cela ne veut pas dire qu'il y ait du style plastique déjà à l'époque du Early Style véritable.

HAWKES: Non, non: d'accord.—La discussion est terminée.

Additional Note

Waldalgesheim Problems

Professor Frey in his communication, and the speakers in the discussion, refrained from dating the Waldalgesheim grave exactly. Within the IVth century, doubtless later than the opening quarter, very well; but why not any closer? Jacobsthal, judging of a date from its Greek-Italian bronze bucket, with the handle-escutcheons of splayed palmettes, voluted scrolls, and flowers, permitted himself to be seen as dating it late. Jope in his recent study was content again with the late IVth century. But each was so much concerned with the accompanying Celtic ornaments, with the art above all on the gold, and with analysis and comparison, that a closer date for the grave was allowed to recede from major attention. Frey in his fresh review, of the style itself and its pre-conditions, its relation to Greek motifs and to Celtic works in the Early Style, has loosed new currents of thought, and has stressed the spatial distribution in which this and the Early differ so much—though holding the Marne in common. This led the discussion to "masters", workshop (*atelier*) locations, relations of these, and the spreading of inspiration. And those led in turn to the place of the *artisanat* in Celtic society.

Thinking from styles to "cultures", however, as social entities static or spreading, must bring one back to chronology. For a culture is an art-style's context in terms of time—for duration or for movement. And the scene in the Celtic Eastern zone, where Kruta has said rather more about dates, puts Early Style in the princely cremation-graves into contrast with art from the flat inhumation-cemeteries. These are signs of a culture supervening, into a distribution different, leading on to Middle La Tène from IVth century commencements. Art here is growing "democratized"; yet the Waldalgesheim Style itself, in its higher manifestations, is as fit for lords and ladies as the Early. If there is a question of two cultures, or of established Celts and expanding Celts (see Jan Filip in *Études celtiques* 1973), dates for the art should help the dates of expansion, shown by the cemeteries. Waldalgesheim Style in Switzerland comes in cemeteries started earlier, so would stiffen their inner chronology—if its initial date were absolute. For that, we have now once more to return to Waldalgesheim itself. And on the famous grave and its facts and problems a book just appearing, by Jürgen Driehaus (a "Vorgeschichtliche Forschungen" volume, Berlin 1974), will start a further stage in our thinking.

Already since the Colloquy it has received an advance conspectus, in *Frühlatène-Studien* (1972: Hamburger Beiträge zur Archäologie I, 2), with the Moscano di Fabriano scabbard (and the Schwarzenbach bowl) treated by Frey, related stamped pottery from Central Europe treated by Schwappach, and the Waldalgesheim bucket itself by Gisela Zahlhaas. On its body and base and rim form, her range of date for it reaches back from 300 to 375; the style of its ornament proves it work of Tarentum (Taranto, the Greek Taras), and can place it at the start of the range ("380–370")—some 50 years earlier than Jacobsthal's indication. Is she too extreme? Or might it be work indeed of before 350, but brought to the Rhine just after? Future debate may be brisker than ours was. Kruta mentioned "around 350" for signs of the style as taken to Bohemia; it anyhow reflects the

Celts' lunges into Southern Italy from the homes north and south of the Po that they had seized some 40 years before. And with that, we may turn from it to the West.

The Marne has less of the contrast between the styles perceived elsewhere. The cemeteries of the Champagne indeed show changes in distribution with the passage from La Tène Ia types of object to Ib, as Denise Bretz-Mahler's maps of them show (PLATE 162–3 of her work cited p. 18, n. 12). Yet the change in style, from the late Vth century manner of (say) Somme-Bionne, is less abrupt than from Reinheim (say)—Early though rich—to Waldalgesheim. From the phaleras of Écury-sur-Coole (*ECA* no. 189) to the disc of Auvers and the helmet of Berru (19, 143) one has symmetry still, yet floralized in ways no longer so "severe". In Armorica, the floral-style vases take it up; in Britain, the Box fibula (p. 9, Fig. 5, centre) and the Cerrig-y-Drudion bowl from North Wales. When Britain receives any true Waldalgesheim derivatives, these do bring a contrast: the design on the Newnham bracelet, or that on the Brentford bronze yoke-tip (cf. *Antiquaries Journal* 1969, 378–81). But the British Isles will soon themselves be getting the promised book, carried forward from Jacobsthal to completeness now by Jope, which the Preface has noted: *Early Celtic Art in the British Isles.* From the art of the Thames dagger-sheaths to the Wandsworth Mask Shield—Jope's contribution to the present book—if the stretch seems rather long, it is partly because of the editors' foreknowledge of that other book and anyhow because their choice of themes was desired to be widely spread.

So lastly, between the lands from middle to east in Celtic Europe, and the insular lands where the art came to be spread in the centuries after (as the next contributions illustrate here), lies France. And France throughout the phases and styles of its own Celtic art—we return to it later—has much to teach us still.

C. HAWKES.

7

The Wandsworth Mask Shield and its European Stylistic Sources of Inspiration

E. M. Jope
Belfast

THIS BRONZE COVER for the boss and spine of a bronze-faced wooden shield (Fig. 4) was taken from the River Thames near Wandsworth in 1849[1]. It can be seen as a complete "Gaulish Shield" in terms of the Witham shield (Fig. 1 a, b) found in that river near Lincoln before 1809[2]. Sufficient survives of the Wandsworth piece to reveal it as a masterwork of subtle spatial modelling, and the mask which gives the shield its name is of considerable dramatic intensity (Fig. 3). This work of thin embossed bronze shows us moreover how Celtic craftsmen in Britain in the IInd century B.C. achieved in full three-dimensional shaping their own sovereign stylistic individuality. Some of their continental sources of inspiration can nevertheless be discerned.

The place of the Wandsworth mask shield in the development of British armour design can be understood if we see the Witham shield in a typologically prior (perhaps even primary) position[3]. This oblong shape and the *décor,* with spine and spindle-shaped boss, had long been current in Italy[4], though it did not spread significantly among the transalpine Celts till the later IIIrd century B.C., becoming widely known as the "Gaulish shield"[5], *le bouclier gaulois.* In the use of a thin overall bronze facing over a wooden shield, the British shield-makers were however employing an ancient southerly tradition not used in transalpine Europe, where shields were of wood virtually throughout, with only scanty metal fittings[6]. The main ornament on the Witham shield is in some respects very classical—the 7-leaved palmettes[7] and the mirror/patera roundels at the ends of the spine[8], for instance—a miscellany of variously ancient ideas such as might have been seen in those *ateliers* producing copies of antique pieces for the Hellenistic market[9]. The maker of this Witham shield evidently had a considerable skill in large-scale bronze-beating, for the boss, spine and end-roundels are hammered out of one continuous piece of bronze basically 0.9 mm thick and 109 cm long (with few annealing flaws); at such a date this must surely again reflect a considerable southerly skill. Only in lesser detail (on the spine, the groove with wavy-line edging, and in the roundel planar annuli, are there signs of the transalpine Celtic world, and even then we need go no further than the Alpine valleys or fringes[10]. These transalpine features are however more informative in giving a sharper time-setting than the ancient southerly features; there is nothing intrinsic in the shield to demand a date after the later IIIrd century[11] B.C., and the transalpine details such as the double involution on the spine would hardly allow much earlier[12].

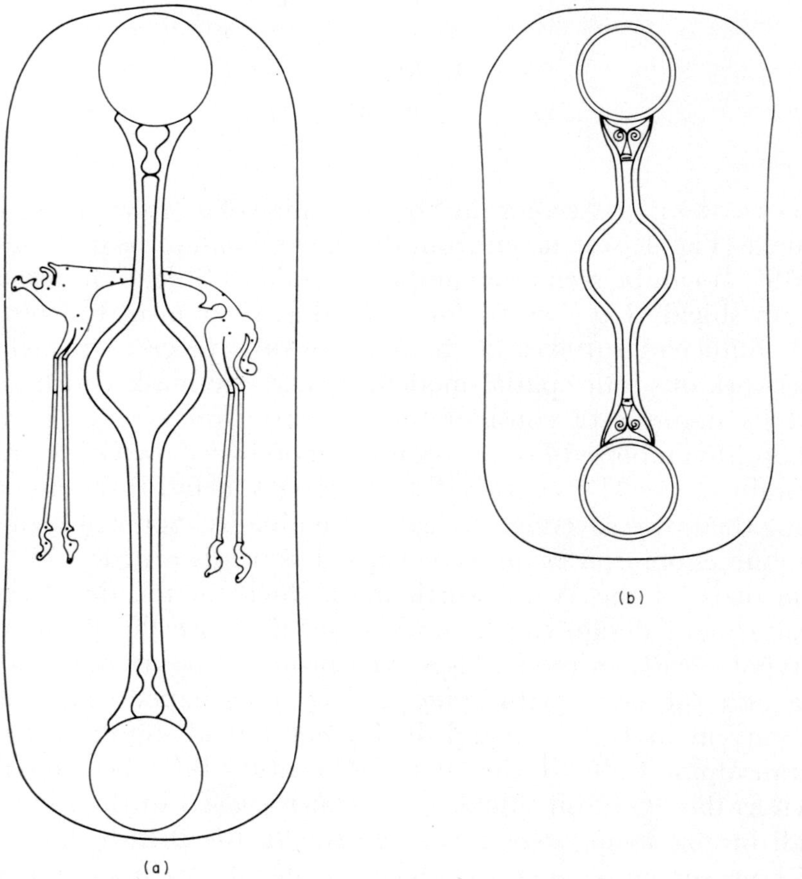

FIG. 1. Diagram showing the proportions of the Wandsworth Mask Shield (b as reconstituted) compared with the Witham Shield (a).

The Wandsworth shield maker followed the same overall southerly design as the Witham (Fig. 1), and in some details of ornament the Witham shield itself seems almost to have been followed (Figs. 3–6a): the darting fangs stabbing along the spine (Figs. 3, 4), the wavy rib[13] (Fig. 4), the slewed layout over the broad almost hemispherical boss[14] (Figs. 3, 6a). The Wandsworth was a considerably smaller shield, less than half the length (Fig. 1), and the spine-ends roundels were separate fittings, lost when the wood shield disintegrated in the river; the more modest scale of metalworking is however more than outweighed by the extreme skill of the bold embossing and the artistry of the spatial composition of the modelling. This high-relief embossing covering the shield boss with a profuse but well-organized encrustation (analogous to a general trend of Hellenistic taste), constitutes the main ornamental scheme, and has in some respects stylistic sources quite different from the flatter relief of the Witham shield, more pervasively transalpine than southerly, and entirely without the classicizing themes. These sources we must now pursue.

Stylistically, the embossed decoration of the Wandsworth mask shield is dominated in many places by a manner translated out of one kind of modelling tool—worked in solid metal, with its consequent deep

FIG. 2. Map showing the distribution (from Bavaria westwards) of Celtic tool-worked solid metal modelling of the later IVth–IIIrd centuries B.C. in relation to its embossed relatives on the Wandsworth Shield (Wa). Other embossed works mentioned; Wi: the Witham Shield; P: Paris; Ch. Châtillon-sur-Indre; T: the Torrs Headpiece; G: Sirmio, Lake Garda.

V-valleys, sharp angles and ledges, and hemisphere bosses rising at the head of spirally-climbing roadways (Figs. 5d, 6a–c). This manner is now most clearly shown by the reconstitution (on an electrotype) of the damage[15], especially in those places of highest relief, where the very thin (0.2 mm) metal has been torn. This very distinctive tool-worked solid metal manner is seen widely scattered (though discretely grouped, Fig. 2) through the transalpine Celtic world[16], in contexts of La Tène Ic[17] and into La Tène II[18]. It is however in NE Gaul alone that this manner has been significantly used to construct human physiognomy[19], which is one of its most effective uses on the Wandsworth mask shield (Figs. 3, 5). Most important are the amusing vehicle fittings labelled "near Paris"[20] (Fig. 6b), and we should not be too sceptical of their Gaulish provenance, for (apart from the specifically westerly use of this manner for human imagery) one of their most unusual features is the wart or "dewdrop" on the ends of the noses (noses upward in Fig. 6b) to be seen otherwise on the anthropoid sword-hilt from Châtillon-sur-Indre[21]. The bird-eyes of the shield boss are also worked over the great bulging embossed hemisphere bird heads in terms of the same tooled manner of spirally-climbing ledges rising into a boss eye at the centre (Figs. 4, 6a), and here the thread trailing away from the eye (not to be confused with the lead-in spiral) relates it again to the formal ornament of the "Paris" pieces (Fig. 6b), to the Brå cauldron ox-heads[22], and ultimately to the "spectacled eye" convention that we see again on the Châtillon-sur-Indre sword, and on other more distant anthropoid swords[23].

There seem thus to have been sufficient exemplars for this tool-worked solid metal manner in western Celtic lands, during the later IIIrd or early IInd century B.C., to have captured the attention of the Wandsworth shield embosser and fired his imagination. We hardly need to look towards East Celtic lands, even though this tooled-metal manner was there used more profusely (but for formal modelling only). This distinctive treatment of modelling also gives an indication of dating for the Wandsworth mask shield, and a time of making in the early IInd century B.C. would be well in accord with its relations to other developing insular work[24], as noted below.

Another feature of this Wandsworth piece is the manner of embossing arrised ribs with fine thread edging along the arris (*faire saillir une côte le long d'une arête en y faisant ressortir un filet*). For this we can look further south; to the curious fragmentary bird-askoi found at Castiglione delle Stiviere near Sirmio on Lake Garda[25], on the southern Alpine fringe (Fig. 6d). On less flowing curves, this technique of a thread roll (*filet arrondi*) along an arris edge (*côtoyant une arête*) is seen on the central cups of the end-roundels on the Witham shield[26], and the use of such edging (*bordure*) on the great bulging hooked beaks and other details of the Wandsworth mask shield (Figs. 4–6a) could perhaps be seen as an

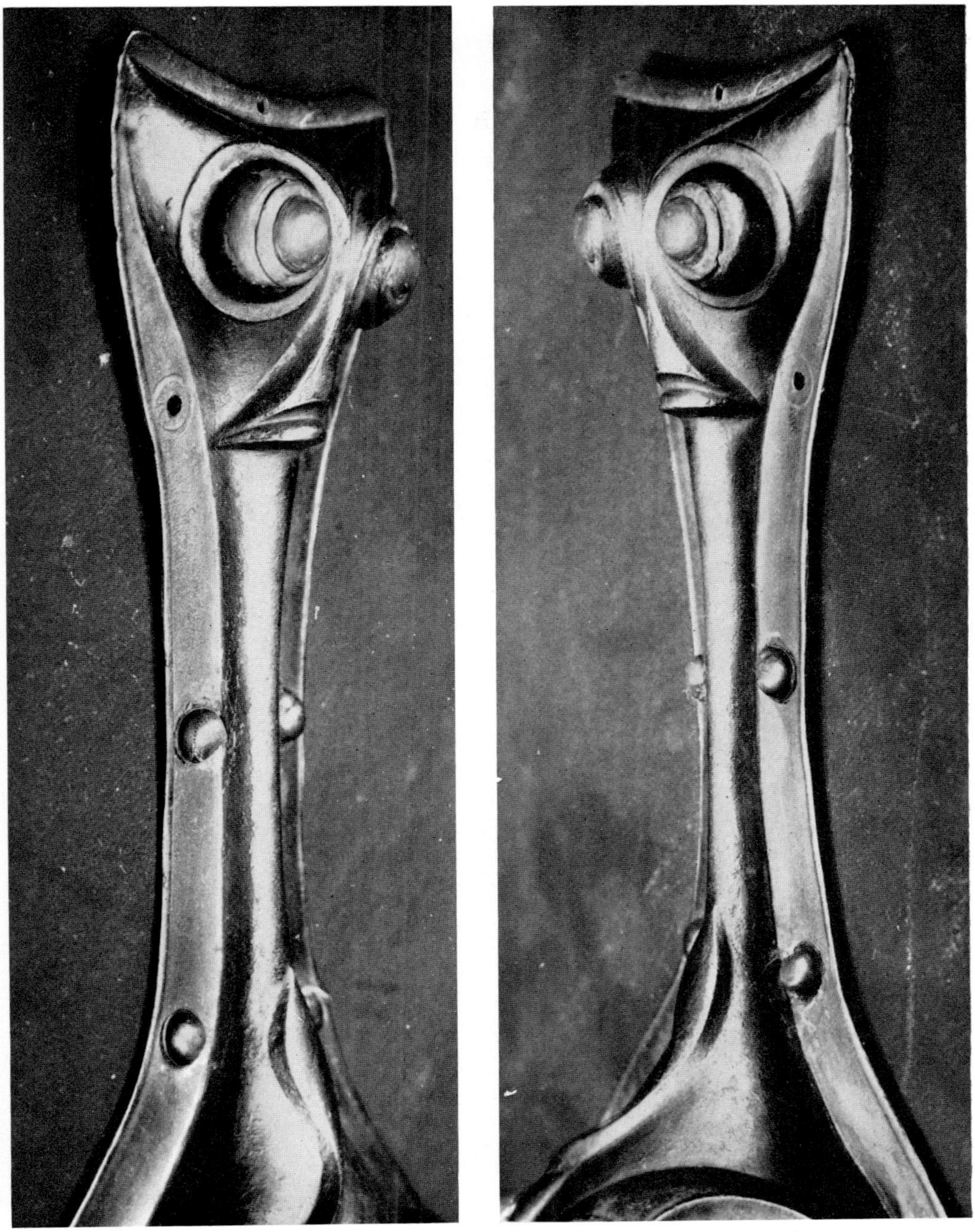

FIG. 3. The Wandsworth Mask Shield. Two views of the mask, with the damaged eyes restored, showing its facial expressions (*Photographs: R. E. H. Reid*).

inspired flowering from such a severely formal model. In the extensive use of embossed very full modelling the Wandsworth mask shield seems to be feeling more towards the lusciousness of Hellenistic taste[27] than other Celtic work of this age.

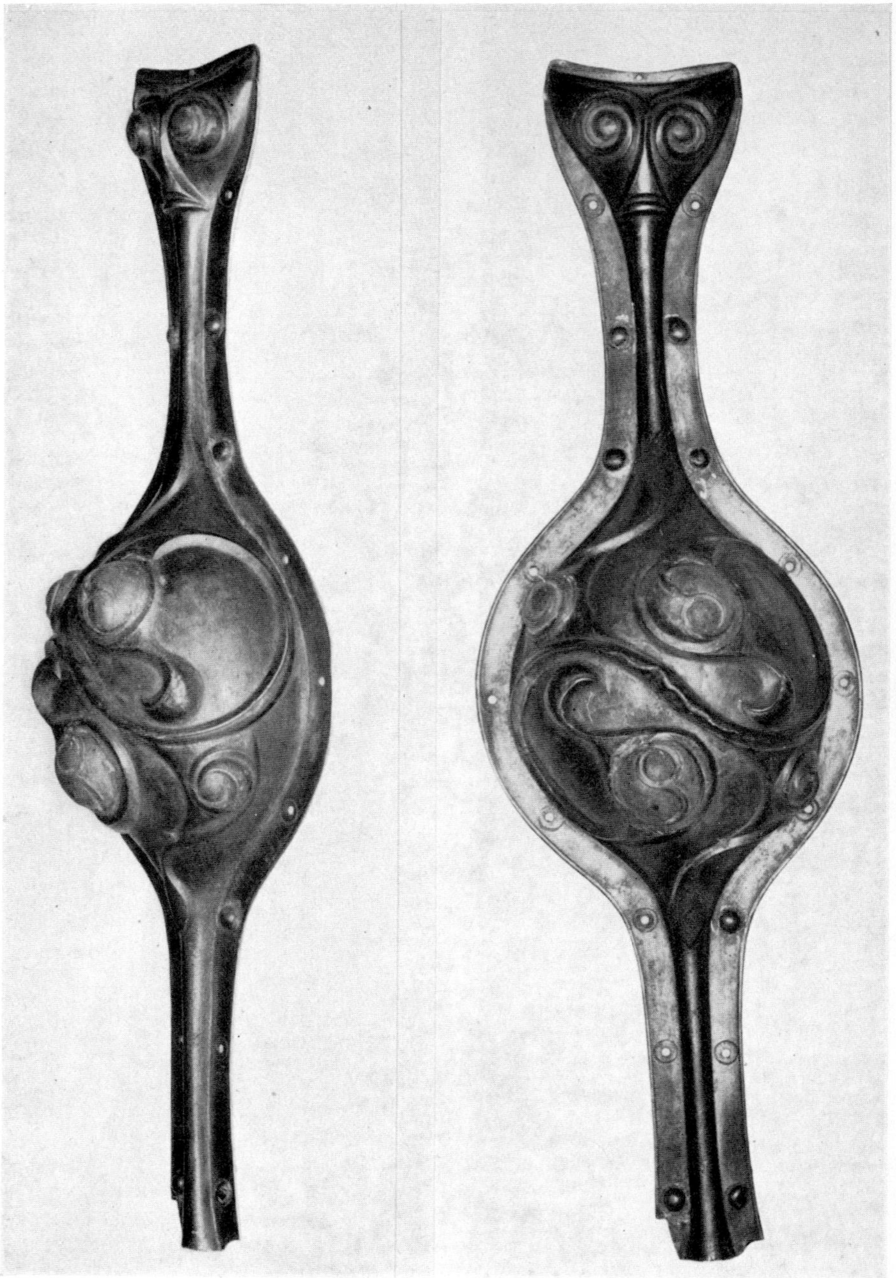

FIG. 4. The Wandsworth Mask Shield. Two views of the central boss, spine and mask, with damage restored (*Photographs: R. E. H. Reid*).

Yet other features of the Wandsworth mask shield composition show the emergence of themes distinctive to Britain, and make it so important a work in studying the rise of insular Celtic art[28]. The *cusp-held roundel* (Fig. 4), so fruitful in later British work, has here grown out of the working up of the double involution within the scroll-end[29] to make the great beaked bird-heads. The *keeled-volute*[30] (Figs. 3 and 4) which we see here in its inverse form, seems to have arisen out of the inevitable spine tectonics that produces an eared physiognomy as a carrier for the end-roundel[31] (Fig. 5a; Fig. 1b), and in another context out of the need to brace the design after the modelling of the great scroll-end has been freed to take its place in the subtly implied spatial composition (Figs. 4 and 6a). The engraved and down-cut micro-detail should also be noted (Figs. 5 and 6), the scalloped or dentated edges (note the real teeth[32], Fig. 5b), and the meticulous micro-designs left in reserve in panels set on the nasal and other strategic places (Fig. 5b), for this manner is related to insular sword-scabbard and other ornament of the IInd or early 1st century B.C.[33].

The mask itself is *sui generis*, a forceful composition created with the most sparing means[34]. It is a face of such *hauteur*, and giving such kaleidoscopic changes of expression with varying light or view-point (Figs. 3–5) that the Celtic world has nothing else to show quite like it[35]. It is wholly different from the bulbous faces of early Celtic Europe, and quite un-Hellenistic in its approach to humanism. The physiognomy is contrived from the severest means, the bare angles of the tool-worked manner, whose sharp V-valleys are put to astonishing effect under the nose (Figs. 3, 5). The full character of the face is revealed by the restoration of the eyes as smooth bosses rising from the spiralling ledges (Fig. 5); the hard-angled curving lines of the nasal give strength as they sweep down to the outer ends of the concave under-surface of the nose-end, and the conflation of this nose-end with upper lip, lower lip, and chin, gives a tenseness which overcomes the ambiguities. The single projection here, created by a deep V-valley, does in fact show teeth (Fig. 5, b, d), making it a protruding, pursed-out lower lip, the tapering shield-spine then becoming a long flowing beard falling from a pulled-in rather than receding chin, yet still strong and tense. It is the assured determined strength of the protruding lower lip, with the incisive lines of the nasal, that capture the attention, and create this forceful personality, a masterly spatial deployment of the severe and strictly formal elements. The face is not absolutely symmetrical about the vertical axis. Perhaps not by intention, but in the result this slight inflection is a source of life and expression; "mask" is after all perhaps not quite the best appellation for so human and alert a character.

The modelling of the whole work, both in the face and over the boss, moves freely in space; the pliant interplay of curving lines and surfaces quite transcends the angularity of manner, and allays any suspicion of spatial construction limited to a few discrete planes. This piece is a peak of insular spatial artistry, and its stylistic mastery has few immediately discernible progeny[36]. In no other insular work, of either embossed or solid metal, is the influence of this tooled solid metal manner so mani-

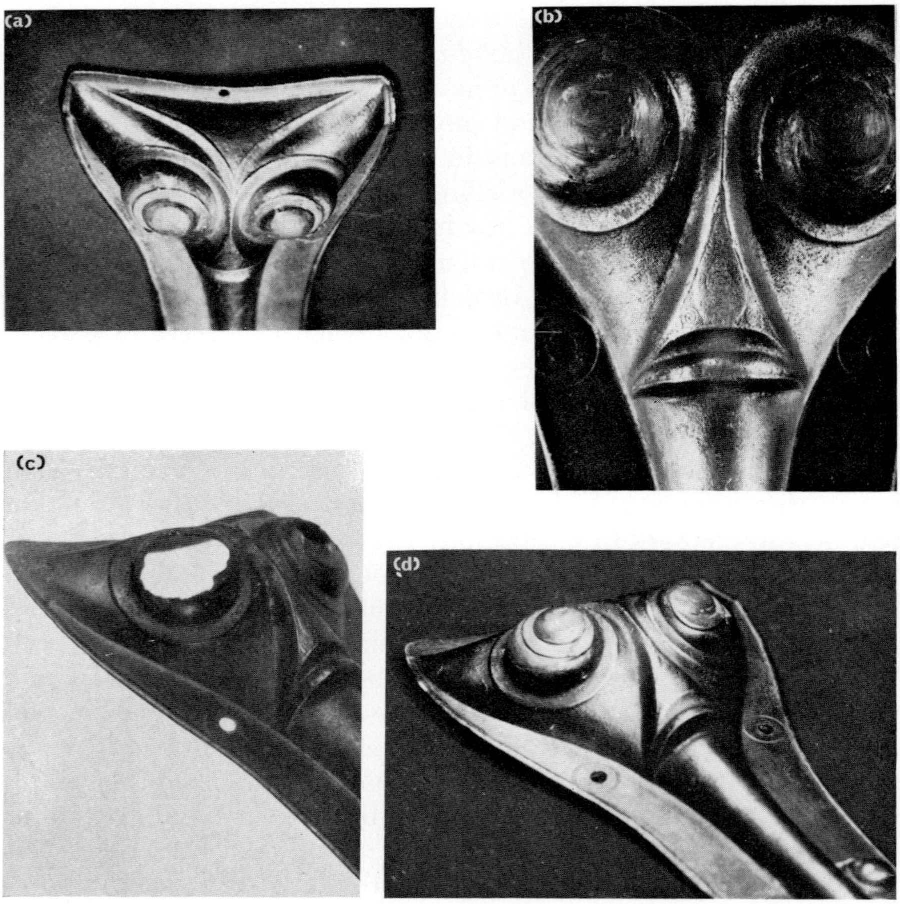

Fig. 5. The Wandsworth Mask Shield. Details of Mask; (c) shows its damaged state (a), (b) and (d) show its reconstituted state (*Photographs: R. E. H. Reid*).

fest; yet it had done its work, for the transplanted root nourished the course of insular Celtic art towards fully free spatial composition, and the lesson was not forgotten[37].

The maker of the Wandsworth mask shield was thus evidently indebted to very diverse sources of design: southerly and transalpine, worked together with copious native wit. His southerly overall design was probably already to hand in Britain for him to see, in a work like the Witham shield; and from here he probably took also some decorative features, though he eschewed its classicizing details. Instead, he sought with great success to translate into his embossing the harder rigid lines of an essentially transalpine Celtic manner of tool-shaping in solid metal; for his alien exemplars of such work he need have looked no further than N.E. Gaul, and probably did not. We have seen how this Wandsworth shield epitomizes the uprise of insular full spatial composition, and shows the emergence of incipient distinctive and most productive insular

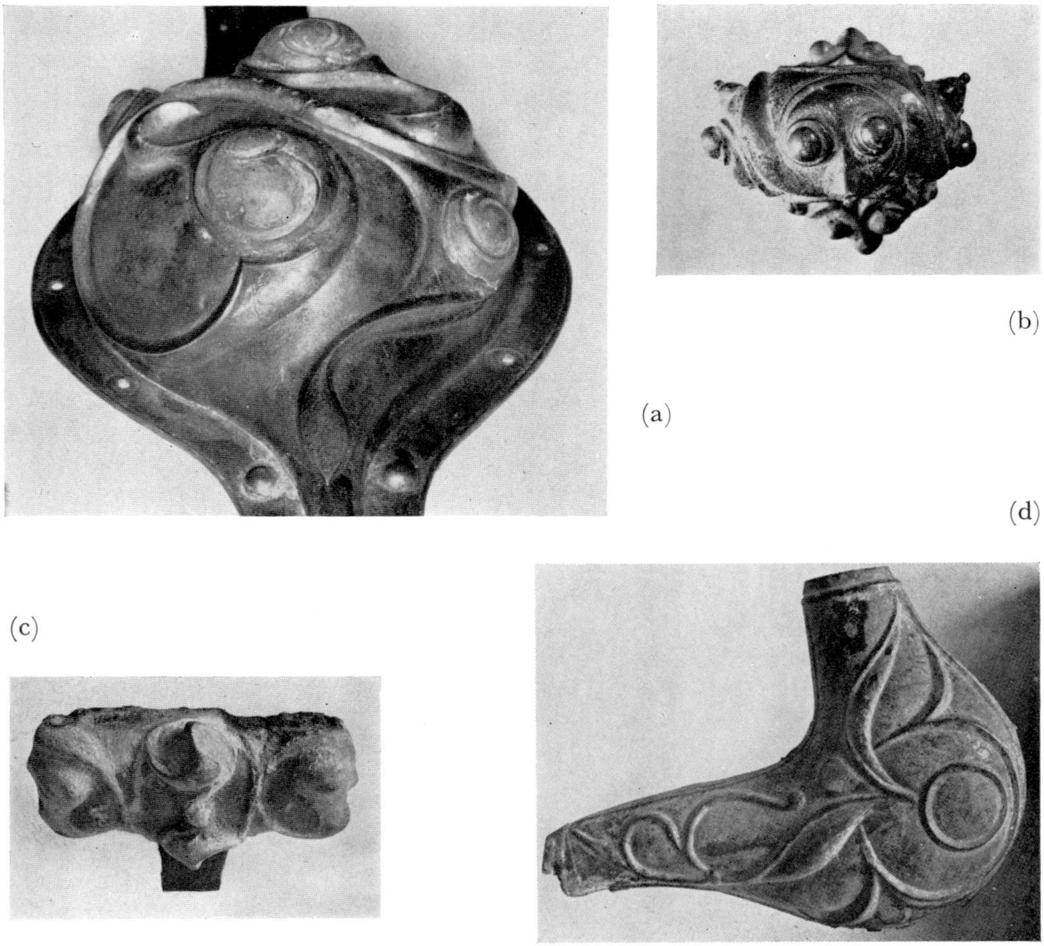

Fig. 6. The Wandsworth Mask Shield. (a) Oblique view of central boss, looking down spine (reconstituted) (*Photograph: R. E. H. Reid*). (b) a small rein-ring "from Paris", to show tool-worked solid metal manner of modelling as it appears in West Celtic lands (p. 170). (c) Head of a linch pin from the River Erms at the foot of the Swabian Alb: an example of work in a soft truly plastic manner (pp. 181, 183). (d) Body of a bird-askos, of beaten bronze, from an inhumation burial near Castiglione delle Stiviere, Sirmio, by Lake Garda. It shows a continental example of arris ribbing worked in beaten metal. (From ECABI: see note 1, p. 177).

themes. This is all consistent with this accomplished artist's intrinsic self-contained outlook. It is a great pity we cannot trace more of the Wandsworth Mask Master's own handiwork.

Notwithstanding the incisive character of his work, the Wandsworth Mask Master must have had a reflective nature sufficient to fashion his stylistically diverse manners into a unified whole. He shows his artistry, for instance, in his grasp of marshalling thematic material, and of treating transitions; the full roundness of the boss encrustation he grades down through simple flowing arris lines into the angular leaf-fang that points sharply at the severe-cut mask, its austerity hardly softened by the discreet swelling of the eye protuberances or the slightly flattened bosses of the eyes themselves. He is perhaps the greatest insular early Celtic artist known to us.

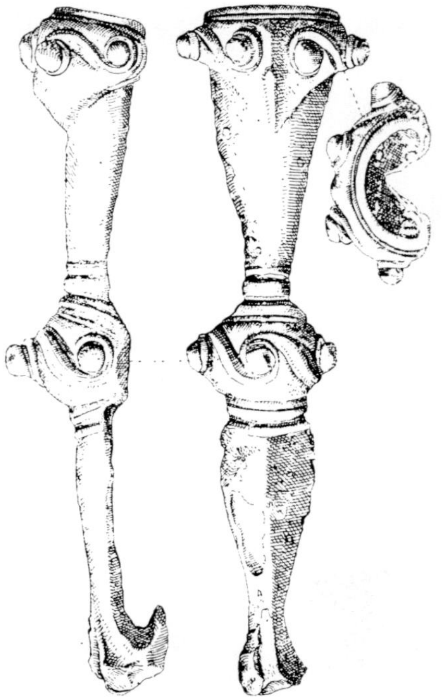

FIG. 7. Belt-hook from Magyarrorazan, Hungary; an East Celtic example of tool-worked solid metal modelling (pp. 169–70, 182).

Summary of Development of British Shield Design

We may thus postulate that the long rectangular shield design, with spindle-boss and spine decor (the "Gaulish Shield"), was introduced into Britain probably in the later IIIrd century B.C., by the maker of the Witham shield, whose experience was mainly southerly, in Italy and the Alpine regions. This design marked the start of a British tradition in shield design. Smaller shields, such as the Wandsworth mask shield discussed here follow the same overall design, but draw upon different, more clearly transalpine sources for ornament. The tradition can be traced in other lesser works that followed on, and it underlines a new tradition of British shield design, with round boss, seen in fine works of the late I^st^ century B.C. or earlier I^st^ century A.D., such as the Battersea shield and the Wandsworth boss-roundel.

Notes

(*Cross references within the notes are indicated by bold italic type*).

1. (1849). *Archaeol. J.*, **6,** 411 (not illustrated); Franks, A. W. (1863). *In* (J. M. Kemble, ed. *HoraeFerales* p. 191, Pl. XVI.2; Leeds, E. T. (1933). *Celtic Ornament,* Plate opp. p. 6 (find-place wrongly given as R. Witham). In the present paper selected topics are discussed; these and others are more fully treated in Jope, E. M. and Jacobsthal, P. *Early Celtic Art in the British Isles* (forthcoming), Chapter 4. This title is here abbreviated *ECABI.* Jacobsthal's *Early Celtic Art* (1944: reprint, 1969) is abbreviated *ECA.*

2. (1831). *Archaeologia,* **23,** 97; (1971) Jope, E. M. in *Brit. Mus. Quart.*, **35,** 61–9: *Prehistoric and Roman Studies,* ed. G. Sieveking.

3. This is an astonishing work, magnificent in its completeness, the largest piece of Celtic metalwork from the whole of Europe. Some of its detail is very classical, and it might well have been the tour-de-force that introduced a whole range of southerly techniques and artistic ideas into Britain (e.g., the rudiments of spatial modelling, though restricted as compared with those of the Wandsworth mask shield). If we see Witham as a IIIrd century work (and the use of coral supports this, see pp. 35–6, 38, 39), there is no distinctive detail that has a currency in Britain before this; the Witham shield would stand in the position of an initiator of many ideas that turn out to be fruitful in the rising traditions of insular workshops.

4. Montelius, O. (1895), *La Civilisation Primitive en Italie.* Plate 175; again in Lucke, W. and Frey, O. H. (1962), *Die Situla in Providence.* For the rare feature of a palmette terminal to the spine (cf. the Witham roundels) note the oval shields on the Early La Tène sword scabbard *ECA*, no. 96, engraved in a manner (*ECA*, p. 1) very Atestine, viz. typical of Este.

5. Déchelette, J. (1927 ed.), *Manuel d'Archéol.* **IV,** 673 ff.

6. Usually no more than small metal mounts on the spindle-boss, or (in Middle La Tène contexts) an iron strap over it; or often none at all. Shields with the boss completely encased in metal are in the Italic tradition, and north of the Alps quite the exception; but it is the overall metal facing and the profuse ornament that enforce the southerly inspiration of the Witham shield.

7. Celtic palmettes hardly ever had more than three leaves, *ECA* p. 88.

8. Jope and Jacobsthal, ECBA (see ***note 1***), chapter 4.

9. Richter, G. M. A. (1955), *Ancient Italy* 58, Figs 188–189.

10. *Brit. Mus. Quart.* **35** (see ***note 2***), 62–64.

11. A date further indicated by the decorative use of coral, which declined in Europe after this time (see above, ***note 3***).

12. See ***note 8***.

13. Here transferred to the spindle-boss from the end-roundels.

14. The hemispherical boss as a central feature was in the main a Late La Tène characteristic, but smaller round bosses can be seen occasionally on earlier representations of shields (G. C. Sansoni, ed.), *Arte delle Situle* (1961) PLATE 35; Bienkowski, P. (1928). *Les Celtes dans les arts mineurs gréco-romains* Figs. 49, 128b).

15. The work of reconstruction was most skilfully carried out by Mr S. Rees-Jones in the Conservation Laboratory, Archaeology Dept., Queen's University, Belfast.

16. The observation that some pieces in this manner seem to be cast does not invalidate the principle, for moulds could have been made from tooled primary pieces, provided undercutting was not too complex (e.g., Hodson, F. R. (1968), *Münsingen-Rain*, tomb 149, bracelet 405, PLATE 111; Hunyady, I. (1944). *Kelták a Kárpátmedencében* (Diss. Pannon., ser. II **18,** PLATE XXX.4).

17. Hodson, F. R. (1968), *Münsingen-Rain*, tombs 75 and 149, bracelets 569 and 405–6;
Viollier, D. (1916). *Sépultures . . . Plateau Suisse* PLATE 13.138, PLATE 24.147.

18. Filip, J. (1955). *Keltové ve Střední Europě* **97,** Fig. 29, nos 3 and 4, the globe feet on La Tène II brooches.

19. *ECA*, nos 161, 163, 175; a possible exception is *ECA* no. 176; in the tomb at Mezek in south Bulgaria, this was far from its homeland.

20. *ECA*, nos 163, 175.

21. Hawkes (1955), *Proc. Prehist. Soc.* **21,** 213–5, 223, no. 28; this is a La Tène III burial, of probably the mid-Ist century B.C.

22. Klindt-Jensen, O. (1953). *The Cauldron from Brå* (*Bronzekedelen fra Brå*), PLATE II and frontispiece.

23. Píč, J. L. (1906) (trans. J. Déchelette), *Le Hradischt de Stradonitz* PLATE XX, no. 8. (No later illustrations show this detail properly).

24. Note particularly the very tentative feeling towards the cusp-held roundel as seen on the embossed work found at Torrs, SW. Scotland (Atkinson and Piggott, 1955; *Archaeologia* **96,** 201, Fig. 1).

25. *ECA*, no. 398, pp. 110, 145 f.; Jacobsthal (p. 110) seems to me to try to relate the bird-askoi to the wrong Wandsworth shield, stylistically perhaps because of the more frankly bird character. The bird-askoi can hardly be isolated work.

26. *Brit. Mus. Quart.* **35** (see ***note 2***), PLATE XXIII.

27. Strong, D. E. (1966), *Greek and Roman Gold and Silver Plate*, chapters 5 and 6;
Boardman, J. (1964), *Greek Art* 237 ff.

28. The crucial role of its maker's fertile imagination in generating a distinctive insular Celtic art has not been adequately recognized.

29. For fuller discussion see *ECABI* (***note 1***), chapter 8.

30. *Ibid*; there are also the related keeled-bosses and keeled roundels. The theme is implicit in some earlier work, but does not really materialize (*ECA*, pp. 104, 109, 437; F. Schwappach in *Fundber. aus Hessen*, Beiheft I (1969), 223, Fig. 6, 57, and Taf. 18).

31. This eared theme also became a regular convention for terminating the ornament in a panel. This follows on from the horse/ox-head carriers of the Witham shield, the pseudo-axillar palmettes being the forerunners of the ear theme.

32. These teeth have not been previously noted.

33. See *ECABI* (***n. 1***) chapter 3, for full discussion.

34. An even more severe subservience to practical tectonics, which is nevertheless most evocative of an analogous human physiognomy, is seen in the enamelwork on a toggle in the Polden Hill hoard (*B.M. Guide Later Prehist. Antiqs.* (1953), PLATE XIII, 4).

35. The nearest in feeling are perhaps the Brå owls: Klindt-Jensen (1953, cit. here ***n. 22***), PLATES I and III.

36. If you seek another interpretation, perhaps a moustache; the protuberance is then the upper lip, and the expression altogether less forceful.

37. This angled manner is used very effectively in later British work to give the key structural lines of three-dimensional animal forms, e.g., the Birdlip knife-handle, or the Bulbury terriers (see *ECABI*, chapter 6).

Résumé

Le bouclier au masque de Wandsworth et ses sources d'inspiration

Ce qui reste du bouclier trouvé dans la Tamise près de Wandsworth en 1849 permet d'y voir un chef-d'oeuvre de l'orfèvrerie celtique et, particulièrement, de l'art celtique de Bretagne au IIe siècle av. J.-C.: le masque en bronze repoussé qui le décore est d'une grande intensité dramatique. On peut lui retrouver certaines sources d'inspiration, sur le Continent principalement.

Le bouclier oblong et décoré à épine médiane et umbo était d'usage courant depuis longtemps en Italie et fut adopté par les Celtes transalpins vers la fin du IIIe siècle av. J.-C., date à laquelle on peut attribuer le bouclier trouvé dans la Witham près de Lincoln en 1809. La fine feuille de bronze recouvrant le bois du bouclier, adopté par les Brittons, était une tradition méditerranéenne. Le bouclier de Wandsworth est inspiré de celui de la Witham ou d'une oeuvre analogue jusque dans certains détails du décor, mais il est beaucoup plus petit. Le masque évoque la Gaule du nord-est: voir les montures de char de "près de Paris", bien que leurs masques soient plutôt grimaçants (nez comme sur la poignée anthropomorphe de Châtillon-sur-Indre). Le modelé du bronze à l'outil avec ses plans différemmenent orientés permettrait de dater le travail du début du IIe siècle av. J.-C., d'après d'autres oeuvres insulaires. Par l'importance des volumes très pleins obtenus au repoussé, le bouclier évoque le goût hellénistique plus qu'aucun autre objet celtique de cette époque.

Toutefois, certains traits sont typiquement insulaires en relation avec des fourreaux de la fin du IIe siècle: les têtes d'oiseaux à bec dérivés de la vrille, les spirales, les micro-dessins gravés en réserve, etc. Le "masque" lui-même (le mot n'est peut-être pas adéquat pour une représentation humaine si réaliste), si impressionnant dans sa hauteur, n'a pas son semblable dans le monde celtique continental. La distribution des plans dans l'espace à trois dimensions est typique de cet art insulaire.

Donc, influences méditerranéennes, influences continentales transalpines. L'artiste a vu aussi une oeuvre telle que le bouclier de la Witham mais il a su éviter ses détails classicisants. Il a surtout essayé de traduire en repoussé les modelés rigides de métal plein de la Gaule du nord-est.

La note ajoutée par l'auteur sur le terme "Style Plastique" (p. 183) doit se lire avec la discussion suivante qu'elle a évoquée.

Discussion

Speakers:— Doctor Kruta, Professors Jope, Duval, Hawkes, Doctor Schwappach, Mr Allen, Professor Klindt-Jensen, Mrs Hawkes.

DR KRUTA began by stating that in Bohemia and Moravia there are far more pieces done in Jacobsthal's "Plastic Style" than were ever known to Jacobsthal, who only noticed the two in Vienna. His French can be given in the words *le nombre de ces pièces en style plastique, inconnues à Jacobsthal, pourrait bien monter à 100; c'est donc un groupe plus grand que les deux groupes voisins réunis, en Hongrie et en Bavière; du reste c'est certainement d'ici, tout au milieu de l'Europe centrale, que le Sud de la France a reçu le groupe de Fénouillet-Lasgraisses.* (He was alluding here to the ornately-modelled collars and rings of gold in the treasures of Lasgraisses (Tarn) and Fénouillet (Haute-Garonne), long perceived as having their stylistic home in Central Europe: see Hawkes above, p. 16 with his Figs. 9–10). Nevertheless, the group of the Marne, with its own version of the style, could in his opinion have arisen in the Marne region itself. He asked for Jope's opinion on these various group-relationships, as background for the growth of the British style. PROFESSOR JOPE replied that this, as seen in the shield he had been presenting, could have immediate sources in the Marne, yet prior origins farther east. He was very conscious that Jacobsthal had never explored Bohemia, and recognized the justice of Kruta's pointing it out. Even so, however, he was still not sure where the primary area was in which this distinctive kind of three-dimensional manner was developed.

The debate took here an important turn, semantic or terminological: what did the adjective "plastic" really denote in this connexion? Jope, observing that he had never used the phrase "Plastic Style", repeated that in ordinary English "plastic" means something soft, like modelling-clay: something that you can mould with your hands. Jacobsthal, however, used it not for this only, but for any kind of modelling or sculpting in three dimensions, including the rigid angular kind displayed on this Wandsworth shield. Soft modelling—clay or wax—gives you soft profiles; it is the hard angular kind that he thought had spread from Central Europe. PROFESSOR DUVAL objected that "plastique", in French, did not mean soft modelling only, but covered all the relief of sculpture, however done, in three dimensions. He believed it was the same in German; DR SCHWAPPACH signified assent. Jope agreed that on the Continent, where the term had a sense so large, the distinction he wanted might not worry anyone. Yet the two kinds of work did differ, nonetheless; "plastic" in English really meant the soft, not the hard, and Jacobsthal was misunderstood through his using it for both. PROFESSOR HAWKES explained that classical sculpture specialists in England, a small and refined circle, practised the Continental usage; so of course did Jacobsthal, moving into the circle from Germany, where he himself had essentially been a classical archaeologist. But to ordinary English, quite oblivious of that circle, "plastic" has never meant hard things like sculpture, but soft like plasticine—the modelling-stuff that is so enjoyed by children. No wonder Jacobsthal's "Plastic Style" was a term that had caused confusion. Jope declared, however, that once the confusion was rightly grasped, English allowed the soft and the hard style to be seen as distinct; as the distinction is here important, that is a very useful thing.

Mr Allen wondered if the hard style had been aided mathematically. Jope demurred, as the mathematics would have surely been too difficult; any three-dimensional art must draw on imagination, and he believed that this was the factor working here. Klindt-Jensen viewed the result of Jope's distinction as most important: it allowed the concept "plastic style" a wider distribution, divided as one now could see it into specific manifestations. Could these, within the wider whole, let movement be better located? Comparing British and Moravian bird-heads, say, as from Torrs and Maloměřice, might we allow this style an origin more to eastward than we used to? or could the linch-pin (*esse*) and the bronze with contorted faces (*masques grimaçants*) be examples of little-known western work and genuinely from Paris? Jope answered that he thought they could; he added however, that their eyes, which looked so easterly, were the kind of thing that had once made him almost call the style "Eastern Celtic" (compare Fig. 7, p. 176). Sources were not to be found for it in the older art of the west.

Hawkes reverted to the Witham shield, and its elements shown to be southern. The bronze *askos* pieces from Castiglione delle Stiviere, which Jope had compared with his Wandsworth shield, deserved remembering also. Schwappach here agreed, calling them the "Milan" askos pieces (from their Milanese museum, the Castello Sforzesco). We had thus, Hawkes continued, factors in west and east and south, besides an export piece in the north, namely the cauldron found at Brå, with Professor Klindt-Jensen's comparisons both with Maloměřice (eastern) and also from the Ceretolo grave, near Bologna (southern again), and of the turn from La Tène Ic to La Tène II. Might not this horizon, around 200 B.C., suggest a historical context partly at least explaining the wide dispersion, of works with features of style in common (in varying degree), made by craftsmen alike progressive, for their society's leading class? The Celts of North Italy, with transalpine reinforcements, made their last assault on the power of Rome in 225. Their defeat was followed by Rome's beginning the conquest of their homeland; interrupted soon by Hannibal, whose invasion forces they joined, it was renewed and re-inflicted 198–5. Around Bologna and Ceretolo they were Boii, and suffered harshly; and if any fled to Bohemia, where the name became so renowned, that has been Wolfgang Dehn's explanation for new modes of fortification—most evident in the long inturned gateway-structure, the *Zangentor*—appearing after this in transalpine *oppida*. Celtic armed movement would have had other contexts too, and we seldom may expect to trace its flux and reflux over our maps. But the Italian events of the 30 years from 225, resounding throughout the Celtic world, could have brought big repercussions; and dispersal of well-armed leaders, with smiths and craftsmen in their retinues, might explain things perplexing us in our distributions of style.

This suggestion did not arouse immediate response. But Schwappach and Jope spoke again of links between Continent and Britain, rare indeed but in the Wandsworth Mask manner besides the Witham. And in reply to Mrs Hawkes on a small but distinctive feature, the chasing of small spirals, tightly coiled, on a pattern's spaces, Jope declared this to be a British insular feature, re-asserting thus the regional factor in a workshop's range of practice, whatever might have been occasional forces intruding over greater distance.

Additional Note

"Plastic Style": a Heterogeneous Concept

This study of the stylistic roots of the embossed work on the Wandsworth mask shield has shown the need for a more exacting analysis of the stylistic diversity that has been clumped under the too-inclusive term "Plastic Style"[1]. There was certainly a general trend towards freer three-dimensional shaping, particularly of ornament, among Celtic artists of Europe from the later IVth century B.C. onwards (in which they seem to follow Hellenistic taste), but the term for this, "plastic style", has been made to embrace two quite distinct—even diametrically opposed—modes of three-dimensional shaping. One is soft, with persuasive almost yielding surface shapes, as if the product of kneading clay or modelling soft wax (p. 175, Fig. 6c); the other is hard, with planes or surfaces meeting at sharp edges, a manner characteristic of working in hard solid materials, metal, wood, bone, with sharp tools or files, giving almost a machined look.

The problem is basically semantic. It arises from the inclusive meaning of the word *Plastik* in German, to embrace any kind of three-dimensional shaping, however done, and uncognisant of whether the result is soft-shaped or angular; Jacobsthal transferred this meaning to the English word "plastic"[2], and did not adequately distinguish the two chief modes of spatial shaping it embraces[3]; he has been followed ever since. English usage is here, however, more restricted, and thereby at an advantage, for the response evoked in most English speakers by the word "plastic" is immediately the softer, kneaded modelling of clay or wax[4], and the attempt to describe the Wandsworth mask shield in English words has brought out the essential stylistic dichotomy of the term "plastic style" in current usage. We must henceforth distinguish carefully these two main aspects of modelled work wherever it may appear in the Celtic world, and new terms are needed: "soft-modelled"[5], and "facetted" might perhaps serve.

E. M. JOPE

Notes

1. As we have seen in the examples just quoted; and in fact, apart from a little small-scale work such as we see under the foot of the Newnham Croft brooch, there is no other insular work in which spatial composition is so fully developed till we come to the free-standing animal or bird figures.

2. *ECA*, pp. 97–103; but the term is not really defined.

3. He is by no means alone in this; many English-writing classical archaeologists also do it.

4. *ECA*, pp. 97–103; but how *ECA* no. 266 could be set directly beside the linch-pin no. 159 as examples of the same homogeneous style it is difficult to see. Yet the overall principle is valid; there was a new trend towards achieving three-dimensional modelling in general, by whatever technique.

5. Hence the trade name "Plasticine".

8

The La Tène Shield in Wales

HUBERT SAVORY
Cardiff

WE POSSESS SOME knowledge of the metal casings (*revêtements*)—more or less ornamental, made of bronze or of copper-zinc alloy—of four, possibly five, La Tène wooden shields found at places in North Wales. This is a small number, but it forms by no means a small proportion of the total recorded from Britain as a whole. As is well known, British La Tène shields are fully representative of the idiosyncrasy of the regional culture which produced them, in that many of them are elaborately decorated and vary greatly in the outlines of their metal sheeting (*couverture*) and the detail of their embossed and engraved ornament. They are representative, too, in another respect, in that the longitudinal arrangement of their metalwork, which nearly all of them show, is related, more or less directly, to a longitudinal, spindle-shaped wooden boss and midrib (*umbo de bouclier et nervure médiane, en bois*) of the continental Hjortspring (earlier La Tène) type, not to the plain transverse strip of iron which commonly covers the wooden boss of continental Middle La Tène shields. Yet there is evidence which suggests that the earlier tradition lasted in Britain till the end of the I^st^ century B.C., if not later, and it is difficult to show that even the earliest of those which have survived was made before the end of the IIIrd century B.C.[1] The same paradox is suggested by much of the ornament on the shield-bosses (*umbos de bouclier ornés en métal*), and indeed of that on other kinds of British La Tène metalwork.

It might seem that the rarity and individuality of British La Tène shields, combined with the fact that most of them either lack associations or belong to votive deposits or to metalworkers' hoards, clearly containing objects of widely differing dates, make the task of arranging them in

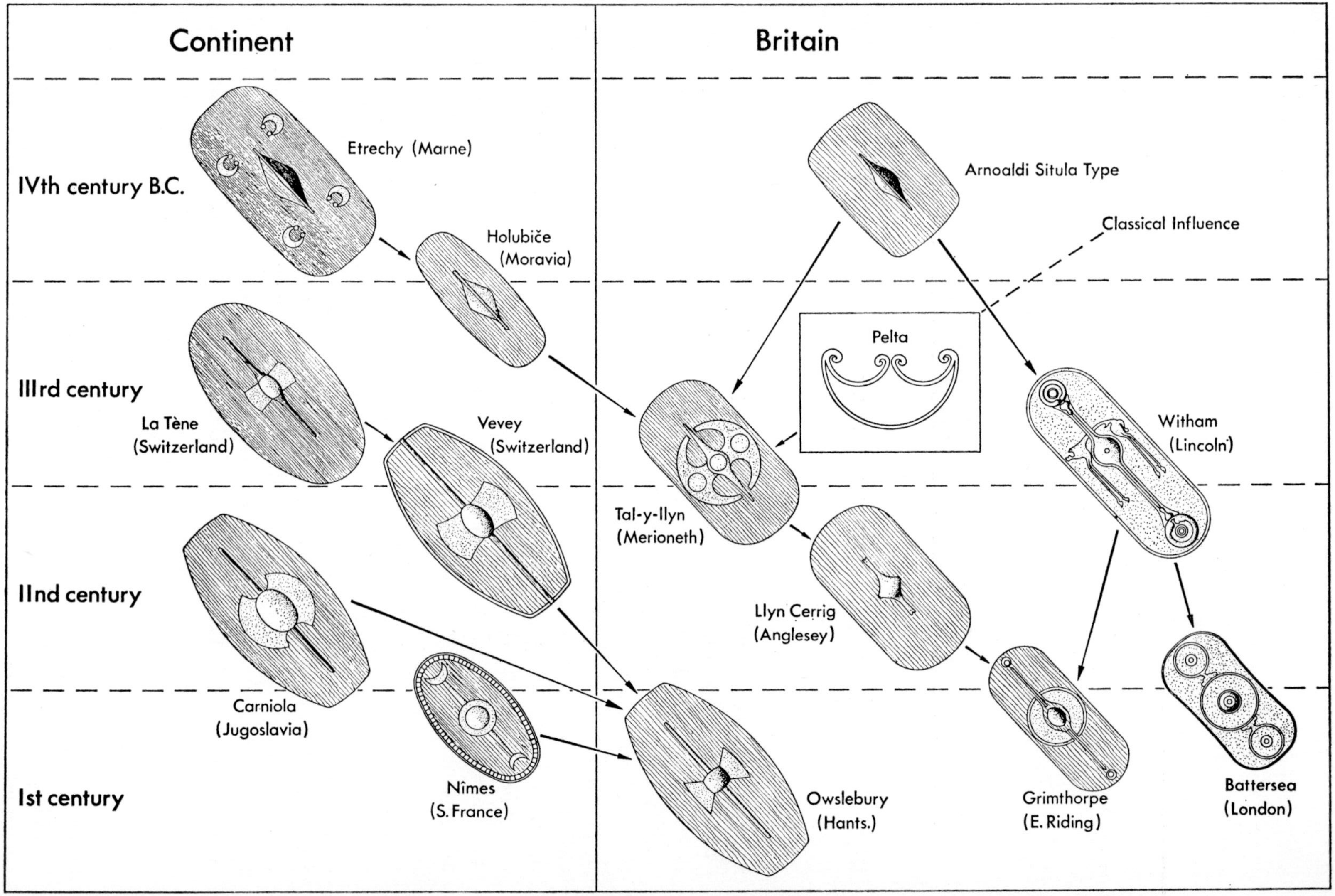

FIG. 1. The evolution of the La Tène Shield in Britain.

a dated typological sequence almost impossible. Just recently, however, some new discoveries have seemed to provide chronological footholds and a control on the purely typological approach, even though this approach must still govern our view of the beginnings of the British tradition. These new finds help not only to fix a little more precisely the time-limits at least of the later stages of the shields, but to strengthen the suggestion that two traditions of shield ornament, at least partly parallel, existed in Britain. The one will be represented by the famous shields from Witham (Lincolnshire), Wandsworth (Thames in London) and their descendants, mainly eastern in distribution, and the other by the North Wales shield-bosses and some others, mostly of poorer quality, from southern England. In the second group, the metal casing of the wooden boss and midribs tend to form a single unit, more closely related to the form of the wooden bosses of the simple Hjortspring type than is the case with the Witham-Wandsworth group (Fig. 1); and their decoration is sometimes rather more closely related to continental earlier and Middle La Tène forms.

It is easy to advocate a low chronology (*tardive*) for each of the North Wales shields that at present are known; but as with other groups of insular La Tène metalwork, prototypes linking them with forms of the Continental Early La Tène (*ancien*) appear to be probable. Above all, it should be noted that the very idea of having ornamental bronze sheeting on shields seems to have its roots shown in the Vth century Marnian shield from Etrechy[2], with its engraved bronze midrib-cover and its crescentic bronze plaques embossed in "La Tène A" style. Later, in the IVth or IIIrd century B.C., central European La Tène shields of the Holubiče group had their bosses cased with sheet iron, sometimes lozengic in outline, held in position by a longitudinal iron rib (*nervure en fer*)[3]. The insular Celtic ornamental tradition, which evolved very slowly indeed during the first five centuries A.D., may have been equally slow during the last five centuries B.C. If so, we can envisage the western British or North Wales shield tradition branching off from the continental stem at some date after Étrechy but not after Holubiče. On similar grounds Professor Jope has recently maintained[4] the accepted early date of the Witham shield, against the greatly lowered date proposed for it by Spratling on his evidence of finds at the South Cadbury hill-fort (Somerset)[5]. Can any of the western group of shields have been made as early as this?

If the famous crescentic plaque from Llyn Cerrig Bach (Anglesey) had been one of a pair arranged at each end of the midrib of a shield, rather after the manner of the two pairs of much smaller plaques from Etrechy, one might be inclined to consider an early date for it, because of this link with the earliest La Tène shield tradition on the Continent. But in fact it is by no means certain that this plaque was part of a shield, and the embossed leaves of its very insular triskele pattern were rightly

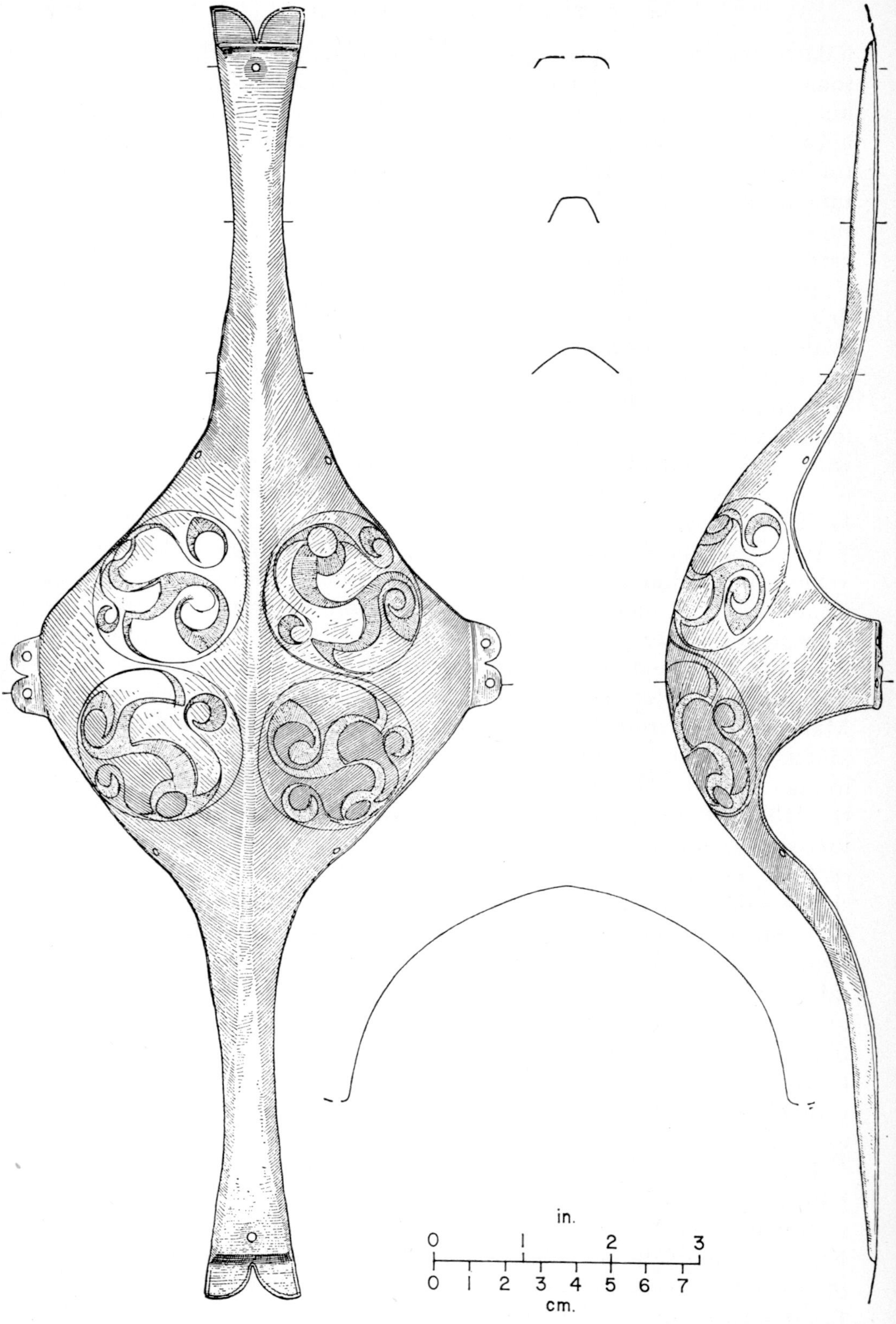

FIG. 2. Bronze shield boss from Llyn Cerrig Bach (Anglesey).

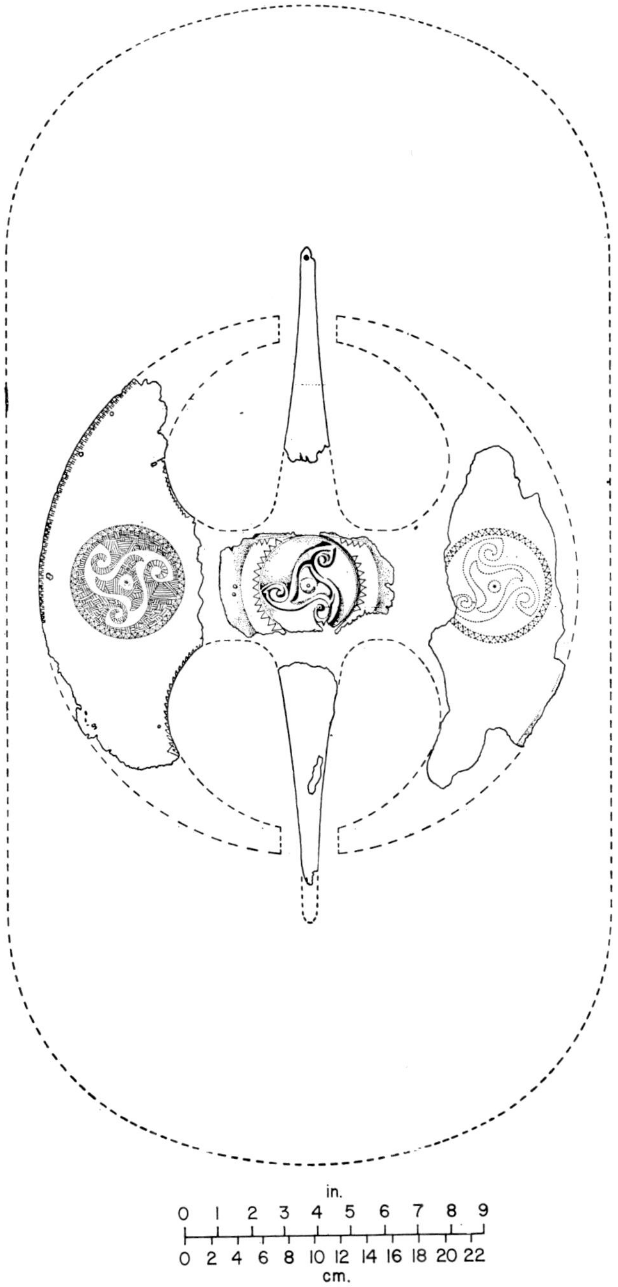

FIG. 3. Shield boss 1 from Tal-y-llyn (Merioneth).

compared by Fox with those on the two terminal roundels on the shield found in a grave at Grimthorpe (East Yorkshire); this also contained an insular La Tène II sword with a scabbard (*fourreau*) ending in a bifurcated chape, which could hardly be earlier than the Ist century B.C.[6] The relationship between the triskele on this plaque and the four engraved triskeles on the undoubted shield-boss from Llyn Cerrig Bach (Fig. 2), which Fox reasonably regarded as a forerunner of the completely insular "mirror style", certainly weighs against a date much earlier than the end of the IInd century B.C. for the plaque. The Llyn Cerrig Bach shield-boss, moreover, with its arcaded sides, has a "poor relation" in an undecorated iron shield-boss recently found, with an inhumation and a late La Tène sword, at St. Lawrence in the Isle of Wight[7]. The plain bronze shield-boss, with casings for midribs and attached pair of peltate plaques, found long ago in the hill-fort at Moel Hiraddug (Flintshire), is linked to the Llyn Cerrig Bach shield-boss by its arcaded sides; but it still may be of somewhat earlier date. The recent attempt by Stead to bring down the date of the Moel Hiraddug shield to the early Ist century A.D., on the strength of a bronze shield-boss found in the immediately pre-Roman chieftain-grave at Stanfordbury (Bedfordshire)[8], is not very convincing, for this boss was not accompanied by midrib-casing, nor pelta-shaped plaques, and in its conical form resembles, more closely than the Moel Hiraddug boss, the central portion of the La Tène II bronze shield-boss recently found in a grave of the early Ist century B.C. at Owslebury (Hampshire)[9].

More significant is the association of the Moel Hiraddug boss, in what was probably a metalworker's hoard (rather than the equipment of a warrior who fell while attacking the hill-fort)[10], of a square plaque with a beautiful embossed whirligig pattern, based on a triskele but of fully-developed insular style. The appearance in this pattern of the stretched pelta, bisected by an elliptical form, which is so characteristic of Romano-Celtic metalwork and the later Irish style,[11] suggests a date hardly earlier than the end of the Ist century B.C. There is nothing, however, to show that this plaque was mounted on the same shield as the shield-boss already mentioned, or indeed on any shield, and in fact it may have been made at a much later date than the boss. But it may be contemporary with another shield-boss—the newly-discovered embossed one from South Cadbury—which incorporates the same late motif, in spite of its formal relationship to the Witham-Wandsworth group. If the South Cadbury shield-boss belongs to our immediately pre-Roman phase, as its associations imply, it helps to fix the horizon on which this motif, one of the principal features of the long-lived later Irish style, began to appear in Britain, no doubt spreading westwards to Ireland through Wales. Thus decorated plaques and shield-bosses like those from Llyn Cerrig Bach and Tal-y-llyn, which lack it, should be earlier than the end of the Ist century B.C.

That the two shield-bosses from the discovery at Tal-y-llyn (Merionethshire), also with midrib-casings and pelta-shaped plaques are indeed much earlier, is suggested in several ways: not only by their simpler form, and with no arcading of the sides, but by their particular range of embossed and engraved patterns, and the special technique of their execution. This links them with each other and with a number of other pieces from western Britain and the Irish Channel area, which have generally been regarded as early: the Standlake sword-scabbard (Oxfordshire),[12] those from Ulster[13] and the Torrs (S.W. Scotland) drinking-horns.[14] For the engraved background of the pattern on the two Tal-y-llyn bronze pelta-shaped plaques, which go with the first shield-boss (Figs 3 and 6a), the technique used was rolling a round-nosed graver to form triangular or rectangular "matting". Chronologically this is certainly ambiguous, because it looks back to the decoration of certain tubular torcs of the Vth century B.C. in eastern France[15] (and to the bronze belt-plates made in the VIth century further south), and also forward to certain British mirror-backs of the early Ist century A.D., such as those from Colchester (Essex) and Old Warden (Bedfordshire).[16] But the true position of these shield-bosses is halfway between the immigrant Celtic crafts of the Vth century B.C. and the fully-evolved and isolated insular style of our immediately pre-Roman period. This is shown by the way in which an identical triskele pattern on the first of them (Figs 4 and 6b) is embossed by the linear use of the roller graver, in the manner of the early pieces from Standlake, Lisnacroghera and Torrs, already mentioned, and by the relative closeness of the patterns to various groups of Continental metalwork of Early to Middle La Tène, "B" and "C". The triskele pattern on the first boss, in which three limbs enclose a sub-triangular void, is one of the favourite *motifs* of the Continental art in Early La Tène, "A" and "B". Certainly the peaked coil or trumpet motif, which here surmounts each of the three corners, is much more characteristic of British art than of Continental. But it is not unknown on the Continent: it appears, for example, on an engraved bronze trefoil binding attached to an iron sword-scabbard of La Tène Ib from the Loire at Nantes,[17] on various early La Tène cast bronze bracelets and neckrings with relief ornament from France and Czechoslovakia[18], and on an iron La Tène II sword-scabbard from Szob in Hungary.[19] The starting point for the Tal-y-llyn type of triskele may lie in contacts with the La Tène Ib workshops of France or the Upper Rhine ("B"); and the similarities with the "Sword

FIG. 4. Shield boss 1 from Tal-y-llyn (Merioneth), Detail.

FIG. 5. Reconstruction of embossed pattern in shield boss 2, Tal-y-llyn.

Style" of Hungary reflect common origins in western Europe (for instance, Switzerland). For this reason the terminal of the fragmentary gold torc from Clevedon (Somerset), with a triskele pattern very like that from Tal-y-llyn, and a palmette pattern related to those found in Continental La Tène "B" work[20], should not be dated too low.

The fragments of the second shield-boss from Tal-y-llyn (Fig. 6c), which was of similar form to the first, are embossed in the early manner with what seems to have been a palmette-derived pattern (Fig. 5) recalling that in the upper part of the early La Tène scabbard from Standlake[21], which can hardly be later than the IInd century B.C. in spite of its "matted" (rolled-graver) backgrounds. This pattern, however, does seem to be in the line of ancestry of those which form the framework of some of the more coherent designs on mirrorbacks, for example, those from Colchester, from Desborough (Northamptonshire), and from Birdlip (Gloucestershire)[22]. Another form of palmette-derived pattern, outlined in the same way with the rolled graver, on the two trapezoid plaques from Tal-y-llyn (Fig. 6d) forms the setting of the unique human masks, connected in "dumb-bell" fashion (*comme des boules d'haltère*), which in their detail stand close to the classic La Tène "A" masks of the Continent[23]. The comparisons which Megaw here

FIG. 6. (a) Detail of pelta shield boss 1. (b) Detail of shield boss 1, Tal-y-llyn. (c) Detail of shield boss 2, Tal-y-llyn. (d) Detail of trapeze-shaped plaque, Tal-y-llyn.

FIG. 7. Pebble with sculptured face from Bont Dolgadfan (Montgomery).

makes[24], with the art of the late La Tène pails (*seaux*) from southern England, are not very convincing. It is true that distant parallels in Czechoslovakia to the "dumb-bell" heads[25] are Middle La Tène rather than Early; but it is important to note that the parallels to the two bronze bracelets recently found in Wales at Coygan Camp (Carmarthenshire)[26] also lie in Central Europe. Probably these parallels, like the metalwork from Mount Batten, Plymouth,[27] reflect the dependence of southwestern Britain, from the IVth to the IInd century B.C., upon contacts through Armorica with the "Jurassic corridor" of the *falaise oolithique*—Burgundy, Franche-Comté and northern Switzerland—where lay the main creative centres of a Middle La Tène culture from which influences radiated northwards and eastwards, as well as westwards. It is probably to this area also that we should look for the origins of the later "Sword Style" and the linear use of the rolled graver sometimes associated with it, as at Neunkirchen in Lower Austria.[28]

So far, I have not ventured to assign the North Wales shields to anything but a generalized western tradition of ornamental metalwork in Britain, to which the makers of the Lisnacroghera scabbards over in N. Ireland obviously owed a great deal. They reflect the general working of the line of cultural development, first from Lower Normandy to Wessex and the Welsh Marches, and later from farther west in Armorica as well, through North Wales to Northern Ireland and south-west Scotland, which is undoubtedly the same as reflected in the spread of hill-fort building, from the Late Bronze Age onwards, and of ordinary La Tène forms, such as brooches and pottery, through the same insular areas. The distribution of the art metalwork should not be considered in isolation from the general cultural pattern. The relatively rich concentration of finds of high quality metalwork in North Wales, however, may not simply reflect the line of contact between western Britain and Ireland; it may be based, at least in part, upon the existence of local workshops which exploited local resources in ores (*minerais*) of copper and of zinc, of which the former certainly were known and used from the Early Bronze Age onwards.[29] Despite the lack of a local pottery industry, for much of the Early Iron Age, this area can no longer be regarded as a barbarous Late Bronze Age enclave locked away in this part of Britain's Highland Zone. The degree to which the distinctive Celtic La Tène culture had penetrated these fastnesses, well before the Roman conquest, has been emphasised by the recently growing number of finds of carved stone heads, single or double (of "Janus" form), which can no longer be relegated, as a class, to the Roman period[29]. One mask, on a large pebble recently found in a river bed near Llanbrynmair, close to the estuary of the Dovey[29] (Fig. 7), probably once occupied a recess in a wooden pillar, in a shrine which would have been a rustic verson of those at La Roquepertuse and Entremont in Provence[30]. Discoveries like this will help us to understand the Turoe stone, just as the metalwork from Tal-y-llyn, near by, helps us to understand the designs on the Lisnacroghera scabbards.

Notes

(*Cross references within the notes are indicated by* ***bold italic type***)

1. Stead, I. M. "The Typology of the Grimthorpe Shield", *Proceedings of the Prehistoric Society*, **XXXIV,** 1968, 173–8;

Savory, H. N. (1971). "The Date of the North Wales Shield Bosses", *Excavations at Dinorben, 1965—9,* Cardiff, 69–75.

2. Morel, L. *La Champagne souterraine*, 95–9, Plate 19. Stead, I. M. (see ***n. 1***).

3. Krämer, W. (1949–50). "Zur Zeitstellung der hölzernen Schilde des Hirschsprungfundes", *Prähist. Zeitschrift* 34–35, i, 354–360.

4. Jope, E. M. (1971). "The Witham Shield", *Brit. Mus. Quart.* **XXXV,** 61–69, and now in his Wandsworth contribution here (pp. 167–184 above).

5. Spratling, M. (1970). "The Smiths of South Cadbury", *Current Archaeology*, **18**, 188–191.

South Cadbury Information Sheet SCC4, **24,** (1).

6. Fox, C. (1947). *A Find of the Early Iron Age from Llyn Cerrig Bach, Anglesey*, Cardiff, 46–50 and

Ibid. (1958). *Pattern and Purpose*, Cardiff. 32–5.

7. Jones, J. D. and Stead, I. M. (1969). "An Early Iron Age Warrior Burial found at St. Lawrence, Isle of Wight", *Proc. Prehist. Soc.* **XXXV,** 351–4, Plate XX; and (see ***n. 9*** (Collis).

8. Stead, I. M. (see ***n. 1***), 176 and Fig. 18, and (1967) "A La Tène III Burial at Welwyn Garden City".
Archaeologia, **101,** 1–62, esp. 55.

9. Collis, J. (1968). *Antiquaries Journal*, **XLVIII,** 23–6; and now on all such British graves with shields in *Germania*, **51,** (1973), 123–133.

10. Hemp, W. J. (1928). "A La Tène Shield from Moel Hiraddug, Flintshire", *Archaeologia Cambrensis*, **LXXXIII,** 253–84.

11. Savory, H. N. (as ***n. 1***), 70 f.

12. Jope, E. M. (1960). "The Beginnings of La Tène Ornamental Style in the British Isles", in (Frere, S. S. ed.), *Problems of the Iron Age*, London, 96.

13. Jope, E. M. (1954). "An Iron Age Decorated Sword-Scabbard from the River Bann at Toome", *Ulster Journal of Archaeology*, n.s. **XVII,** 81–91.

14. Atkinson, R. J. C. and Piggott, S. (1955). "The Torrs Chamfrein" *Archaeologia*, **XCVI,** 197–235.

15. Joffroy, R. (1964). "Les torques tubulaires à décor gravé", *Celticum* **XII**: Actes du IVe Congrès International d'Etudes gauloises, celtiques et protoceltiques, Sarrebruck, 1964, 11–18.

16. Fox, C. *Pattern and Purpose*, 84–8.
Spratling, M. (1970). "The Late Pre-Roman Iron Age Bronze Mirror from Old Warden", *Bedfordshire Archaeological Journal*, **5,** 9–16.

17. *Bulletin Archéologique du Comité des Travaux historiques*, 1913 (Paris), 14–16, PLATE I.

18. Savory, H. N. (1966). "Further Notes on the Tal-y-llyn (Mer.) Hoard of La Tène Metalwork", *Bulletin of the Board of Celtic Studies*, **XXII,** 88–93.

19. Ibid. PLATES II–IV.

20. Ibid. 88 and Fig. 1, 4.

21. Jope, (see ***n. 12***).

22. Fox, C. (see ***n. 16***), 85–91, PLATES 56–57.

23. Jacobsthal, P. *Early Celtic Art*, PLATES 21, 30, 58, (nos 20, 34 and 93).

24. Megaw, J. V. S. (1970). *Art of the European Iron Age*, 157 f.

25. Filip, J. *Keltové ve Střední Europě*, Figs. 13–15 and PLATES XX, 1–2, and LXXVIII, 1.
Klindt-Jensen, O. *Bronzekedelen fra Brå*, 69 f., PLATE VIId.

26. Wainwright, G. J. (1967). *Coygan Camp*, 83 f.

27. Clarke, P. J. (1971). "The Neolithic, Bronze and Iron Age and Romano-British Finds from Mount Batten Plymouth, 1832–1932". *Proc. Devon Archaeological Society*, **29,** 137–161.

28. Pittioni, R. (1900). *Urgeschichte des Österreichischen Raumes*, Fig. 470.

29. Savory, H. N. (1966). (as ***n. 18***), 101 f.; (1971). (as ***n. 1***), 64–68.

30. Ross, Anne. *Archaeologia Cambrensis*, forthcoming; Savory, H. N. (1973). "Pagan Celtic Shrines in Wales and Provence". *Amgueddfa*, no. 14, 28–34.

31. Benoît, F. *L'Art Primitif Méditerranéen de la Vallée du Rhône*, Gap 1955, PLATES XXV–XXVII.

Résumé

Le bouclier laténien en Galles

Quatre et peut-être cinq boucliers en bois de l'époque de La Tène sont connus au Pays de Galles. Ils présentent, comme tous les autres boucliers insulaires, une disposition longitudinale de la partie métallique ouvragée qui est dûe à l'échine saillante du bois, caractéristique du bouclier continental du début de La Tène ancienne (I) et différente de la traverse de fer qui distingue le bouclier continental de La Tène moyenne (II). Ils se datent entre la fin du IIe et au plus tôt la fin du Ier siècle avant J.-C.

On peut aujourd'hui risquer un classement des boucliers laténiens britanniques, en deux groupes: l'Est de l'île (Witham, Wandsworth) et le Nord du Pays de Galles augmenté du Sud de l'Angleterre (la partie métallique y est plus étroitement adaptée aux saillies du bois et le décor est plus influencé par ceux des deux premières périodes de La Tène sur le Continent). La couverture de bronze gravé du second groupe remonte au bouclier d'Etrechy (Marne), qui est du début de La Tène.

Comparaisons. L'*umbo* aux quatre triscèles du bouclier de Llyn Cerrig Bach (pas avant la fin du IIe siècle av. J.-C.);—plus récemment étudiés ou découverts: l'*umbo* en fer de Moel Hiraddug (un peu plus ancien, peut-être; l'*umbo* en bronze de Stanfordbury et celui d'Owslebury, différents, sont du début du Ier siècle av. J.-C.); les *umbo* de Tal-y-Llyn; les fourreaux de Standlake et de Lisnacroghera, les cornes à boire de Torrs, datés assez haut, etc. Les fourreaux irlandais de l'Antrim doivent certainement beaucoup à cette tradition de la Bretagne occidentale. C'est probablement dans la région Bourgogne-Franche-Comté-Suisse septentrionale qu'est né, vers La Tène moyenne, le "style des épées" de Jacobsthal.

Les ressources en cuivre et en zinc de la région nord-galloise expliquent, au moins en partie, la quantité et la qualité des objets en métal travaillé qui y ont été trouvés. Les productions de cette région ont influencé celles de l'Irlande centrale et septentrionale, aussi.

Discussion

Speakers:— Dr Kruta, Mrs Champion, Dr Savory, Drs Harding and Schwappach, Professors Duval and Piggott.

The subject first approached, in French by DR KRUTA, and developed by MRS CHAMPION, was the character of the "matting" (called formerly basketry-pattern, *décor en mode de vannerie*), so typically British, on the pieces from Tal-y-llyn. As in Central Europe for instance on the Panenský Týnec fibula, or the Borscher Aue flagon-handle, both of them Early La Tène, this was formed of little squares, hatched alternately downwards and sideways, as again on the Asperg torc; whereas on the Hallstatt tubular torcs (as in the Bronze Age already), the units were little triangles, with alternate diagonal hatching. Matting in the British Isles would thus be La Tène, and not matched any earlier. DR SAVORY replied that the Tal-y-llyn matting had both, and showed Mrs Champion and DR HARDING where the triangles entered in. They answered that this was only where the curves of the space required: the basic form was in squares, with no recourse to triangles otherwise.

Before this subject was taken further, a technological one was raised. Mrs Champion quoted from R. F. Tylecote the highly volatile nature of zinc: smelting from a copper ore containing natural zinc could perhaps leave only 1% of zinc in metallic form. Dr Savory agreeing that the Tal-y-llyn analyses showed 17–18% of zinc, and even 20%, she averred that it must have been added to the copper to make the alloy intentionally, showing a process that only Roman technology was likely to have mastered first. While not suggesting a date so late as the Roman conquest of Britain (in spite of the find's including a plate from a lock not probably older than that), she did incline to a date for the shield in the I^st^ century B.C., rather than as shown on Dr Savory's chart, stretching from the IIIrd to reach the IInd. He referred her, however, to his article of 1971, where techniques of roasting copper ore with zinc were shown as overcoming the zinc's volatility. And if those could be only Roman, they would here be 1st century A.D.: he would exclude any possibility of their reaching this region any sooner. He therefore still believed that the work was British, and of earlier date.

Returning, thirdly, to the "matting", now in its aesthetic bearing on style, Dr Harding saw it on the Tal-y-llyn piece Fig. 3 as used with ambiguity, perceived so often by Jacobsthal, which leaves one in doubt of what to view as background and what as pattern. DR SCHWAPPACH thought that this could be taken back as far as the Early Style, and to eastern France where it first appeared on the ornament of the flagon from Besançon, well known from its publication by Professor Frey. PROFESSORS DUVAL and PIGGOTT joined in, the one suggesting that this illusionism had its origin in openwork, which the matting rendered as shadow, the other calling it a "bi-colour" or light-and-dark effect, such as Sir Cyril Fox had commented on in his study of the British mirror-backs, by publishing the same one in two contrasting photographs with different lighting, so that one showed the background dark and the other one light: *Pattern and Purpose*, 84, Plate 56*a*, A1, A2. On Duval's point about openwork, Schwappach compared the gold bowl from Schwarzenbach, where the inner container (of wood) would show up dark in the voids of the gold-work; this was of course again of the Early Style. Tal-y-llyn thus showed an older artistic tradition from the Continent, rendered in an advanced and distinctively British form.

9

The Turoe Stone: its place in insular La Tène art

MICHAEL DUIGNAN
Galway

THE PURPOSE of my paper is to present for your consideration a hitherto unpublished, 1968, reading[1] of the curvilinear decoration of the well-known, but imperfectly understood, La Tène stone at Turoe, Co. Galway, in western Ireland, to argue that, in essence, it represents an advanced stage of insular La Tène art, and to provoke a discussion of its "elusive images" from which I may hope to derive considerable profit.

The stone (Fig. 1) was brought to the notice of scholars in 1903 by George Coffey[2]. For Coffey the ornament "does not require description". Because it is "not constrained geometrically, as in late La Tène, especially . . . in Britain and Ireland", because the fret pattern is frequent in the Hallstatt period, rarely combines with La Tène ornament, occurs in simplified form on a La Tène I scabbard from Hallstatt and on pottery from the La Tène I and II cemeteries of the Marne, and because the Turoe "scroll-work" is comparable with that on torques figured by Morel[3], the stone should be as early as La Tène II, if not indeed later La Tène I, and it bears "a relationship of the highest interest" to the art style of the Marne region.

In 1914 Déchelette[4], while finding it difficult to date the Turoe stone and its fellows, recognised a relationship between them and Armorican (Breton) La Tène stones, the Irish stones providing an additional instance of that parallelism between Insular and Armorican La Tène finds which he had already noted, particularly when treating of La Tène pottery. His chief Armorican stone here was the Kermaria stele

Fig. 1. Turoe Stone, seen from the ESE. Photograph by courtesy of the Commissioners of Public Works in Ireland.

(Finistêre). Since Déchelette's time, and doubtless as a result of reading into his words more than he ever intended, there has been a general tendency to regard the Turoe stone as proof of a direct connection between Brittany (La Tène Armorica) and Ireland.

In his 1929 article for Ebert's *Reallexikon*[5], Bremer advances but little beyond Coffey's position. For him the Turoe decoration is coherent, Early La Tène, plastic, spiral, ornament. It shows close connections with the decoration of the wooden tubs from Glastonbury, as well as with that of the Marne culture. Coffey's dating may be correct; but the Glastonbury relationship suggests a somewhat later date.

Four years later Françoise Henry acutely perceived a relationship between the ornament of the east face of the Turoe stone and that of British metal pieces like the Trelan Bahow (St. Keverne) mirror and the Weston spoons. For all that her sketch of the east face is inaccurate, she was within an ace of recognising the organisation of the whole Turoe scheme of decoration. More recently it seems to have eluded her altogether[6].

In 1944 came Raftery's publication[7] of the stone, with its gallant attempt to lay out the decoration in a single plane. Raftery's analysis of the decoration is not easy to follow. Having drawn attention to the long life in Ireland of certain details, he nevertheless regards the Turoe design, taken as a whole, as "clearly early and not too provincial". The misreading of one particular detail, combined with a jumbling of Déchelette figurations of painted pots from Finistère and the Ardennes, leads him "to think of a Breton sculptor working in Ireland", and this notwithstanding the fact that he rejects the comparisons of the Turoe and Kermaria stones made by other writers.

In *Pattern and Purpose*[8], published fourteen years after Raftery's paper, Fox—though familiar with the Atkinson-Piggott paper on the Torrs pony-cap (see below)—could still see only one explanation of the Turoe stone, namely independent contact of Ireland with Brittany by the western sea route.

Writing in the year Fox's book was published, Jope[9] thought that the Turoe sculptor must have been familiar with Rhenish or Gaulish work of the later IVth or IIIrd century B.C. That same year Rynne[10] was claiming that "it would appear that" the western Irish La Tène carvings "must have derived from" Brittany, probably in the late IIIrd century, one of the closest Breton parallels being Kermaria.

Powell's *Prehistoric Art* (1966)[11] reflects a similar point of view: the Turoe stone seems to have retained some direct memory of the rounded Etruscan *cippi*; Raftery's comparison with Armorican painted pottery is valid; an early IIIrd century date is acceptable for the stone, which, together with the Clonmacnois torque, provides leading evidence for "a direct Gaulish contribution to Celtic art in Ireland".

Now, as far back as 1953, in their paper on the Torrs pony cap[12], Atkinson and Piggott had drawn attention to the "general indebtedness" of the Turoe patterns also those on the Castlestrange Stone (pp. 214–15 below) to the Newnham Croft (Cambridge)—Torrs (S.W. Scotland)—Coleraine (N. Ireland) tradition. They might, perhaps, also have adverted to the fact that the relief patterns of both the Torrs pony-cap and the Turoe stone are—as Raftery's text and illustration make quite clear—in the same *two-plane* mode. While two-plane relief ornament has a good Waldalgesheim Style ancestry (e.g. a small bronze from Brunnam-Steinfeld)[13], it is particularly well exemplified on insular pieces such as the Llyn Cerrig plaque, the Grimthorpe disc, the Thames helmet, the Ulceby bridle bits, to name but a few.

In linking Turoe to the Newnham Croft ornaments, Torrs pony-cap, Wandsworth circular shield-boss, and Coleraine (R. Bann scabbard), Atkinson and Piggott are, I believe, on the right track. At the same time

I would suggest that the art relationships of Turoe are much more complex than these scholars seem to appreciate.

As early as 1945, and in complete ignorance of Françoise Henry's 1933 observations—which, indeed, I overlooked until our new drawing had been completed—it seemed to me that Raftery's drawing revealed details on the Turoe stone which had counterparts on British "Mirror Style" bronzes, thereby suggesting a relationship, if at several removes, between Turoe and the Mirror Style. This relationship appeared to be confirmed by Fox's Llyn Cerrig Bach studies[14], and by the relevant parts of his *Pattern and Purpose* synthesis, for all that Fox himself failed to recognise it. The relationship seems likewise to have eluded Megaw, the latest writer on Turoe.[15]

The Turoe stone is a glacial erratic of fine-grained granite, 168 cms in maximum length. The stone is not *in situ* (see pp. 216–17). It has been dressed to a flattened cylinder over most of its length, and the top given a steeply domed shape. The upper 78 cms are covered with baroque, three-plane, curvilinear, and, in places, ambivalent, ornament bounded below by an incised fret pattern. Assuredly the ornament was originally picked out in contrasting pigments.

A groove at the junction of the north and west faces of the stone[16] conspicuously divides a sunken, and otherwise unitary, background into two separate fields. If the line of the groove is followed upwards across the top of the stone and down the other side, the curvilinear ornament of the west face is found to constitute a separate, unitary composition, scutiform or hemispherical on plan, and with what Fox calls a "domed trumpet with one lateral coil or boss or roundel" filling each of the base angles. It then becomes obvious that the north and south faces present each a triangular composition with similar domed trumpets filling the base angles, and that the east face presents a second, independent, scutiform composition, again with single-boss, domed trumpets filling the base angles. In a word, the organisation of the Turoe ornament is quadripartite (Fig. 2), is an adaptation, to the contrived shape of the stone, of a decorative scheme appropriate to a four-faced stone, e.g. an obelisk!

Megaw, who had seen a copy of my reading of the stone, speaks of the "unequal quartering of pelta designs by separate tendrils"[17]. To me, the terminology employed by Megaw in treating of the stone, and indeed of other La Tène pieces as well, is ambiguous[18]. He is not, of course, alone in this respect. In fact, one of the difficulties in discussing La Tène art stems from the lack of an agreed English terminology. In what follows, and purely to avoid ambiguity, I shall adhere as closely as possible to the terminology employed by Fox in *Pattern and Purpose* and other publications.

Scrutiny of the four Turoe compositions shows, I submit, that they present us with an anthology of La Tène motifs which are either dis-

FIG. 2. Turoe Stone: developed scheme of the curvilinear ornament.

tinctively insular or at least handled in insular fashion, and which include representatives of four or five of the eleven categories set out in Fox's "Grammar"[19]. I begin with these:

(1) *Palmette derivatives:* Fox's B 10 (Brentford "chariot horn-cap"): The one plausible Turoe example of these (south face; Fig. 3, a) could instead, conceivably, be read as an example of Fox's next class, particularly in view of the interlocking negative variant (Fig. 3, b).

(2) *Sub-triangular, curvilinear forms* (otherwise "trumpets with two lateral coiled tendrils", alias "designs with two coils or knobs"); Atkinson and Piggott's "asymmetrical domed motifs in which both ends bend downwards and inwards to terminate in spirals or bosses"[20]: Fox's C 16–17 (Newnham Croft arm-ring) and C 21 (Weston spoon)[21]. At Turoe this motif, so familiar from a long insular series of metal pieces, appears twice—in evolved forms—on the west face, once positively (Fig. 3, d) and once negatively (Fig. 3, c); on the south face it occurs once in negative form (Fig. 3, b) and possibly also, as already suggested, once in positive form (Fig. 3, a).

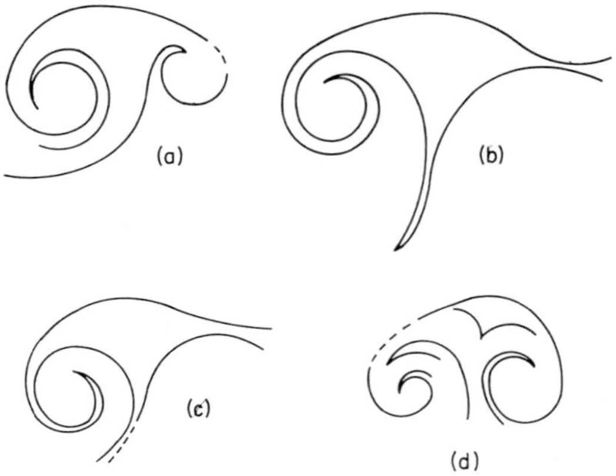

FIG. 3. Turoe Stone: palmette derivative (a) and other sub-triangular, curvilinear, forms (b, c, d).

(3) *Domed "trumpets" with one lateral coil or boss (or roundel)*: Fox's D 24–26 series (Llyn Cerrig Bach plaque). The Turoe versions are closest to No 7 B of figure 24 of the 1946 Llyn Cerrig report. For Fox, this motif makes a tentative appearance on the Torrs pony-cap, and appears in developed form on the Ulceby bridle bit, the Snettisham rope-twist torque, and the Llandyssul collar, as well as on the Llyn Cerrig plaque. At Turoe there are two to four examples on each of the four faces of the stone (Fig. 4).

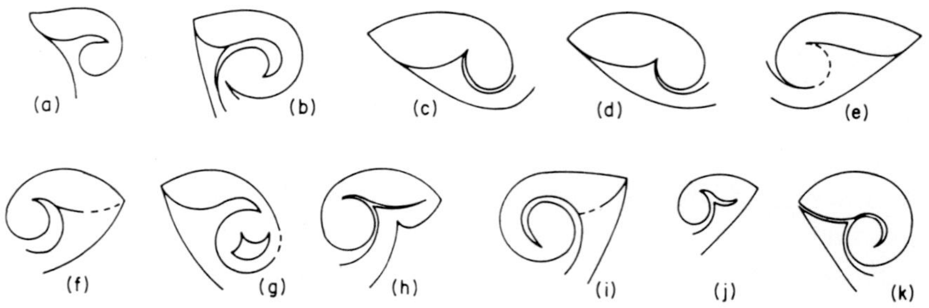

FIG. 4. Turoe Stone: domed trumpets with one lateral coil or boss: a, b, north face; c, d, e, south face; f, g, east face; h, i, j, k, west face.

(4) *Three-sided, alias "Llyn Cerrig", voids*: Fox's L 98, 99 (Llyn Cerrig Bach plaque) and variants thereof. The long catalogue of insular works in stone, gold, bronze, and bone which bear these motifs includes such Irish pieces as the Attymon "horse pendant"[22] and some of the puzzling bone objects from Sliabh na Caillighe (Loughcrew)[23], as well as both the Turoe and the Mullaghmast stones. At Turoe we see them (Fig. 5) on at least three of the four faces (east, north, and west).

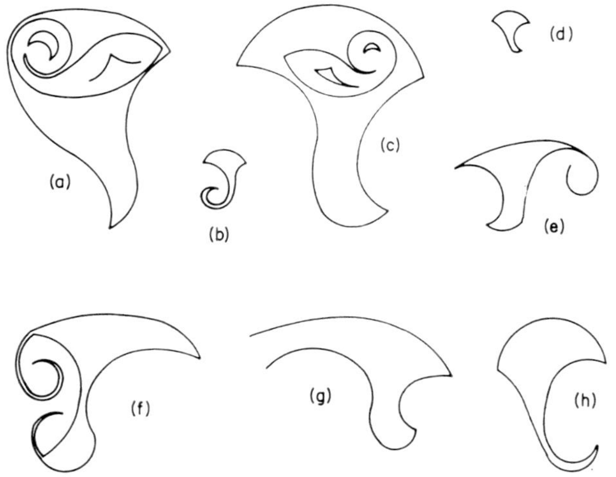

FIG. 5. Turoe Stone: three-sided, alias "Llyn Cerrig", voids: a, b, c, d, east face; e, north face; f, g, h, west face.

(5) *Lobe patterns*: Derivatives, or variants, of Fox's J 70 (Witham shield) and J 71 (Snettisham tubular torque) are present on both the north and east faces of Turoe—four times on the east face (Fig. 6). With these should probably be considered the half dozen simpler leaf-commas (Fig. 2) on the west, north, and south faces, some of them "floating" rather haphazardly in background spaces. This haphazard Turoe use of "floating" leaf-commas is surely far removed from the manner of (say) the Waldalgesheim gold torque[24].

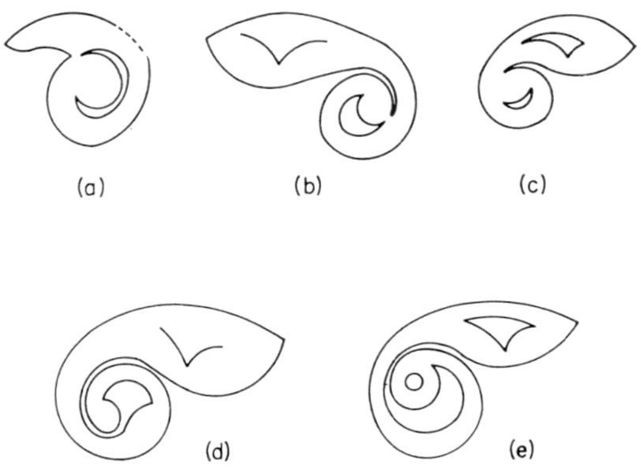

FIG. 6. Turoe Stone: lobe patterns: a, north face; b, c, d, e, east face.

Besides these motifs from Fox's "Grammar", the following call for brief notice:

(6) *Ornithomorphs:* Three terminal coils on the east face (Fig. 7, a, b, c) and one on the north face (Fig. 7, d) have an ornithomorphic (bird-like) quality. The north-face coil forms one foot of a triskele whose head (Fig. 7, e) is the clearest ornithomorph on the stone. This last recalls a detail of the Tal-y-llyn anthropoid plaques[25]; better still, a detail of the Llandyssul collar; best of all, perhaps, a detail of some Romano-British pelta brooches (e.g. those from Wolvershill[26] and Leicester[27]) to which my colleague, John Waddell, has drawn my attention.

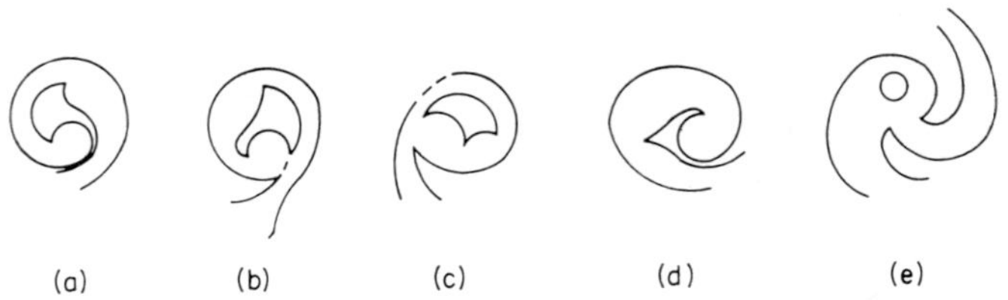

FIG. 7. Turoe Stone: ornithomorphs.

FIG. 8. Turoe Stone: triskeles, alias whirligigs.

(7) *Triskeles, alias whirligigs*: There are at least four on the stone: one on the west face (Fig. 8, c), perhaps one on the south face (Fig. 8, d), and three on the north face (Fig. 8, a, e, b). These north-face triskeles present the most striking composition on the stone: a highly evolved,

static, triskele of the triangular variety (Fig. 8, a) encloses a spinning triskele with central "disc" and "peaked-coil" terminals (Fig. 8, e), and interlocks above with the ornithomorphic triskele (Fig. 8, b) already mentioned.

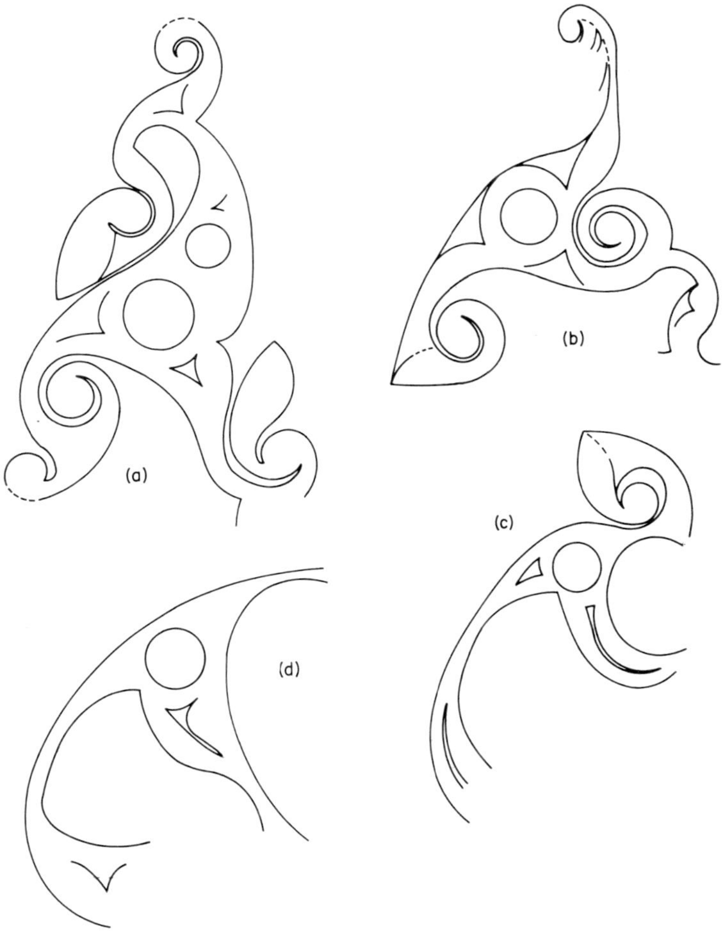

FIG. 8. Turoe Stone: capped triskele-limbs: a, south face; b, west face; c, d, east face.

(8) *Capped triskele-limbs*: Highly evolved, relief, versions of a capped triskele-limb on the west (Fig. 9, b), south (Fig. 9, a), and east (Fig. 9, c, d) faces of Turoe bring us back yet again to the tradition of the Tal-y-llyn openwork discs, the Llyn Cerrig shield boss, the Bugthorpe scabbard, the Hunsbury chape, and of several mirrors, including Great Chesterford[28]. As Fox has pointed out, the Bugthorpe and Hunsbury versions are "controlled" by the use of pairs of "Llyn Cerrig" voids as background. One Turoe east-face rendering is flanked on one side by such a void, on the other by a sunken roundel (Fig. 2). On the west face is a variant which is flanked on one side by a complex void ("trumpet"

with lateral coil, etc.) and on the other throws out a fleshy, lateral volute (Fig. 2). On the south face yet another version is flanked by a "trumpet" void and a lateral, comma-leaf, "tendril" (Fig. 2).

Consideration of details like these leads, I suggest, to but one conclusion: the Turoe Stone shows us a mixture of insular traditions and styles, and represents an advanced stage of insular La Tène art.

Notes

1. The drawings are by my friend, Pádraig O hÉailidhe, and represent many hours of joint study of the stone. I am greatly indebted to Dr Joseph Raftery, National Museum of Ireland, for having the drawings reduced for publication.

2. Coffey, G. (1902–4). *Proc. Roy. Ir. Acad.* **24,** 260 ff.

3. Morel, L. (1898). *La Champagne souterraine,* Reims, PLANCHE 37.

4. Déchelette, J. (1914). *Manuel d'archéologie préhistorique celtique, et gallo-romaine,* **2,** Part 3, Paris, 1522–3 (1927 ed., 1028–9).

5. Ebert, M. (1929, ed.). *Reallexikon der Vorgeschichte,* **13,** Berlin, 487.

6. Henry, F. (1933). *La sculpture irlandaise pendant les douze premiers siècles de l'ère chrétienne* Paris, **1,** 33 ff.;
Henry, F. (1965). *Irish Art in the Early Christian period (to 800 A.D.),* London, 7.

7. Raftery, J. (1944). *J. Roy. Soc. Antiq. Ireland,* **74,** 42 ff.

8. Fox, C. (1958). *Pattern and Purpose. A survey of Celtic art in Britain,* Cardiff, 57, (***n. 13***).

9. In Frere, S. S. (1961, ed.). *Problems of the Iron Age in Southern Britain,* London, 80.

10. In (1961). *Bericht über den V. internationalen Kongress für Vor—und Frühgeschichte, Hamburg 1958* (Berlin), 706.

11. Powell, T. G. E. (1966). *Prehistoric Art,* London, 209 f.

12. Atkinson, R. J. C., and Piggott, S. (1955). *Archaeologia,* **96,** 197 ff.

13. Jacobsthal, P. (1944). *Early Celtic Art,* Oxford, PLATE 177, no. 377; cf. PLATE 277, *P* 450a.

14. Fox, C. (1945). and (1946). *Archaeol. Cambrensis,* **98,** 202 ff. and *A find of the Early Iron Age from Llyn Cerrig Bach, Anglesey,* Cardiff.

15. Megaw, J. V. S. (1970). *Art of the European Iron Age. A study of the elusive image* Bath, 97 (no. 129) and 125 (no. 194).

16. Clearly visible, Coffey, (***note 2***). PLATE XX, Fig. 2; Déchelette, (***note 4***) Fig. 700; and Raftery, (***note 7***), Fig. 5.

17. Megaw, J. V. S., (see ***note 15***), 97.

18. With the quotation just cited compare his "trumpet or pelta junctions", his "peltas or curved-sided triangles"—both with reference to the Turoe stone —and his "peltas or hollow-sided triangles terminating in pseudo-birds' heads", this last (p. 98) à propos the ornament of the Brentford "chariot horn-cap". It is not only his terminology which is hard to follow: I, for one, cannot see the relationship he claims to recognise between the ornament of Turoe and the "spiralling and trumpet terminal tendrils" of a Coriosolites stater (p. 125, no. 194 f) from Armorican Gaul.

19. Fox, C., *Pattern and Purpose*, 147 ff.

20. (1955), 218 (see ***note 12***).

21. No citations are given here for these and other insular pieces conveniently illustrated in *Pattern and Purpose*.

22. Henry, F. (1965), PLATE 4, top (see ***note 6***).

23. Henry, F. 1965 PLATE 8 (see ***note 6***).

24. Jacobsthal, P. (see ***note 13***), PLATE 227, *P*. 450; cf. P. 450a (Brunn am Steinfeld).

25. Savory, H. N. (1965). *Celticum* **12,** 197 (PLATE 107).

26. *Victoria County History of Somerset*, **1** (1906), 357.

27. *Archaeolog. J.*, **25** (1868), 53.

28. Fox, C. (1960). *Antiquity* **34,** 208.

Résumé

La pierre de Turoe: sa place dans l'art laténien insulaire

Présentation de relevés intégraux du décor curvilinéaire de ce monument conservé en plein air, à Turoe, dans le comté de Galway en Irlande occidentale. On avait déjà fait des rapprochements soit avec des pierres ornées armoricaines, en supposant une datation dans la première époque de La Tène, soit avec les pierres sculptées rhénanes des IVe–IIIe siècles, soit avec des objets insulaires en métal (Newnham, Torrs et Coleraine, selon Atkinson et Piggott).

Le décor en relief sur deux plans, comme dans la plaque de Llyn Cerrig, le "couvre-chef de poney" de Torrs, le disque de Grimthorpe, le casque de la Tamise, les mors d'Ulceby, se montre ici en forme plus élaborée encore, les plans sûrement à l'origine peints en contraste.

Analyse du décor: un sillon où se rencontrent les faces du nord et de l'ouest, et dont la prolongation passerait par le sommet pour descendre de l'autre côté, délimitant ainsi la face de l'ouest, permet de déchiffrer le plan du décor, constitué de quatre compositions unitaires, dont deux sont en forme de bouclier et deux sont triangulaires. L'origine est à chercher dans une pierre décorée de forme pyramidale quadrangulaire. La série des motifs, dénommés d'après Fox (*Pattern and Purpose*) est fortement insulaire: dérivés de la palmette, formes sub-triangulaires curvilinéaires, (trompettes etc.), vides à trois côtés, lobes, motifs ornithomorphes, triscèles et tourbillons etc. Métamorphoses insulaires, en effet, du style dit de Waldalgesheim, qui ont parfois des rapports avec le style britannique des miroirs.

"Turoe offre un mélange de traditions et de styles insulaires; elle représente un stade avancé de l'art insulaire de La Tène".

Discussion

Speakers:— Dr Schwappach, Professors Jope, Hawkes, Piggott, Duignan, Frey, Duval, Mrs Hawkes.

SCHWAPPACH: The Turoe Stone is highly important for Continental relations: above all because of what clearly are its two distinct components—the stone itself in its shape, with the band of pattern around its base, and the ornamental designs on its convex surface. It is of different type from the pillars (as that of Pfalzfeld) in the Rhineland: they were tall, with shaft most often quadrilateral and tapering. With Brittany alone (the Armorican north-west of Gaul), where besides stones that are tall there are many essentially hemispherical, can we certainly connect it: through its shape, and its basal band, on which the pattern is maeandroid—not quite a classical step pattern. The presence of the band, and the pattern on it too, are distinctive of the many such stones in Brittany still in place (though above the base, the stone may have been destroyed). But the other Turoe component, that of the ornamental designs, is not to be matched in Brittany. The famous designs on pottery, St Pol de Léon or Kélouer en Plouhinec, have issued out of the Early Style; and I stand with Duignan entirely, when he insists that the Turoe ornament is La Tène that has grown from Waldalgesheim Style, through mediation chiefly to be sought in Britain.

JOPE: I congratulate Duignan both for at last giving really accurate drawings, and for treating the design with a sensible logic that goes right down to details. Ever since Piggott's and Atkinson's work on the bronze ornament from Torrs, over in S.W. Scotland, one could guess the range of the style that grew so ingrained in insular work, and passed to the mirrors, would have to be what the Turoe designs go back to. That and the Brittany connection are separate things, which here are meeting. Getting the one from Atlantic tradition, and the other from Continental, is normal for all our western regions, and typically right for Galway.

HAWKES: Must there not have been hundreds of stones, in Ireland, now disappeared? The Castlestrange Stone, again complete (Co. Roscommon), has designs quite different, as Duignan (I am sure) will be soon reminding us; so have the Killycluggin and any further surviving fragments. The differences must be due to there having been various forms of the style—various deployments of the art, all Irish—of which chance gives us just these samples. And as also in Brittany, where the carved stones surviving show an art that is different again (as Schwappach says), how many that were never carved may have been not meant to be plain, but painted? So I would say that the custom of the stones itself can have come from Brittany first, and the art of the Turoe or other British-insular designs came later, and was joined in Ireland to what existed there already.

PIGGOTT: I too should like to mention the Castlestrange stone, and in connection with the piece from Torrs. Both of them show that striking shape, the "asymmetric dome" shape (or whatever the best phrase is). But the Castlestrange pattern, I fancy, differs from the Turoe, in being an overall pattern with no division into quarters. I am entirely convinced by all that Duignan has said to us of Turoe; would he say something also of Castlestrange?

DUIGNAN: I will take the comments in order, going back first to Schwappach's. One must of course relate the Brittany stones to the Irish in idea. But the contrast between the low rounded ones and the various sorts of taller ones —obelisk shape, cylinder, or cylinder tapering upwards—is not apparent in Ireland, from what material we know. Not only have I long believed that we could have had many more stones, now vanished, but have found it very tempting to think of such things made also of wood. Isn't there a La Tène wooden carving from a lake site in Scotland? Painting, without carving, is a further possibility. I intend a more thorough study, and of course to include Castlestrange. Drawing this is a highly difficult operation technically. I agree with Piggott on its affinities. But its art, in my opinion, is inferior to Turoe's. I would call it a degenerate piece of work.

PIGGOTT: The wooden carving you mentioned must be the one from Lochlee crannog (in Ayrshire). You are right: its design does have elements of this same sort. I must look at it again. And another thing occurs to me: is the pattern round the Brittany stones, which Schwappach called "maeandroid", the same that becomes the step pattern round the edges of the Grimthorpe shield?

FREY: This shield has not exactly a maeandroid: rather it has a true step pattern.

SCHWAPPACH: To return to the Turoe design: we have seen it has a four-field composition. Was this the artist's device to make the hemisphere amenable to treatment? Or what may we see behind the idea?

DUIGNAN: The stone had been purposely dressed to its shape, rounded both in its steep upper dome and its cross-section. But the four-field decoration, I agree, is appropriate to a four-faced stone. So there is, I believe, a kind of contradiction here.

SCHWAPPACH: In Brittany, where the low hemispherical stones have as yet not shown any ornament (though they need examination for traces whether of painting or of carving), the "maeandroid" lower bands that survive may at times have belonged to tall ones. And these, above, can of course have a rectangular cross-section, just as the small stone from Kermaria has, which has ornament on all four faces. So might the four-field Turoe ornament have come from four-faced stones like these? More work is needed on the Brittany stones; few have been studied, of either type, and there are more than are yet recorded.

DUVAL: Personellement, je pense que le décor à quatre parties doit venir d'une pierre à quatre faces; il n'a pas pu être inventé pour une pierre ronde, comme celle de Turoe. Ce serait ici donc une influence d'un type de pierre rectangulaire; rectangulaire et probablement pyramidale.

DUIGNAN: Should we agree that in essence, as a work of La Tène art, the decoration of the Turoe stone is insular?

PIGGOTT: That of all the upper part, yes; only not the maeandroid band below.

SCHWAPPACH: This band, I would say, is the element closest to Armorica. I think it need not imply, as Hawkes suggested, a tradition from there in Ireland at all long prior to the Turoe ornament. An Armorican immigrant from Brittany might have combined both kinds of stone.

PIGGOTT (*with* HAWKES *assenting*): There is the small stone found at Barnwood, the site of a late British Iron Age cemetery outside Gloucester. It is a dome, rather pointed at the top, but with a base very nearly circular, and with carved decoration on the base as well as the body. The style should be certainly insular, with even some likenesses to Turoe. It must be a miniature version of such sacred stones in general.

FREY: The motifs at Turoe include a possible Romano-British pelta; this would then be the latest element there, in what as a whole may be traced down from the period of Waldalgesheim.

SCHWAPPACH: A date, for Turoe, is something we have hardly yet discussed. I would gladly agree with Hawkes that it is somewhat later than stones in Armorica, even if not through dating it by anything on those, as they themselves are so very difficult to date. It ought to be dated in terms of its British-insular style.

DUIGNAN: The ornament above the maeandroid is what must indicate the date. I have been happy to work believing it later than anything in Armorica.

JOPE: It seems to me that you cannot put the date very much after the latter part of the I^st^ century B.C.

MRS HAWKES: May I lastly turn from time to place, and to topographical context? Are there any such stones in Ireland still *in situ*?

DUIGNAN: Unfortunately the Turoe stone was moved, to be a garden ornament for Turoe House; so was the Castlestrange stone, to adorn the frontage of Castlestrange House. The stone from Mullaghmast (Co. Kildare) is in the National Museum. The only one *in situ* is the broken one at Killycluggin (Co. Cavan), which remains just outside the prehistoric stone circle there. I hope there may be the chance of an excavation.

HAWKES: But the Turoe stone did stand, I believe, near the Iron Age fort of Feerwore?

DUIGNAN: It did: somewhere near, but with exact location unknown.

HAWKES: Hence Joseph Raftery's disappointment, in his excavation of that fort, at not being able to attempt to fix a relationship on the ground—though the date he got from his ironwork there could be not much later than the stone's—if this is approaching A.D. 1—or even about the same.

DUIGNAN: I am very grateful to all my colleagues for their comments. If anyone cares to send me further suggestions, I shall welcome them.

10

Celtic Design with Compasses as seen on the Holcombe Mirror

PHILIP LOWERY AND RICHARD SAVAGE
Cheltenham

THE BRITISH Celtic mirror from Holcombe, in south-west Britain near Uplyme, Devon (Fig. 1), was found during excavation in 1970[1]. It has been assigned, from comparison with other British decorated mirrors, to the early part of the Ist century A.D. At the suggestion of Lady Fox, we undertook a study of the techniques of decoration of its back, and the backs of the other bronze mirrors of the British series. In the publication of the study[2], we suggest that the design on the Holcombe mirror is produced by formal systems of construction with compasses. In it will be found an account of the compass constructions we find, and our methods of analysing them. To the roundels of the mirror's design whose compass constructions are given as examples there, we here add another. It is drawn by the same methods and to the same tolerance, 0.1 mm in the drawings: since the drawings are based on non-distorting photographs at a magnification of $1\frac{1}{2}:1$, the equivalent tolerance is 0.06 mm in the object itself.

Throughout our present contribution, we use *arc* to mean arc of a circle. Arcs which appear in the design are represented in the drawings by solid lines. Extensions of these, and arcs whose use in the construction is inferred, are represented by broken lines. Arcs whose centres could not be established within 0.1 mm are omitted from the drawing. The nearly complete circles placed in eccentric pairs in the design, to form crescents, we draw as complete. Centres are marked by crosses. We have found no suitable method of connecting centres to their arcs without producing confusion, in drawings which are inevitably already crowded. So the reader, until his eye accustoms itself to attributing the centres, may find a pair of dividers, or a piece of tracing paper marked with concentric circles at (say) 5 mm intervals up to 5 cm, and showing their common

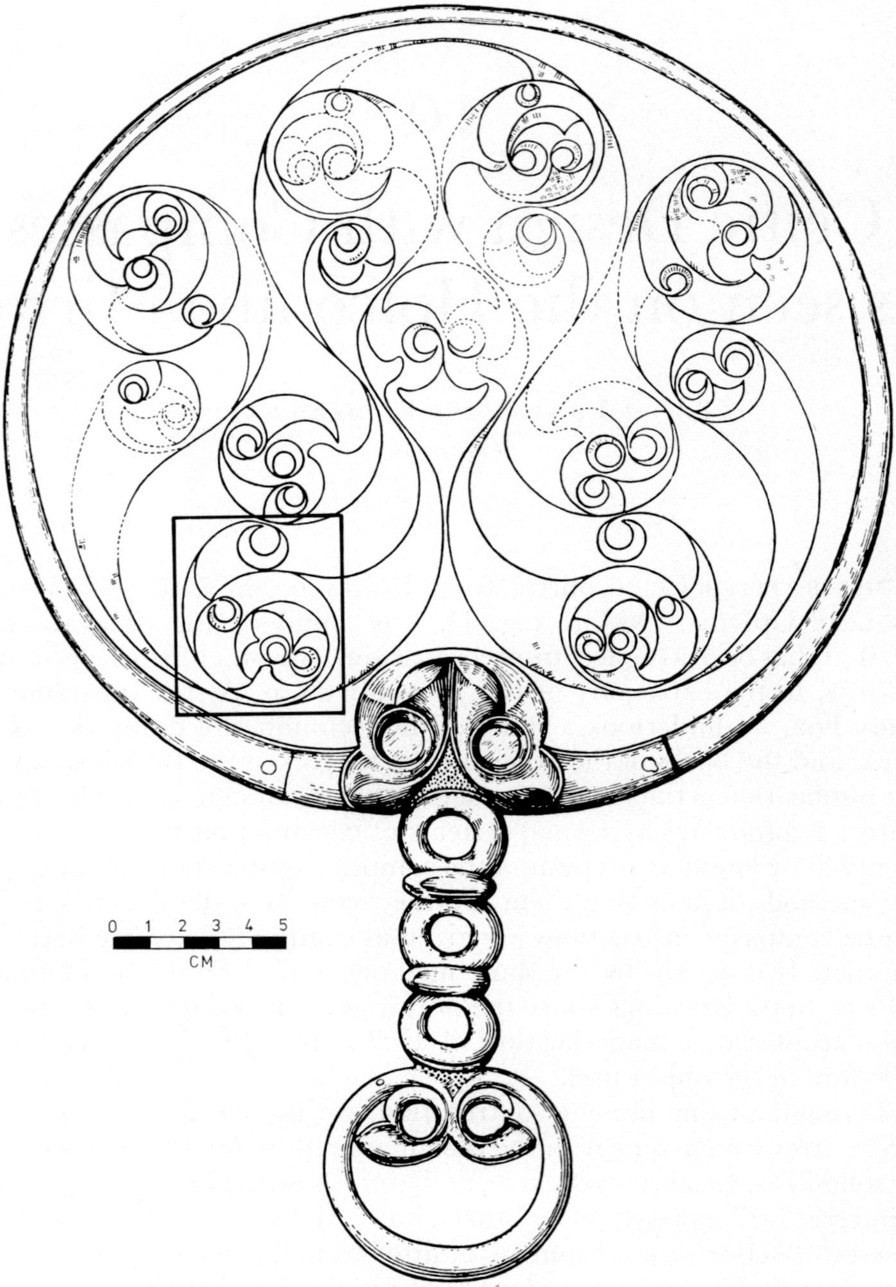

FIG. 1. The Holcombe mirror: drawing by Philip Compton, British Museum. The rectangle marks the roundel here studied.

centre, a helpful guide. We have left gaps between arcs to distinguish them. In many cases they would, if extended, run smoothly into one another; in others there may have been intervening lengths of arc too short for determination by our methods. The drawings are simplified by the omission of some construction-arcs whose inclusion would over-crowd them. We do not claim that the construction-systems we suggest, form, in themselves, a sequence complete enough to let the entire design be built up, but we do believe that they truly present the method.

FIGURE 1 shows the Holcombe mirror as drawn for publication, (see n. 1) in the British Museum, by Philip Compton[3]. The roundel we now discuss is that outlined with a rectangle in this figure. See also Fig. 6.

FIGURE 2 (2:1) shows some elements of the compass construction of the motif which occupies the sector of the inner ring of this roundel,

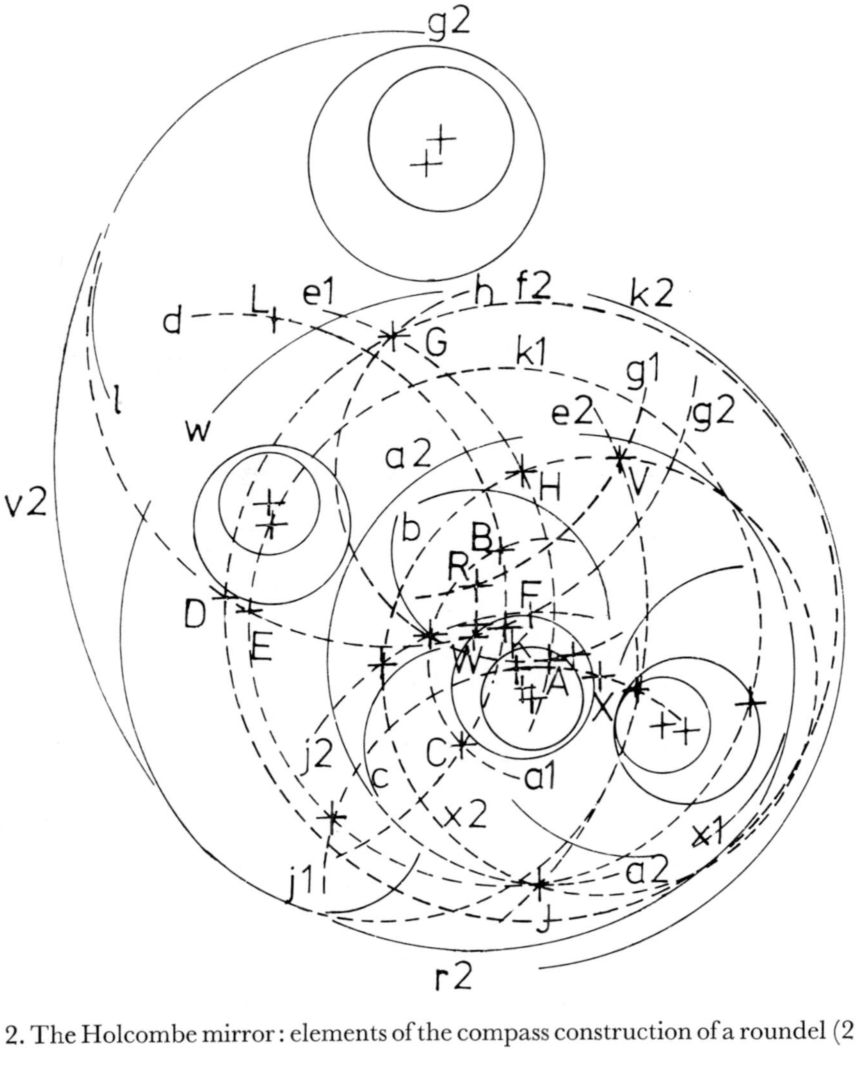

FIG. 2. The Holcombe mirror: elements of the compass construction of a roundel (2:1).

between about 8 o'clock and 10 o'clock. The motif is formed of three arcs: *b*, *c*, *a2*, with centres *B*, *C*, *A* respectively. *B* and *C* lie on arc *a1*; this has a common centre, *A*, with arc *a2*. *A* lies on arc *e1*, with centre *E*; on this lie also the points *G* and *H*. *G* is the centre of arcs *g1* and *g2*; *g2* appears in the design, and on it lie *D*, *E*, *K*, and *F*. *H* is the centre of arc *h*, on which lie *G* and *A*. *B* and *C* lie not only on *a1*, but also on arc *d*, of which *D* is the centre. On this arc *d* lie *L*, centre of the arc *l* which appears in the design (for this arc, see further Fig. 3), and *K*, centre of circle *k1* and arc *k2*. *D* lies on circle *f2*, on which lies *G* (for circle *f2* see also Figs. 3 and 5). *F*, which lies on *g2*, is the centre of this circle *f2*.

The circle *k1*, which has a common centre, *K*, with the arc *k2* visible in the design, is intersected at *J* by arc *a2*. *J* is the centre of arcs *j1* and *j2*, on which lie the centres of five arcs. All five are visible in the design of the motif occupying the sector of the roundel between about 4 o'clock and

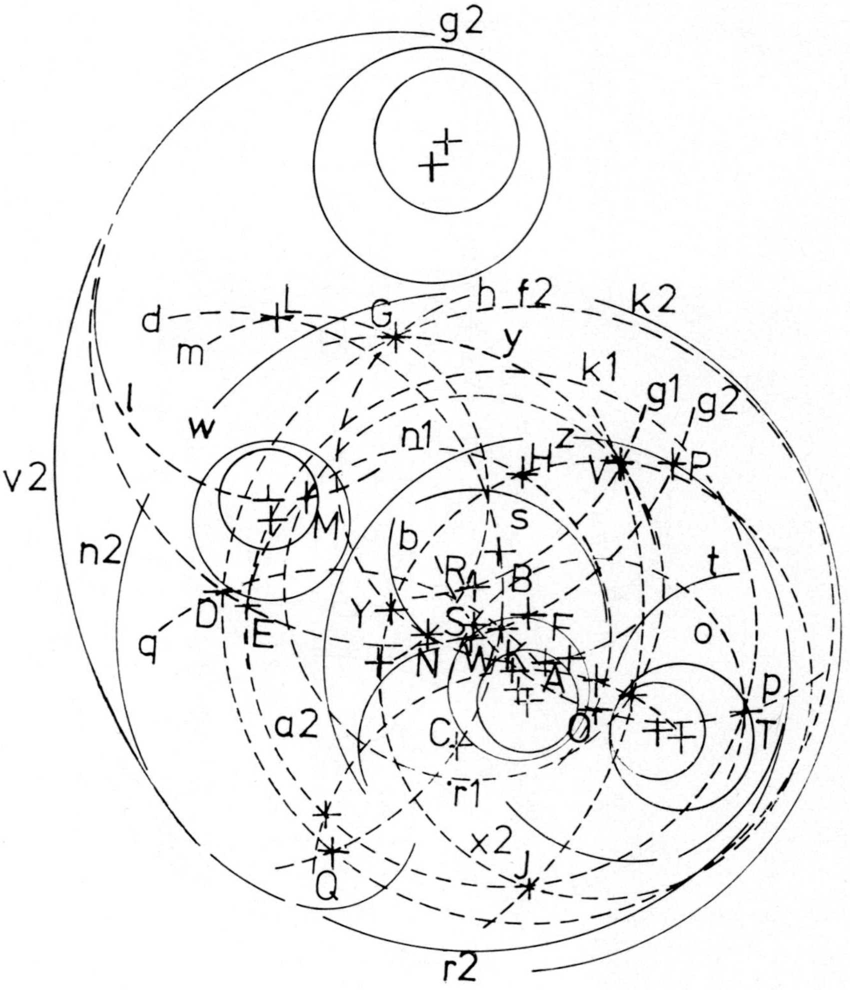

FIG. 3. The Holcombe mirror: elements of the compass construction of a roundel (2:1).

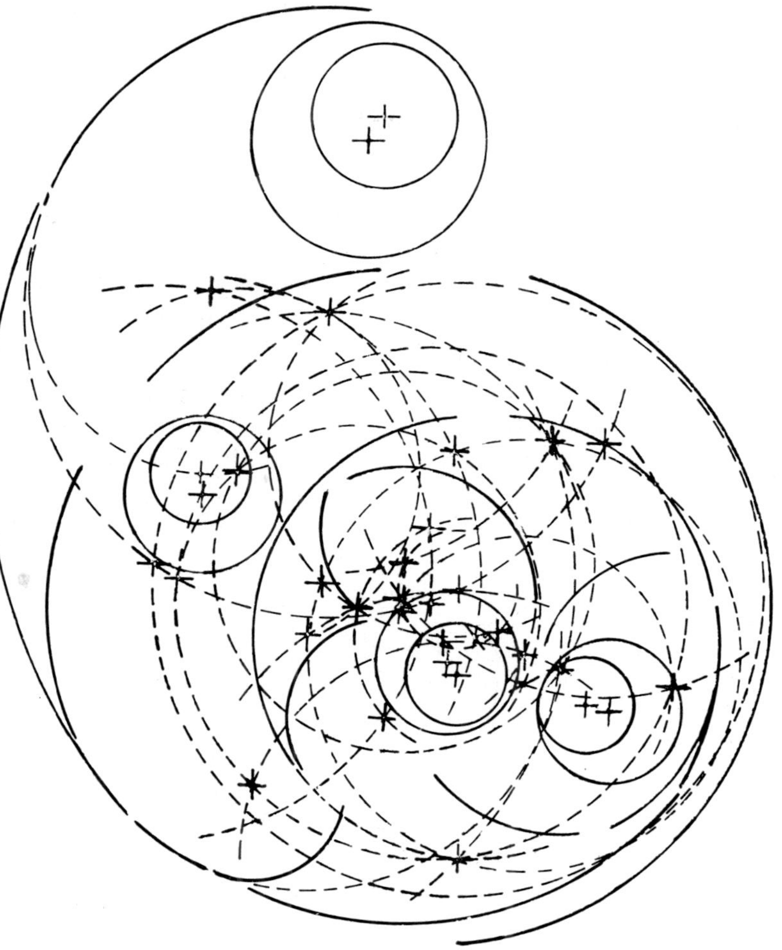

FIG. 4. The Holcombe mirror: elements of the compass construction of a roundel (2:1).

7 o'clock, transitional between its inner and outer rings. For circle *k1*, see also Fig. 3. On arc *j2* lies also *F*. On arc *j1* lies *X*, centre of arc *x1* which appears in the design, and centre also of circle *x2*. On circle *x2* lie *H*, *V*, *J* and other centres, for which see again Fig. 3. On circle *f1* lie *R*, *Z*, and *U*, centres of arcs *r2*, *z* and *u*, all of which appear in the design (see Fig. 5).

FIGURE 3 (2:1) shows some other elements of the compass construction of the roundel. The centre *V* of the arc *v2*, which appears in the design, lies on circles *x2* and *r1* and on arcs *y* and *g1*; for *v1* see Fig. 5. On the arc *g1* lies also *R*, common centre of the circle *r1* and the arc *r2*. The arc *r2* appears in the design. On the circle *r1* lies *M*, which lies also on arc *l*; *M* is centre of the arc *m* on which lie *L*, *G*, and *N*. *N* is centre of arc *n1* on which lie *E*, *M*, *H*, and *O*, and of the arc *n2* which appears in the design. *O* lies also on the arc *p*, whose centre *P* lies on the arcs *z* (which appears in the design) and *g2*. On arc *p* lie the centres *S* and *T* of the arcs *s* and *t* which appear in the design. *S* and *T* lie also on the arc *o*, centre *O*. On arc *g2* and circle *f2* lies *D*, centre of the arc *d* on which lie *L*, *B*, *C*, and *Q*; *Q* is the centre of arc *q* on which lie *D* and *K*. On arc *g2* lies *W*, centre of the arc *w* which appears in the design.

In FIGURE 4 (2:1) some of the elements from Fig. 2 and Fig. 3 are combined, and in Fig. 5 (2:1) are shown constructions, partly independent of the rest, by which the crescents are placed.

All these constructions are comparable with those found in other roundels in the Holcombe design, and with the analogous systems which link the roundels to one another.

We believe it is best for the purpose here to present the facts of the compass-work, disclosed on this roundel, simply one among all that we have studied; comment on them is left for the Discussion.

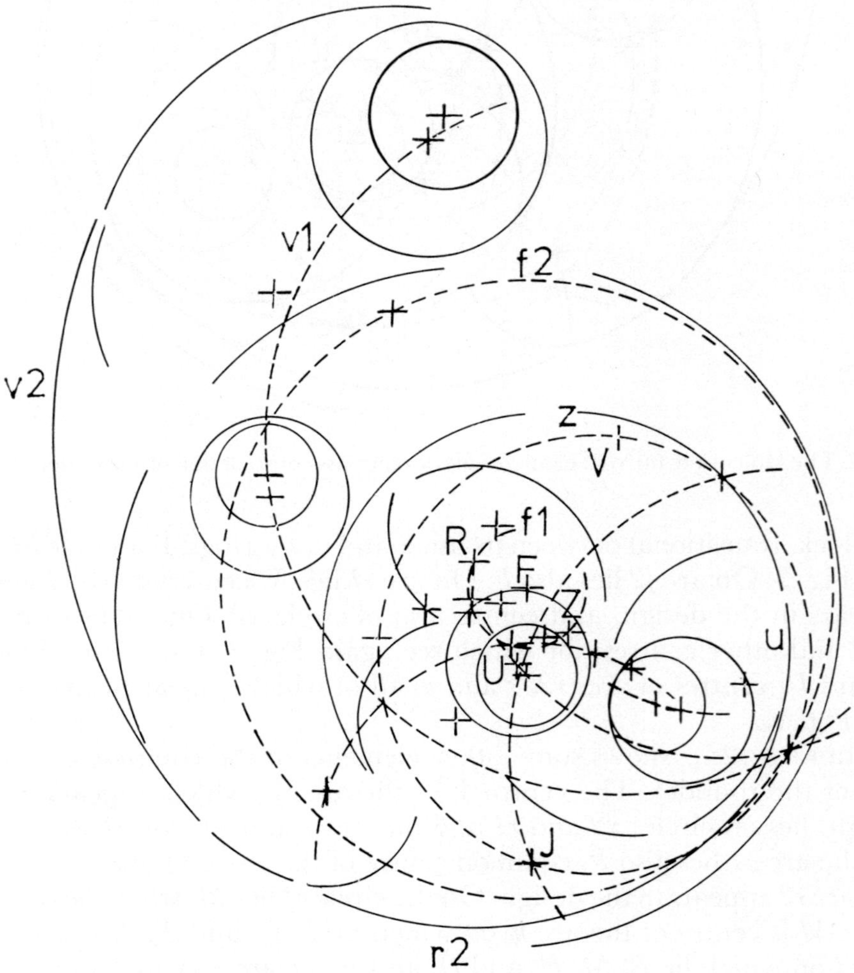

FIG. 5. The Holcombe mirror: elements of the compass construction of a roundel (2:1).

FIG. 6. The Holcombe mirror: silicone rubber mould of a roundel ($1\frac{1}{2}$:1).

Notes

1. Sheila Pollard and Aileen Fox, *Antiquaries Journal* **53,** 1973—Mrs Pollard is publishing her excavation on the Holcombe site, an Iron Age settlement, where the mirror had been purposely buried in a pit, in the *Proceedings of the Devon Archaeological Society* for 1973.

2. Lowery, P., Savage, R. D. A., Wilkins, R. L. *Archaeologia* 105 (forthcoming).

3. Also appearing in the preliminary short article: Aileen Fox (1972). *Antiquity* **46,** (December), 293–296. The mirror, acquired by the British Museum, is displayed in its Iron Age Gallery (Dept. of Prehistoric and Romano-British Antiquities). We desire to thank Mrs Pollard, Lady Fox, and Philip Compton (Fig. 1).

Résumé

Dessins celtiques exécutés au compas

Les miroirs de bronze britanniques portent au revers un décor gravé qui a été construit à l'aide du compas. Le présent exposé fait la démonstration à propos d'une partie du décor du miroir trouvé en 1970 à Holcombe (Uplyme, Devon). "Arc" désigne un arc de cercle, indiqué par une minuscule et distingué par un trait plein sur les dessins, tandis que les prolongements sont exprimés par des traits interrompus ainsi que les arcs qu'on suppose avoir été utilisés dans la construction. Les centres des cercles (complets ou complétés, par exemple, à partir d'un "croissant") sont marqués par des croix et désignés par des majuscules: on peut, en cas de besoin, les retrouver sur les figures à l'aide d'un compas ou d'un calque portant des cercles concentriques distants de 5 mm à 5 cm. Certains arcs ont été omis pour ne pas surcharger les dessins.

FIGURE 1. Dessin du miroir de Holcombe.

FIGURE 2 (2:1). Montre certains éléments de la construction au compas du motif qui occupe le secteur de l'anneau intérieur du décor, entre 8 et 10 heures d'horloge. Le motif est formé de trois arcs *b*, *c*, *a2* avec centres respectifs *B*, *C*, *A*. *B* et *C* sont sur l'arc *a1* qui a un centre commun (*A*) avec *a2*. *A* est sur l'arc *e1* (centre: *E*), sur lequel se trouvent également *G* et *H*; *G* est le centre des arcs *g1* et *g2*; *g2* apparaît sur le dessin et sur cet arc se trouvent *D*, *E*, *K*, *F*. *H* est le centre de l'arc *h*, sur lequel se trouvent *G* et *A*. *B* et *C* se trouvent aussi sur l'arc *d* (centre: *D*). Sur ce même arc se trouvent *L*, centre de l'arc *l* qui apparaît sur le dessin (pour cet arc, voir aussi Fig. 3) et *K*, centre du cercle *k1* et de l'arc *k2*. *D* se trouve sur le cercle *f2* (centre: *F*), sur lequel se trouve *G* (pour ce cercle *f2*, voir aussi Fig. 3 et 5); *F* est sur l'arc *g2*.

Le cercle *k1*, qui a un centre *K* en commun avec l'arc *k2* visible sur le dessin, est recoupé en *J* par l'arc *a2*. *J* est le centre des arcs *j1* et *j2*, sur lequel se trouvent les centres de cinq arcs visibles sur le dessin du motif qui occupe le secteur, faisant la transition avec les anneaux intérieurs et extérieurs du décor, entre 4 et 7 heures. (Pour le cercle *k1*, voir aussi la Fig. 3). Sur l'arc *j2* se trouve aussi *F*. Sur *l'arc j1* se trouve *X*, centre de l'arc *x1* qui apparaît sur le dessin et aussi centre du cercle *x2* sur lequel se trouvent *H*, *V*, *J* et d'autres centres (voir Fig. 3). Sur le cercle *f1* se trouvent *R*, *Z* et *U*, centres des arcs *r2*, *z*, et *u*, qui apparaissent sur le dessin (voir Fig. 5).

Figure 3 (2:1). Montre quelques autres éléments de la construction au compas du décor. Le centre *V* de l'arc *v2* qui apparaît sur le dessin se trouve sur les cercles *x2* et *r1* et sur les arcs *y* et *g1*. (Pour l'arc *v1*, voir Fig. 5). Sur l'arc *g1* se trouve aussi *R*, centre commun du cercle *r1* et de l'arc *r2*. L'arc *r2* apparaît sur le dessin. Sur le cercle *r1* se trouve *M*, qui est aussi sur l'arc *l*: *M* est le centre de l'arc *m* sur lequel sont *L*, *G*, et *N*. *N* est le centre de l'arc *n1* sur lequel sont *E*, *M*, *H*, et *O*, et l'arc *n2* qui apparaît sur le dessin. *O* est aussi sur l'arc *p*, dont le centre *P* est sur les arcs *z* (qui apparaît sur le dessin) et *g2*. Sur l'arc *p* sont les centres *S* et *T* des arcs *s* et *t*, qui apparaissent sur le dessin. *S* et *T* sont aussi sur l'arc *o* (centre: *O*). Sur l'arc *g2* et le cercle *f2* se trouve *D*, centre de l'arc *d* sur lequel sont *L*, *B*, *C* et *Q*; *Q* est le centre de l'arc *q*, sur lequel sont *D* et *K*. Sur l'arc *g2* se trouve *W*, centre de l'arc *w* qui apparaît sur le dessin.

Figure 4 (2:1). Combine certains éléments des Fig. 2 et 3.

Figure 5 (2:1). Montre des constructions en partie indépendantes du reste, et par lesquelles on met les croissants à leur place.

(Nous laissons les commentaires sur ces faits à la discussion suivante).

Discussion

Speakers:— Professors Hawkes and Klindt-Jensen, Mr Savage and Mr Lowery (Mr Savage having given the lecture), Professor Duval, Dr Schwappach, Professors Frey and Jope, Mr Allen.

HAWKES: I want to begin by stressing the date, relatively late, of our decorated mirrors. This is well established for Britain, and their study has amply sufficed—most of all through the work of Sir Cyril Fox—for indicating a new discovery's place, when it occurs. At any rate this seems to be true for the mirror discovered at Holcombe. I would entirely agree that the years just after Christ are the best for placing it.

KLINDT-JENSEN: I certainly think not before the early I^st^ century A.D.

HAWKES: Long after the compass-work of the Early Style of La Tène, as seen on the pieces in openwork from Somme-Bionne, of the Vth century, or the disc from Cuperly, not far off them: both studied by Jacobsthal, both from the Marne. And now among the mirrors from British soil, unknown with such work till at least three centuries after, we have here this amazing demonstration, for a piece four centuries after, of what had been attained through development in between.

KLINDT-JENSEN: The "basketry" pattern, or "matting", that fills some spaces, is British. How was it done?

SAVAGE: With a chasing tool or tracer, tapped into the surface of the mirror: a very characteristic British "mirror style" technique. There was a varied range of techniques, and of tools for employing them. (The recent article here mentioned was that in *Proc. Prehistoric Soc.* **37,** 1971, part I (July), 167–182; same authors as above, note 2: see especially 173, and 177 mentioning mirrors.)

HAWKES: Their use suggests a craft tradition, does it not? Carried on by a succession of masters who had begun as masters' apprentices. Would Philip Lowery expect it to be necessarily continuous, over such centuries of time? Or could it be started up again, in Britain, after a break in the transmission?

LOWERY: The quality of work like this, I think, must mean a continuing tradition. I should find it very difficult to accept the notion of any break whatsoever. The remarkable degree reached here, on this particular mirror, is something I can only see coming from quite a terrific lot of work going on and on beforehand: work by many successive generations. It might, I suppose, start late, but this isn't what either of us thinks.

DUVAL: A terrific lot of work indeed; and its tradition at least as long, I should suppose, as what we see in the Gaulish coin work.

SAVAGE: I don't think one ought to see the workers as "scientific", with geometrical, mathematical or numerical combinations. Jacobsthal, when he wrote about the earlier Celtic compass-work, said that that would be quite wrong: and I am with him. It is simply an extraordinarily elaborate employment of the craftsmanship of compasses *per se*. The properties of compasses are the properties of the circle, but their use need not be in any way scientific or mathematical: the purpose here was simply decoration.

DUVAL: What about precise "fold-over" symmetry, in this or in any of the British mirrors' designs?

SAVAGE: This mirror's design, at first glance nearly symmetrical, is not quite: the constructions on the two sides are similar but not identical.

DUVAL: Why then has the engraver done this enormous work of geometry?

SAVAGE: It was simply the way to produce what he wanted. I don't see any other way of producing such a design.

DUVAL: So the designers didn't carry the composition to exact equality throughout, but did want to make it very precise.

SAVAGE: Aesthetically, even psychologically perhaps, it gives a particular impression of a kind of tension. Whether an arc gives the mind a sense of the presence of its centre, I don't know; but the tension, I think, gets something from the element of asymmetry, which could probably have been got in no other way. The compass-constructions give the design two halves not quite alike.

DUVAL: Like a human face, in fact. (*Assent by Savage.*)

SCHWAPPACH: The design is indeed astonishing, and I agree that it was not the work of a mathematical genius, but the result of a development in playing with compasses. These very complicated patterns, British and late, have their earlier sources. In the Early Style, you can see the palmette rendered in compass-playing, more simple, as in the Schwarzenbach gold openwork; Bohemia shows it on pottery (though not frequently) besides, and on the Dürkheim bronze lid you can still see centre-holes for the arcs. These earliest patterns are simple; but continuity with the complex, as here so late in Britain, goes through the discs from the Marne (as Cuperly): very few, but showing already very complicated constructions. I think they were worked out before being brought on to the bronze; then executed there with compasses free-hand.

HAWKES: For an openwork piece, could the whole design be drawn out first on the wax, and taken by the mould used for casting by *cire perdue*, the "lost-wax" method?

FREY: No, the bronze has signs that show that the rendering was free-hand compass-work on its surface.

HAWKES: Yet on a casting-product like the discs the operation must differ from drawing on a plane metal surface like a mirror-back.

LOWERY: I ought to say that plane drawing, with compasses or with single tools, is easier in comparison with decorating cast objects. The problems of these we ourselves have not yet studied. Technical problems are enormously many and take much time today; it will have been equally true for working men in the Iron Age.

JOPE: The Holcombe mirror and the Desborough mirror have a feature of design in common, not present on any others, in the use of long continuous line: from the lower left, up and round and out to the right-hand side. Of the others, there are quite a number in fact symmetrical.

ALLEN: When this mirror was shown in London first, reason was given to believe that it would be held with the handle upwards. With it downwards, then, the design will be upside down.

JOPE: More than that: the Great Chesterford Mirror, quite as heavy a thing as this, and one of my symmetrical ones, should be held hanging slightly slanted. Then one appreciates its symmetry of design.

HAWKES: I am sure that a heavy mirror was held for a lady by a lady's-maid: the *femme de chambre* held it, while the lady's face was reflected for her of course by the polished front, not by the decorated back.

ALLEN: But the handle would still be upwards when it hung on the wall betweenwhiles; and the back would then be outwards, and so be looked at.

HAWKES: Yes! on the wall of the "bower".

DUVAL: And when the servant held the mirror, I think she would hold it still, while the lady turned her face to consider her charms.

11

L'Est, le Nord et l'Ouest dans l'art de la fin du IIème et du Ier siècles avant J.-C.

OLE KLINDT-JENSEN
Aarhus

MÊME SI NOUS avons réussi à éliminer certaines cartes de répartition et certaines limites injustifiées, on peut encore définir des voies de pénétration traditionelles des influences culturelles. Il est cependant curieux de constater qu'à travers les différentes époques, ces échanges se faisaient dans des conditions qui n'étaient pas immuables, et qu'à certains moments ils étaient interrompus, à d'autres, extrêmement actifs. Si l'on s'en tient à la fin du IIème et au début du Ier siècle av. J.-C., les contacts étaient alors nets et importants entre les Celtes et des peuples plus lointains, dans le Nord comme dans l'Orient et le Sud. Nous pouvons leur imaginer des événements historiques, même si nous ne les connaissons pas tous avec exactitude. Il n'est pas moins difficile de définir les voies par lesquelles circulaient les éléments orientaux ou orientalisants. Ceux-ci sont facilement discernables dans l'art celtique; mais pénétraient-ils par la voie du Danube? Ou bien par la Méditerranée et l'Italie septentrionale? Cela reste sujet à discussion.

Il est peut-être plus facile de commencer par étudier les relations entre l'Europe du nord-ouest et la région de la Mer Noire, parce qu'elles se sont établies directement le long des grandes voies fluviales, à maintes reprises déjà, et, après une pause, s'intensifièrent à partir de la fin du IIème siècle après J.-C. Nous ne savons pas exactement si l'initiative fut prise par les Germains du Nord à tradition culturelle de Jastorf, ou les peuplades du Sud-Est. Mais, au début de La Tène III, des tribus du

Nord-Ouest du Continent envahirent le Nord de l'estuaire du Danube; ils enterrèrent leurs morts dans des cimetières comme ceux de Poieneşti et de Lukashevka[1]. Les urnes contenant des fibules et d'autres bijoux décèlent une origine directe et lointaine, même située en Scandinavie. A la même époque, les anneaux en forme de couronne ("crown rings") et d'autre objets s'étendirent du Nord au Sud-Ouest[2].

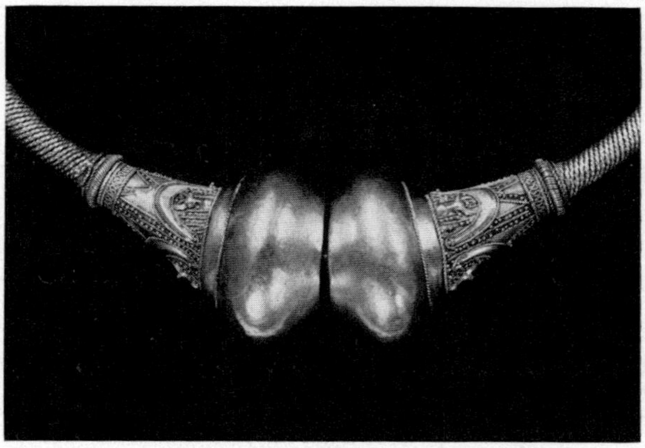

(a)

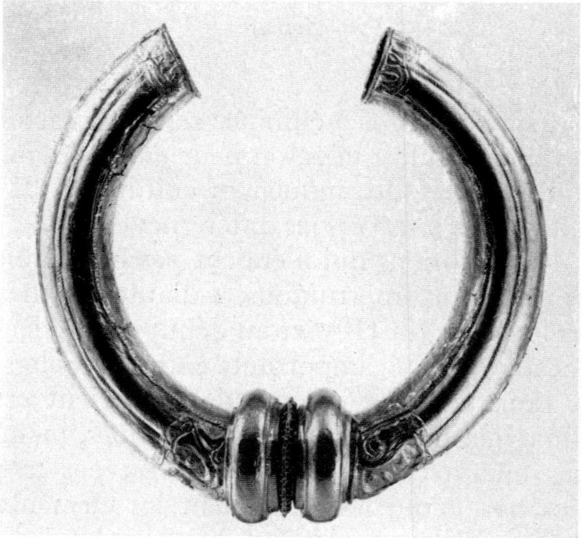

(b)

FIG. 1 (a). Boutons du torque de Havor, Gotland (Suède) (photo de E. Nylén). (b). Torque de Mailly-le-Camp (Aube) (d'après R. Joffroy).

D'un autre côté, de lourds colliers d'or arrivèrent dans le Nord-Ouest: l'un d'eux a été trouvé à Dronninglund (Jutland) et un autre, récemment, à Havor, dans l'île de Gotland[3] (Fig. 1a). Dans la même île ont été découverts d'élégants bijoux en or de même provenance que les colliers et anneaux, c'est-à-dire la Russie méridionale. Là des contreparties peuvent être étudiées p. ex. à Olbia[4]. La balance du profit penche nettement en faveur du Nord; et l'on peut se demander si ce ne serait pas de là que l'initiative est partie, pour établir des contacts avec le Sud-Est.

Ces échanges donnèrent naissance à la production de bijoux, au style semblable à celui de ces objets en or importés, dans le Gotland même, comme l'a montré récemment Erik Nylén[5]. Des perles en double cône et des pendants d'oreilles ronds sont décorés en filigrane, et par des têtes de boeufs stylisées, offrant des ressemblances avec les bijoux cités de la Russie méridionale.

Des échanges par la voie danubienne, nous avons d'abondantes preuves, parmi lesquelles on peut mentionner les phalères d'argent, matériel qui a reçu récemment de splendides compléments tels que le trésor redécouvert de Sark, les nouvelles découvertes d'Oberaden (Westphalie) et celles de Dalboki (Stara Zagora, Bulgarie). On a de bonnes raisons de dater toutes ces pièces du Ier siècle avant J.-C., et les phalères d'argent de la Bibliothèque Nationale portant des inscriptions, une au nom de "Mithradate", permettraient d'aboutir à la même conclusions si, comme nous pouvons le supposer, la dédicace concerne Mithradate le Grand (110–63 avant J.-C.).

Par leur forme comme par la technique utilisée, ces pièces sont en rapport les unes avec les autres mais ne constituent pas un groupe tout à fait uniforme, comme D. F. Allen, dans sa récent publication du trésor de Sark, l'a si clairement souligné[6]. Nous ne pouvons pas non plus suivre ce développement avec une constante certitude. Mais dans la partie orientale de la région danubienne, en Dacie et en Thrace, nous trouvons un travail de l'argent plus ancien, qui constitue le fondement de la fabrication des phalères et des pièces d'argent de cette région. En Russie méridionale, où l'or était aussi utilisé, le style peut être différent.En général, cependant, nous avons dans l'art scythe tardif un élément de liaison qui, dans des découvertes comme celles de Hagighiol (Dobroudja), est irrécusable[7].

Ces oeuvres ont en commun la technique du repoussé, le traitement des fonds au moyen de points etc., les formes arrondies, à peu près naturalistes, des animaux et des hommes. Les peaux des animaux comportent des hachures ou des points, ou des cercles. On constate une prédilection pour des êtres exotiques comme les éléphants, sans parler des griffons, et pour des scènes féroces de combats. La composition est nettement de caractère antithétique. La ressemblance avec une phalère de Sark et l'une des phalères de Mithradate est claire; il y a certainement eu là une connection.

Si l'on compare ces pièces d'argent avec le chaudron de Gundestrup, on constate une certaine ressemblance mais aussi de nettes différences[8]. Ici, les motifs sont aussi disposés de façon antithétique, mais sans liaison intime entre eux comme sur les phalères. Chaque motif est isolé (avec évidemment des exceptions). Il n'y a pas de combats entre animaux, tandis que le taureau, sur la plaque centrale du fond, est dessiné de façon conventionnelle, par opposition à l'homme combattant. La technique est très semblable, l'emploi de l'argent également, de même que les caractéristiques des peaux des animaux et du fond, mais le style est différent. On ne doit certainement pas sous-estimer l'importance de la technique du repoussé pour la représentation des ornements au naturel, comme partie du travail. Les motifs de Gundestrup ont une forme schématique et rigide; et c'est un art élaboré, très conscient des effets de la composition et de l'intention qui l'inspire. Plusieurs artistes différents étaient à l'oeuvre, mais le résultat est extraordinairement impressionnant: c'est le travail d'un véritable atelier d'art. Le but était de représenter les dieux celtes et leurs symboles, d'illustrer les cérémonies religieuses au cours desquelles—qui sait?—des combats de taureaux peuvent avoir eu lieu.

Nous connaissons bien certains de ces dieux dans l'art religieux gallo-romain; avant tout Cernunnos, avec son serpent à tête de bélier et ses torques. D'autres, comme le dieu de la guerre et du ciel, Taranis, sont figurés aussi nettement. Les armes et d'autres détails prouvent clairement que le milieu était celtique, et il est difficile de croire que l'époque en est postérieure au Ier siècle avant J.C. L'*umbo* des boucliers est d'un type courant à cette époque et ne doit pas être plus ancien, dans la période de la Tène.

D'où venait la manière orientalisante de présenter les dieux dans toute leur puissance? Les artistes ont délibérément choisi cette composition pour souligner la puissance divine. Ils ont inventé une scène mettant en présence Cernunnos avec le cerf et le loup dont les regards plongent dans ses yeux puissants, ce qui souligne le lien profond existant entre les trois individus. D'une façon analogue, les artistes gallo-romains donnaient de l'expression à la représentation du dieu.

Nous pouvons chercher une composition orientalisante tardive sur les phalères d'argent, mais elle n'y est pas, comme nous l'avons vu, aussi explicite. On trouve peut-être des traces plus nettes de cette composition dans l'art celtique lui-même: René Wyss l'a montré en relevant des marques comportant de tels motifs sur des épées de La Tène tardive comme celle de *Korisios*[10]. Sur un certain nombre d'autres pièces, nous avons de bons exemples, en particulier en Italie septentrionale, où cette composition peut avoir été traditionelle[11].

Il vaut la peine de se rappeler que des bustes semblables à ceux de Gundestrup étaient traités en repoussé à Waldalgesheim. Ici, comme à Gundestrup et souvent dans l'art celtique, les oreilles des dieux ou des hommes ne sont pas apparentes, tandis qu'elles le sont toujours dans l'art de la phalère[12]. D'un autre côté, il serait impossible de nier le rapport entre Gundestrup et l'art de la phalère. Même si le travail du métal repoussé était très répandu dans le monde celtique—comme sur le seau de Marlborough—, l'emploi de l'argent fut très limité jusqu'à La Tène III et les façons caractéristiques de rendre la peau et le fond se retrouvent dans les deux arts de manière frappante. On doit se demander si les dieux comme Cernunnos, qui étaient adorés en Gaule à l'époque gallo-romaine, peuvent être considérés comme témoignant d'une origine gauloise, ou si l'on doit supposer qu'ils étaient adorés dans les pays celtiques orientaux. Cependant, jusqu'ici, il n'y a pas de preuves à cet égard. Certains chaudrons comme celui de Rynkeby (Fionie), au Danemark, semblent avoir été fabriqués à l'Ouest et, à l'époque gallo-romaine, nous avons des oeuvres comme le masque en argent de Notre-Dame-d'Alençon dont les yeux ont été fixés exactement de la même façon que sur le chaudron de Gundestrup. On peut se demander si ces pièces n'étaient pas fabriquées en Scandinavie, peut-être par des artistes venant du sud ou du sud-est, mais tout le milieu est nettement celtique et nous n'avons aucune tradition de dieux et d'animaux fantastiques dans la technique de repousser l'ornementation. J'inclinerais donc à considérer Gundestrup—et quelques autres chaudrons trouvés dans le Nord—comme dû à un travail gaulois, mais influencé par l'Orient. Les traits caractéristiques des figures, des ornements, des parures, des vêtements, des armes etc., ne vont pas contre un tel rapport. On pourrait par exemple choisir les *torques*, qui sont, il faut l'avouer, distribués très loin, entre l'Occident et la Russie méridionale. On ne sait pas exactement le lieu d'origine, et il y a des rapports évidents, entre Ouest et Orient, qui rendent la question difficile. Les *torques* figurés sur le chaudron de Gundestrup représentent du moins trois types, dont un se rapproche du type de Havor-Olbia (Fig. 2a; cf. Fig. 1a); il est toutefois possible de se référer à des *torques* d'Occident d'à peu près la même forme[15]. Le *torques* le plus commun est aussi bien connu en Gaule (Fig. 2b; cf. Fig. 1b)[16]. Et les *torques* du dieu Cernunnos, d'un anneau tordu, aux bouts ronds, ont des parallèles également en Gaule (Fig. 3a et b).

(a)

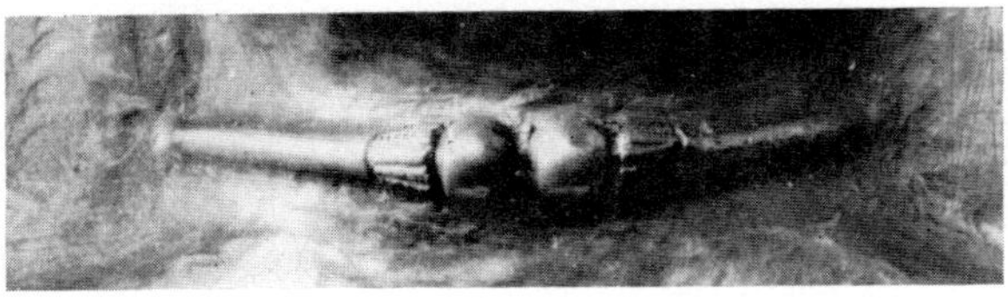

(b)

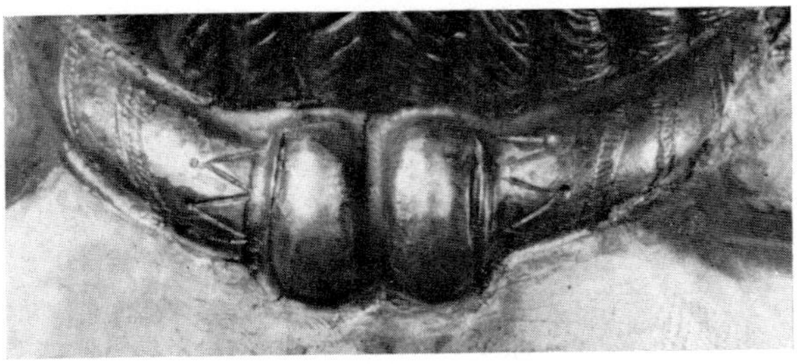

FIG. 2. Torques figurés sur le chaudron de Gundestrup. (a) de type comme Fig. 1 a; (b) de type comme Fig. 1 b.

Un travail en métal de type celtique semble cependant avoir débuté en Scandinavie. Une statuette de Scanie, fondue par moitié, a une certaine ressemblance avec la statuette de bronze accroupie de Bouray[17]: un exemple de plus de la façon de s'asseoir mentionnée par Poseidonios et caractéristique de Cernunnos.

(a)

(b)

FIG. 3 (a). Torque dans la main de *Cernunnos* figuré sur le chaudron de Gundestrup. (b). Torque de Le Pual-sur-la-Touche (Ille-et-Vilaine) (Musée de Cluny, Paris).

Comme l'une des sources de cet art, on a mentionné l'Italie septentrionale où, par exemple à Este, la technique du repoussé pour les frises et les statuettes de bronze est bien connue. Dans ce cadre, il est tentant de placer un étrange objet en or, faisant actuellement partie d'une collection privée. C'est une statuette montée sur une fibule: un guerrier nu combat un lion; il ressemble beaucoup aux pièces du Fondo Baratela, à Este, mais démontre aussi des rapports avec e.a. la Gaule[18]. L'umbo du bouclier est de La Tène II et l'épée, avec son étrange forme asymétrique, pourrait l'être aussi; de même, le casque, avec son décor à cordes et sa bosse, est bien connu dans les tombes de l'Italie septentrionale; d'un autre côté, le guerrier a une certaine ressemblance avec ceux du chaudron de Gundestrup.

Ce réseau compliqué d'influences et de rapports entre des éléments fort éloignés les uns des autres ne pourrait pas être mieux illustré que par le casque du Negau, que Christopher Hawkes a récemment examiné dans une étude éminemment stimulante[19], ce casque qui porte un nom germanique incisé en lettres d'Este et qui peut même se rapporter à l'influence de cette région sur le Nord qui pourrait expliquer la création des runes. Cette époque pleine de forces créatrices a encore beaucoup à livrer pour de nouvelles recherches.

Notes

Cross-references within the notes are indicated by bold italic type.

1. Vulpe, R. (1955). *Le problème des Bastarnes à la lumière des découvertes archéologiques en Moldavie*, Bucarest.
Hachmann, R. (1961). "Die Chronologie der jüngeren vorrömischen Eisenzeit", *Bericht der rom.-germ. Komm.* **41,** p. 123.

2. Babes, M. et Untaru, I. (1969). *Dacia* **XIII,** p. 283, avec références.
Babes, M, und Mihailescu-Birliba, V. (1970–71). "Germanische latènezeitliche Feuerböcke aus der Moldau", *Bericht der rom.-germ. Komm.* **51–52,** 1972, p. 176.

3. Nylén, E. (1962). Skatten från Havors fornborg, *Proxima Thule*, p. 94.

4. Müller, S. (1900). Dans *Aarb for nord. Oldkyndighed* p. 142.
Ouvaroff, A. (1855). *Recherches sur les Antiquités de la Russie Méridionale*, p. 38.

5. Nylén, E. (**n. 3**), p. 112. Une tête apparentée sur le torque de Frasnes-les-Buissenal (Belgique), Jacobsthal. *ECA*, no. 70.

6. Allen, D. F. (1971). "The Sark Hoard", *Archaeologia* **CIII,** p. 12.

7. Nylén, E. (1967–68), en *Tor*, p. 133.
Powell, T. (1971), en *The European Community in later Prehistory* (*Studies for C. F. C. Hawkes*), p. 189.

8. Klindt-Jensen, O. (1961). *Gundestrupkedelen* (Copenhagen, Nat. Mus.).

9. Duval, P.-M. (1957). *Les dieux de la Gaule*, p. 23.

10. Wyss, R. (1954). *Jahrbuch des bern. historischen Museums in Bern* **XXXIV**, p. 285.

11. Par exemple Fr. Studniczka, *Arch. Jahrbuch* **XVIII,** p. 1.

12. Jacobsthal, P. *ECA*, p. 183 (no. 156).

13. Arbman, H. (1948) en *Tor*, p. 109.
Klindt-Jensen, O. (1950). *Foreign Influences in Denmark's Early Iron Age*, p. 109.

14. Müller, S. (1892). "Det store Sølvkar fra Gundestrup", *Nordisk Fortidsminder* **I,** p. 35.

15. Jacobsthal, P. (1944). *ECA*, nos 55–56 (Waldalgesheim).

16. Joffroy, R. *Monuments et Mémoires Piot* 1969, p. 45.
Jacobsthal, P. *ECA*, passim.

17. Halbert, L. (1956–57). *Medd. från Lunds universitets hist. museum* p. 105.

18. Klindt-Jensen, O. (1960), dans *Civilta del ferro*, Bologna p. 363. La pièce sera publiée en détail par M. R. Rowlett.

19. Hawkes, C. (1970). "Runes and the Caput Adriae", *Adriatica Praehistorica et Antiqua, Mélanges Novak*, Zagreb, p. 399.

Résumé

Study of cultural transmission, even with older mistakes eliminated, can still achieve results, if we allow for changes in its conditions. A time when conditions promoted it, between Celts and more distant peoples, was the end of the IInd and the Ist century B.C. Historical events may be presupposed as a background even if not known precisely, just as routes of transmission may be open to debate. Between the North-West of the Continent and the Black Sea region, as in earlier times and later, the routes were along the big rivers, such as Vistula and Danube, whether the initiative was South-Eastern or from Jastorf-culture peoples. But about the beginning of La Tène III, some of these plainly moved down to the northern side of the estuary of the Danube: in cemeteries like Poienești and Lukashevka, a start from a Scandinavian area is implied by the urns, fibulas, etc., and connected with this are the "crown rings" and other objects distributed in South-East Europe out of the North. Conversely, great gold neck-rings (Dronninglund, Jutland; Havor, Gotland) and more elegant ornaments (Gotland) are of Black Sea origin (e.g. Olbia). The North had the best of the exchange, so perhaps the initiative came from there. And Erik Nylén has in Gotland shown that the gold novelties aroused there production of imitations: bicone beads and pendants, with filigree and ox-head features, having clear similarities to their prototypes in South Russia. Common despite the differences, however, are embossed technique, forms fairly lifelike, human and animal, conventions for showing pelts or hides of animals, some exotic (elephants, griffins), fierce fighting scenes, and antithetic composition.

Denmark's silver Gundestrup cauldron presents an art both like and unlike. Forms if antithetic are not so intimately paired; more are self-contained; no scenes are animal fights. The embossing, and surface conventions, are like, but the style is schematic and stiff: an elaborate art, contrived for effect, conveying idea, and strangely vivid. Its team of artists was set to show Celtic gods, their symbols and attributes, and scenes and ceremonies of Celtic religion.

Turning then to silver, we can be confident now of connections by the Danube, and of datings at this same time, for the well-known decorative phaleras. From Oberaden (Westphalia) and Dalboki (Stara Zagora, Bulgaria) new finds indicate both, along with the Sark hoard (rediscovered in its old engravings); thus the Mithradates named on the unlocated Paris phaleras may be taken as Mithradates the Great of Pontus (110–63 B.C.). Late Scythian silver, as at Hagighiol (Dobrogea), is related undeniably, yet the art is not quite uniform throughout (see Allen on Sark). Earlier Dacian and Thracian silver-work certainly gives a background. In South Russia, using gold as well, the style may somewhat differ, and the story is not everywhere equally certain. Some of the gods we know from later, Gallo-Roman religious art: Cernunnos, with ram-headed snake and torc, above all. Weapons and details are plainly Celtic; some would be out of place before the I[st] century B.C. (shield-bosses), and the whole is scarcely credible any later. The purpose, of presenting the gods in their might, is oriental in spirit, yet the composition fulfilling it much excels that of the phaleras, and might have emerged from Celtic art itself. Suggestive examples are Swiss (stamps on swords: René Wyss) and others including North Italian. For busts, like Gundestrup's, even Waldalgesheim art employed embossing. And in both, the heads lack ears; phalera art portrays them always.

The links with phalera art are clear. Whence else came the use of silver? Yet were not the gods here Gaulish? Was Cernunnos worshipped in the East? This and e.g. the Rynkeby cauldron (Denmark, island of Fyn), suggest production in the West (like the later mask from Notre-Dame-d'Alençon); they seem too Celtic for making in the North itself, by immigrant artists. So I believe they were made in Gaul, under powerful influence there from the East. The faces, dress, armaments, and ornaments that they show, notably the torques (of at least three types) give nothing against this. Their bringing to the North had no artistic precedents, only some sequels: the rare squatting bronze statuettes, Northern but Celtic in pose, like one from Scania.

Lastly—neither Western nor Eastern, but North Adriatic—the art of Este (neighbour of Italian Celtic) might be a supplementary source. Suggestive here is a work in gold (made known from a private collection), a warrior nude and fighting a lion, the whole set on a fibula; the style is like Este (Fondo Baratela). His helmet is North Italian, shield-boss still La Tène II, yet he does have some resemblance to the Gundestrup cauldron's warriors. The suggestion by Christopher Hawkes of an Adriatic-Nordic link, implied by that between "North-Etruscan" scripts and Runic, and reflected in one of the Negau helmets (Slovenia), with lettering as at Este yet for a Germanic wearer's name, points again to the period's network of connections over distance. They were creative forces, and have much to teach us yet.

Discussion

Speakers:— Professor Hawkes and Klindt-Jensen, Miss Sandars, Mr Allen, Professors Piggott and Jope, Dr Schwappach, Mrs Hawkes.

In reply to PROFESSOR HAWKES, PROFESSOR KLINDT-JENSEN explained the initial movement, by people of Jastorf tradition down to the region of the Danube mouths, as unlike the almost contemporary Cimbric-Teutonic movement from the North, aiming wherever there was plunder, but as an armed bid for a dominance over trade in precious products. That of the sketchily-known Bastarnae might be related, although comparison based on finds was better from several centuries later (as in Bornholm: fibula matched at both the Vistula and Danube mouths, when the IIIrd century A.D. again offered entry into Black Sea markets). To MISS SANDARS, who recalled that Black Sea art had its background in Hellenistic, and mentioned this and a barbaric style together on an Oxus phalera, contrasting, as on the Gundestrup base do the bull and the smaller figures, he replied that though he did not know her silver phalera from the Oxus, he was sure that the phaleras, in their art and in their silver-work, had themselves some Hellenistic background too. Miss Sandars added that the ram-headed snake recalled Near Eastern art's extremely ancient creature, the horned serpent. He replied that altogether there was surely a fusion of elements, difficult indeed to clear up.

On the fibula mounted with warrior and lion, remarked by Miss Sandars and questioned by MR ALLEN, the genuineness of the figure-group, and of its mounting and of the fibula, was commented on by PROFESSOR PIGGOTT, quoting opinion given to him previously: the warrior's feet suggest that the group was originally fixed to a base, as a statuette, while the fibula appears of a different gold, and plainer; thus the whole seemed composite, with the figure-group alone authentic. Klindt-Jensen repeated his own acceptance of the group, though its strangeness should prompt some further investigation.

Hawkes then returned to Klindt-Jensen's exposition in general, for confirming of the range of date: late IInd and on into Ist century B.C.; in La Tène terms, later than the lapsing of the high Plastic Style. In historical terms, at the Black Sea end, the period then was that of Mithradates the Great, who from the Pontus in Asia Minor made a political hegemony also north of the Black Sea, which he tried to extend all round it; at his death (63 B.C.), expelled from Asia by the Romans, he was still trying all he could on the side of Europe. Klindt-Jensen confirmed the archaeological chronology, and saw Mithradates' role as both political and commercial. Replying to Hawkes on the phalera inscriptions, including the same name, Allen explained that two phaleras were known that had inscriptions, one with the Mithradates name and the other very fragmentary: its single remaining word is not this name, but both are in Greek letters, and presumably equally genuine. Jope, supporting this, remarked that no modern forger would be likely to give the fragmentary one a word that was not significant. The phalera chronology thus, including the link with the great Mithradates, was as a whole found acceptable by the speakers.

Reverting to Gundestrup, SCHWAPPACH asked if the sword of the man on the base plate, wielded against the bull, and seeming certainly La Tène, could not well have been La Tène from Dacia? Klindt-Jensen agreed in taking the sword as La Tène: like the three (anyhow two) on the inner plate where bulls are assailed, it has twin knobs, to be seen as enclosed in a palmette form on the pommel—a normal La Tène sword feature, as against the one-knob pommel of the Roman. Whether this might have spread to Dacia, through the La Tène influence known there, he could recall too little of any Dacian swords to say.

Lastly, MRS HAWKES, on the gold collar from Havor (Gotland: his Fig. 1a), was assured by Klindt-Jensen that the grave-associations claimed for it were of the 1st century A.D., so let it be an older piece itself: exactly resembling one of the Gönesborg gold collars, it is astonishingly large—as big as the silver ring from Trichtingen—and suggests that it might have been worn by the wooden image of a god.

12

Matériaux pour l'étude stylistique des monnaies celtiques

Paul-Marie Duval
Paris

Les monnaies gauloises et, plus largement, les monnaies celtiques, ont longtemps souffert d'un discrédit de la part des numismates, des historiens de l'art et des historiens de l'Antiquité. Les uns leur reprochaient leurs irrégularités, leur anonymat presque général, leur frappe incomplète et le manque de séries issues d'un même coin. Les autres déploraient leur aspect souvent incomplet ou informe et voyaient en elles des imitations maladroites de modèles grecs ou romains. Quant aux historiens, ils se heurtaient à l'absence trop fréquente de légendes monétaires, au manque de provenances certaines, à l'absence d'une chronologie sûre. Tout au plus, les amateurs d'art reconnaissaient-ils aux pièces les plus réussies un air d'étrangeté intéressant.

La situation s'est retournée il y a un peu plus d'une vingtaine d'années. Un numismate, le Dr J.-B. Colbert de Beaulieu, a heureusement mis au point une méthode d'examen qui permet d'identifier les pièces, si mal frappées soient-elles, qui sont issues d'un même coin: désormais, les monnaies celtiques pouvaient être étudiées sur le même pied que les monnaies grecques ou les monnaies romaines, et les travaux de Derek Allen, de Castelin, de Colbert de Beaulieu, l'ont bien montré. En même temps, les historiens de l'art, instruits par l'évolution des formes dans l'art moderne et particulièrement par la peinture abstraite, découvraient avec André Malraux une valeur originale aux effigies des monnaies gauloises[1] et y retrouvaient certains caractères de l'art celtique, linéaire, décoratif, curviligne ou géométrique; Bianchi Bandinelli analysait la décomposition du modèle grec et la recomposition des éléments en une création originale[2]. Simultanément, un reclassement géographique plus exact permettait d'entrevoir l'existence de styles régionaux.

Au moment où un important matériel s'offre ainsi aux historiens de l'art, il convient de définir ses caractères au regard de l'art celtique antique en général et d'examiner les conditions dans lesquelles on peut tenter de l'exploiter pour l'histoire des formes.

Dans le temps, les monnaies celtiques se rapportent à une période d'environ trois siècles: entre le début du IIIe au moins et la fin du Ier av. J.-C. Leurs auteurs sont donc contemporains des deux phases les plus récentes de l'art laténien: la phase médiane, qui voit s'épanouir un art plastique et plus libre après le Premier style, encore sévère, des Ve—IVe siècles, (et c'est alors, aux IVe—IIIe siècles, la grande période de l'art celtique),—et la phase finale, qui voit l'invention s'appauvrir et le géométrisme reprendre ses droits avec la prédominance triomphante des influences méditerranéennes, d'où un style qu'on pourrait qualifier de "néo-sévère", nettement moins riche que le précédent. L'art monétaire est ainsi, par rapport à l'art laténien du continent, approximativement dans la même situation chronologique que l'art celtique des Iles britanniques et de l'Europe danubienne: il ne connaît pas réellement la première période, celle de l'assimilation encore timide et sage des motifs méditerranéens;—il profite des grandes expériences de continuité des lignes, de liberté et de plasticité, des styles dits par Jacobsthal "de Waldalgesheim" et "des épées"; et aussi des premiers essais des Celtes en sculpture lapidaire: c'est d'ailleurs, dans une certaine mesure, un style plastique, puisque toute effigie monétaire comporte un relief, au moins léger;—il connaît même, dans sa période terminale et en particulier dans le Nord de la Gaule et en Bretagne, un retour marqué au géométrisme non curviligne.

Comme les autres arts celtiques, l'art monétaire a son point de départ dans des motifs importés. Plus particulièrement, ce sont ici, pour l'essentiel, des modèles grecs—la tête d'Apollon lauré et le bige des statères macédoniens, principalement—, puis des modèles romains—ceux des deniers. Des motifs secondaires s'ajoutent à ceux-là, importés eux aussi: triscèles, palmettes, rinceaux, "lyres". Toutefois, des motifs celtiques viennent se mêler à ces importations: torques, chaudrons, serpents, "jougs", mains, etc., et une prédilection pour les motifs curvilignes, anneaux, rouelles, liens sinueux, tiges et feuilles, esses, spirales, etc., relève aussi du goût celtique le plus authentique. Enfin, des motifs propres à l'art monétaire celtique naissent de la décomposition du modèle: grilles, filets, rubans, notamment.

Au point de vue de la qualité, l'art monétaire celtique comporte des réussites techniques parmi les plus raffinées qui soient: le bon graveur en monnaies est un artiste d'une habileté exceptionnelle, la gravure de ces surfaces minuscules et concaves est une sorte de tour de force perpétuellement renouvelé. Toutefois, il faut bien tenir compte du caractère quasi industriel de cet art: comme l'étaient déjà certains objets de l'Age du bronze (les haches, les épingles, par exemple), comme le sont de nombreux objets de l'Age du fer (les fibules, par exemple), comme le seront les céramiques gallo-romaines, et comme l'ont été toutes les monnaies de l'Antiquité classique, les monnaies celtiques sont faites à l'aide de moules (qui sont ici les coins de frappe et aussi, vers la fin, des moules proprement dits): d'un coin, on sait aujourd'hui qu'on tirait plusieurs centaines au moins, peut-être plusieurs milliers d'exemplaires en certains cas. Il faut donc compter, au point de vue de la qualité, avec les degrés divers de l'usure ou de l'encrassement du coin, qui provoquent des imperfections variées. En revanche, nous sommes assurés que ces petits chefs-d'oeuvre passaient sous les yeux ou dans les mains de tous les Celtes, quelle que soit leur appartenance sociale, et l'on ne pourrait en dire autant d'aucune autre catégorie d'oeuvres d'art, pas même de la céramique.

Les monnaies celtiques sont heureusement d'une grande variété: la plupart des cités de la Gaule, par exemple, frappèrent monnaie et s'efforçèrent de diversifier leurs effigies, ne fût-ce que par un motif de détail, pour qu'il n'y ait pas confusion avec le monnayage voisin. Cette obligation a grandement contribué à la richesse d'invention de cette forme d'art. D'autre part, une telle diversité donne à l'art monétaire, dans une certaine mesure, les caractères d'un art régional: il y eut un style belge, et breton insulaire, un style armoricain, un style parisien, et les monnaies des régions périphériques—belges et bretonnes, languedociennes, alpestres—se signalent par une stylisation particulièrement forte (Figure 1, a, b). En bref, l'art monétaire est la forme d'art qui, à l'époque celtique, présente la plus grande variété et la seule qui, à l'intérieur d'une unité géographique comme la Gaule, peut se prêter à la distinction de styles provinciaux, tout en participant de l'unité du style celtique car un certain nombre de motifs typiques se retrouvent d'un bout à l'autre du monde celtique.

L'art celtique est essentiellement un art de petits objets: la monnaie est l'un de ces objets par excellence et peut-être le plus petit de tous. Elle partage avec d'autres la forme circulaire: miroirs, couvercles, phalères, ornements divers, mais sa petitesse est une contrainte d'une force exceptionnelle. La composition s'en trouve orientée souvent dans le sens de la surcharge: les vides sont rares et, en tout cas, ne jouent pas le rôle de motifs négatifs qu'ils ont dans les oeuvres de métal ajouré. La forme circulaire peut être aussi favorable au choix de motifs curvilignes mais ce n'est pas toujours le cas (dans le style belge, par exemple). Il n'y a pas, non plus, de "zones de raccord" (les triangles curvilignes, par exemple) entre les vides et les pleins ou entre deux motifs comme dans les fusions et les enchaînements du style continu (Waldalgesheim) et

Fig. 1

(a) La tête dérivée de l'Apollon grec sur le statère de la classe I des *Parisii* (BN 7789).

(b) Ce qu'est devenue la tête d'Apollon sur une monnaie belge. Pour les monnaies armoricaines, voir les figs. 6 et 7.

(c) Monnaie de Vercingétorix, frappée incomplètement en surface et, à cause de la mauvaise frappe ou de l'encrassement du flan, en épaisseur. C'est la seule pièce connue de ce coin. (Collection particulière).

(d) Monnaie gauloise complètement frappée, des *Turones*. Peut-être y avait-il un grènetis circulaire périphérique.

(e) Statère d'or de la classe V des *Parisii*, l'un des moins incomplètement frappés (D2, R3). Voir le dessin complété, fig. 4.

du style libre. Enfin, l'art monétaire est, comme l'art celtique presque tout entier, fonctionnel: il s'agit de décorer d'une façon significative, bien reconnaissable et originale, deux surfaces données et inséparables. Il est peut-être aussi parfois symbolique ou religieux, du moins de l'avis de certains auteurs: si cela était vrai, la signification artistique de ces monnaies s'en trouverait grandement enrichie; toutefois, aucune preuve n'a encore été donnée d'un symbolisme éventuel des monnaies et c'est une question qu'il vaut mieux réserver actuellement.

La diversité extrême des monnaies celtiques est née du nombre très limité des images modèles, qu'il fallait à tout prix modifier de cité en cité: principalement une tête humaine, un char attelé de deux chevaux. C'est la tête qui a été le plus profondément transformée, au point d'en devenir parfois méconnaissable, même comme point de départ de la nouvelle composition. L'attelage s'est réduit en règle générale à un seul cheval avec son aurige; ce dernier s'est transformé en un petit personnage fantastique mais le cheval, lui, est toujours resté reconnaissable. Il est important que ces motifs de base soient des formes vivantes, des sujets naturalistes: l'artiste celtique a une prédilection pour les lignes souples et il y ajoute volontiers des formes végétales. Toutefois, il lui arrive aussi de les déformer (notamment dans les styles périphériques) en motifs géométriques rectilignes; et, naturellement, il les traite parfois avec un sens aigu de la caricature (le sanglier-enseigne des monnaies armoricaines, par exemple: Figure 7).

Du point de vue de l'analyse des motifs, le travail essentiel, qui se fera sur les monnaies incomplètes comme sur les complètes, sera double: (1) identifier et dénommer les motifs nés de la décomposition du modèle pour trouver les règles de leur composition en un ensemble, dresser la liste de ces motifs, soit réalistes, soit inventés et purement décoratifs; (2) chercher ceux qui se trouvent également sur des oeuvres d'art d'autres catégories et isoler du même coup ceux qui seraient la création des artistes monétaires ou employés seulement par eux. Quand ce travail sera fait, on pourra déterminer la place exacte qu'occupent les monnaies dans l'ensemble de l'art celtique ancien.

Or, un tel travail se heurte à un obstacle sérieux mais qu'il n'est pas impossible de surmonter: c'est le caractère fréquemment incomplet de ces images monétaires. Les effigies des monnaies celtiques, en effet, sont souvent incomplètes, de plusieurs manières, en surface et en épaisseur: le flan est plus petit que le coin gravé (Figure 1, a)[3], le flan est mal placé dans les coins et frappé incomplètement au droit et au revers (Figure 1, c); le coin étant usé ou encrassé, l'image est en partie floue (Figure 1, c); la monnaie elle-même, enfin, est usée par le temps. Très souvent, même pour les plus belles monnaies d'or, l'image frappée est nettement incomplète par rapport au coin gravé; c'est alors une question de savoir pourquoi on gravait de si beaux coins pour n'en tirer couramment, notamment pour le droit, qu'une image incomplète; il y avait sans doute la nécessité d'économiser le métal, mais aussi une indifférence étrange à l'égard du travail artistique, parfois de grande valeur, réalisé par le graveur du coin (c'est d'ailleurs une autre question, de savoir pourquoi on gravait sur les monnaies antiques, par exemple sur les grecques et les gauloises, de si belles images, de véritables oeuvres d'art et même de grand art).

Quoiqu'il en soit, nous possédons un certain nombre de monnaies celtiques à image complète, et parmi les plus belles (Figure 1, d). La grande masse, toutefois, des monnaies trouvées en trésors, comme les milliers de pièces des trésors de Jersey, sont incomplètes ou floues ou les deux à la fois. Certes, l'archéologue est habitué à s'occuper d'objets incomplets ou abîmés. L'historien de l'art antique, aussi. Le numismate, non: il prend la monnaie telle qu'elle est. L'historien de l'art des monnaies celtiques, qui est une espèce de spécialiste en train de naître, ne peut se contenter ni de trop rares pièces complètes ni des innombrables pièces incomplètes. On trouvera donc ci-après la définition d'une méthode pour compléter en toute sécurité scientifique, avec une certitude parfaite, les coins complets que nous ne connaissons que par des monnaies incomplètes.

Déjà un numismate français, Marcel Baille, avait eu, en 1945, l'idée d'assembler des morceaux de plusieurs pièces incomplètes pour retrouver toute l'image originale[4]. Il a fait l'expérience avec des monnaies "à la croix" du Languedoc, qui sont particulièrement et systématiquement incomplètes. Je pense qu'il a opéré avec des pièces issues de coins différents car l'assemblage n'est pas parfait: M. Baille a découpé matériellement des pièces incomplètes (sept pour le droit) en morceaux qu'il a assemblés, ne pouvant juxtaposer les pièces, pour obtenir une seule monnaie complète. Le résultat n'est pas très satisfaisant et l'expérience ne saurait évidemment être répétée sans des sacrifices inadmissibles.

Depuis cette époque, nous avons appris, grâce aux travaux de J.-B. Colbert de Beaulieu, que nous pouvons reconnaître avec certitude les pièces, à images complètes ou incomplètes, sorties d'un même coin. Dès lors, il suffit de calquer sur des photographies toutes les images incomplètes issues d'un même coin et de superposer ensuite ces calques pour obtenir sur un dernier calque une image beaucoup plus complète que chacune des pièces incomplètes et, si l'on est favorisé par la chance, une image tout à fait complète, qui nous restitue le coin originel sans aucune erreur possible pour les contours des motifs, avec parfois une marge d'erreur inévitable pour le relief car, ici, l'exactitude dépend de la bonne qualité de la frappe et du bon état de conservation de la monnaie. La figure 6 illustre le procédé graphique. Il va de soi que seules des pièces du même coin doivent être utilisées si l'on veut atteindre une exactitude absolue (j'ai donné Fig. 7 pour le revers, un exemple de ce qu'il ne faut pas faire: compléter une pièce en pointillé d'après une ou plusieurs autres du même type mais non du même coin. L'exiguïté des

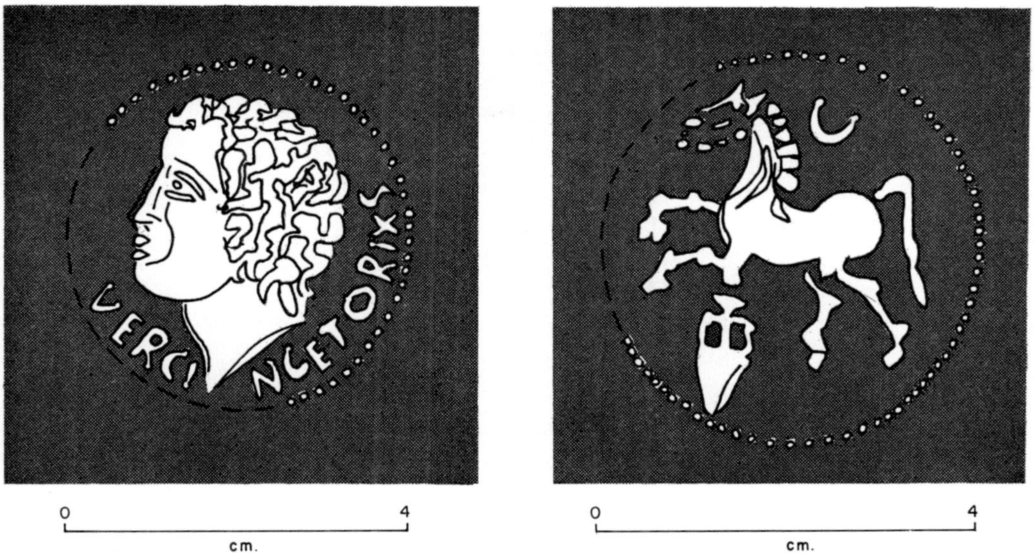

FIG. 2. Statère d'or de Vercingétorix, complété graphiquement à l'aide de 6 pièces pour le droit et de 6 pièces pour le revers, issues des mêmes coins. (Dessins A. Marguet).

motifs ne fait que rendre plus grave l'inexactitude la plus infime de forme ou de mise en place).

J'ai donc tenté l'expérience sur des monnayages bien étudiés, dont les coins différents sont maintenant connus, chacun étant représenté par plusieurs pièces au moins, qui sont toutes publiées: le monnayage de Vercingétorix et celui des *Parisii*. La tentative a réussi et nous a restitué une monnaie complète de Vercingétorix (Fig. 2)[5], droit et revers (mises à part quelques perles du grènetis périphérique) et au moins une pièce complète ou presque complète de chacune des six classes sur sept que compte le très beau monnayage des *Parisii* (Figs. 1, e, et 3–5).

FIG. 3. Droit du statère d'or de la classe I, la plus ancienne, des *Parisii*, complété graphiquement à l'aide de 3 pièces issues du même coin. Voir figs. 1, a, et 8, a–d.

FIG. 4. Statère d'or de la classe V des *Parisii,* complété graphiquement à l'aide de 10 pièces pour le droit et 3 pour le revers, issues des mêmes coins. Voir fig. 1, e.

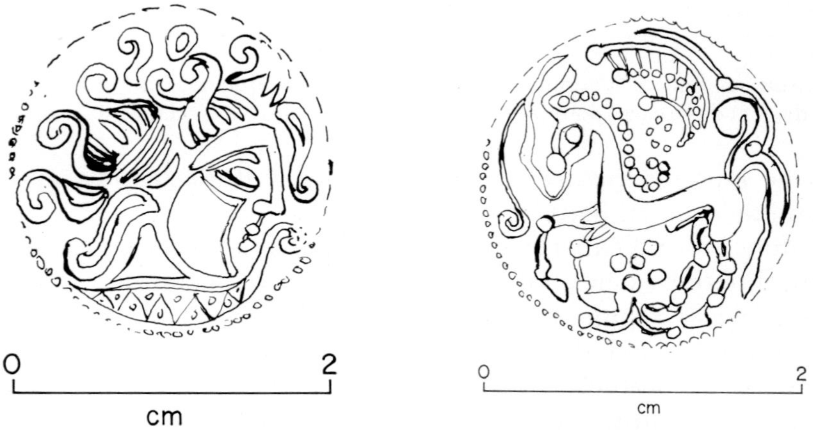

FIG. 5. Droit et revers de deux quarts de statère de la classe V des *Parisii,* complétés graphiquement à l'aide de 2 pièces pour le droit et 3 pour le revers, issues des mêmes coins.

Les conditions nécessaires à une telle opération sont, toutefois, difficiles à réunir dans la grande majorité des cas: il faut tout d'abord disposer de plusieurs monnaies issues d'un même coin et seul le numismate peut fournir ce matériel à l'historien de l'art; or, on sait que souvent les monnaies gauloises d'une même famille ont voyagé dans toute la Gaule et se trouvent dispersées dans des musées ou des collections très nombreux: le numismate doit les trouver, reconnaître les pièces identiques, nous procurer des moulages ou des photographies réduites strictement à la même échelle, sans quoi la superposition des calques est vouée à l'échec. Ce travail d'enquête est rendu d'autant plus difficile que les publications numismatiques reproduisent généralement les pièces de types différents à raison d'une par type, et non toutes les pièces d'un même type reconnues du même coin. D'autre part, il faut que les pièces issues d'un même coin qu'on a pu rassembler aient été frappées assez différemment pour offrir toutes les parties de l'image complète. Enfin, il faut que la frappe ait été bonne, sans encrassement ou usure du coin et que la monnaie elle-même ne soit pas usée. Et il est rare qu'on dispose de plus de cinq ou six, parfois dix pièces reconnues du même coin (surtout pour le revers), dans l'état actuel de la recherche des coins, tout au moins.

L'historien de l'art choisira, pour commencer ce travail lent et difficile, les plus belles parmi les monnaies gauloises: outre celles des *Parisii*, les armoricaines, d'or, d'argent ou de bronze. Elles présentent en effet des images d'une composition à la fois riche et savante, faites de motifs tantôt propres aux monnaies, tantôt analogues à ceux que comportent d'autres objets d'art celtique (Fig. 6). Complètes, ces monnaies sont des oeuvres d'art originales, interprétations celtiques de modèles grecs, à divers degrés d'évolution, et leur composition permet, par exemple, d'étudier la coexistence de motifs statiques combinés avec des motifs dynamiques, combinaisons fréquentes sur d'autres oeuvres postérieures au Premier style (Fig. 7). On peut reconnaître aussi, sur les pièces des *Parisii*, des motifs issus de la chevelure d'Apollon: esses, spirales, mèches, spirales à mèche accolée, esses à mèche accolée, esses percées à un bout, "haricots" percés, et des motifs de remplissage qui sont courants, par exemple, dans les différents styles celtiques (Fig. 8). D'autres motifs sont propres aux monnaies, par exemple l'espèce de conque développée des quarts de statère de la plus belle classe du monnayage parisien (Fig. 5) ou le filet visible sur le revers des autres classes (Fig. 4) ou le signe naviforme sur le droit du dit quart de statère (Fig. 5).

Cette méthode élémentaire, fondée sur le dessin, ne permet pas seulement de nous rendre une image monétaire qu'aucun être humain n'a peut-être vue (pour peu que toutes les pièces de l'émission aient été frappées incomplètement commes celles qui nous sont parvenues, ce qui est vraisemblable puisque la quantité de métal était constante pour une même émission) après l'auteur du coin dont elle est issue et les ouvriers qui s'en sont servis: elle doit fournir aussi à l'historien de l'art celtique un abondant matériel d'oeuvres de qualité, qui risque d'enrichir considérablement la connaissance des deux dernières périodes de la Tène. Seulement, ce matériel ne sera obtenu que par le concours apporté par le numismate à l'archéologue et au prix d'un double et énorme travail d'enquête et d'analyse. On voudra bien n'en trouver ici qu'un modeste commencement, avec les premiers éléments d'une terminologie des motifs, qui reste à établir[7].

La tâche à accomplir, qui sera de longue haleine, devra comprendre les opérations suivantes: sélectionner les monnaies complètes parmi celles qui présentent une qualité artistique; parmi ces dernières toujours, compléter sur calque les monnaies incomplètes, après reconnaissance des coins; d'après l'une et l'autre série, dresser la liste des motifs isolés, soit réalistes, soit d'invention décorative; étudier les principes et les caractères de la composition d'ensemble de chaque image; comparer

Fig. 6. Droit d'une monnaie armoricaine (*Osismii*) : quatre pièces issues d'un même coin et, en bas, à droite, la monnaie complétée par superposition des quatre calques (seule, la petite feuille de droite, en haut, est reconstituée par analogie). Les légères divergences de traits sur les quatre dessins incomplets sont dues au fait que ceux-ci ont été calqués non sur des photographies mais sur des frottis de pièces qui avaient été frappées plus ou moins fortement et dans un coin qui a dû s'user progressivement. (Dessins A. Marguet).

Fig. 7. Droit et revers d'une monnaie armoricaine (*Osismii*), complétés graphiquement à l'aide de 2 pièces pour le droit (BN 6555, 6559); pour le revers, presque toute l'image est donée par BN 6571, les parties en pointillé ont été reconstituées approximativement à l'aide de pièces du même type mais issues de coins légèrement différents: BN 6555 quasi complète, 6560, 6563, 6570, 6572. Si bien que l'emplacement exact de la petite boucle de gauche n'est pas tout à fait connu; cette façon de faire est évidement beaucoup moins sûre.—*A droite*, le revers avec ses trois éléments reconstitués, dont deux sont statiques: le motif symétrique du haut, composé de deux "têtes coupées" à l'envers, entourées de tiges feuillues se réunissant en haut en une sorte de fleuron, et, en bas, le sanglier-enseigne et l'aigle—et dont l'un est dynamique: le cheval à tête humaine cabré ou en plein galop (mouvement dans le sens des aiguilles d'une montre) avec un motif de remplissage, plutôt qu'une petite aile, au-dessus du dos.—*A gauche*, le droit avec deux éléments statiques, la tête centrale et le sanglier et un motif d'encadrement qui, lui, est libre et dynamique: trois "têtes coupées" et des tiges feuillues, se suivant vers la droite et disposées dans le même sens. C'est le procédé de composition inverse de celui du revers.

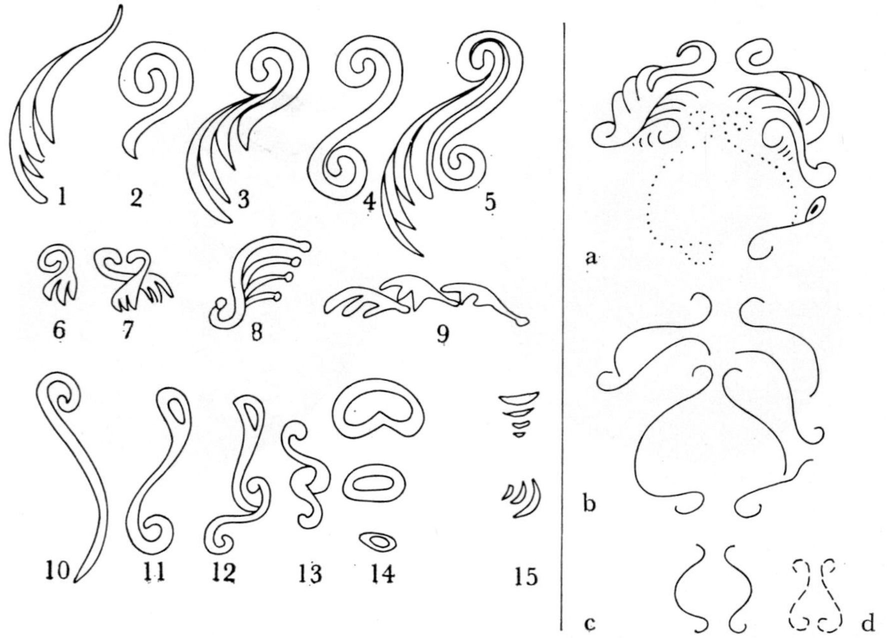

FIG. 8. Quelques motifs isolés tirés de monnaies parisiennes (1 à 7, 10 à 15), danubienne (8, 9), armoricaines (a, b, c). 1: mèche; 2: spirale; 3 et 6, 8: spirale chevelue; 4: esse; 5: esse à mèche accolée; 7: esses à mèches accolées, entrecroisées; 9: suite de spirales à mèches accolées, simplifiées; 10: spirale à queue; 11: esse percée; 12: esse percée et esse combinées; 13: esses combinées; 14: haricots percés issus de la boucle de cheveux; 15: motifs de remplissage; — a, b, c: schéma progressivement simplifié de la chevelure du droit de la classe I des *Parisii* (fig. 2 et pl. I, a), redressée à la verticale. Le motif principal de cette composition est une sorte de fausse lyre, surmontée de deux accolades superposées (en d, schéma de la "lyre" issue de la palmette grecque).

enfin, sur le plan des motifs et de la composition, avec les autres oeuvres d'art celtiques. Peut-être, d'ailleurs, les numismates retireront-ils un bénéfice de la reconstitution graphique des coins à laquelle ils auront bien voulu contribuer: la connaissance de l'image complète peut aider à identifier plus facilement les types et les coins de monnaies incomplètement frappées, mal venues ou trop usées.

J'espère déjà avoir montré l'intérêt, souvent allégué mais non prouvé jusqu'ici, des monnaies celtiques et, particulièrement, gauloises et bretonnes, pour l'historien de l'art celtique. Il ne réside pas seulement dans leur qualité, leur variété, leur nombre et dans la possibilité d'une chronologie: il tient encore au fait que ces compositions exiguës présentent des caractères et même des motifs qu'elles partagent avec d'autres oeuvres d'art celtique. Elles font partie intégrante de ce grand processus d'assimilation, de libération et d'évolution qui, à partir de modèles méditerranéens et de motifs empruntés, a produit chez les peuples celtiques un art subtil, raffiné, original. Ni les Scythes, ni les Ibères n'ont rien eu de comparable: seuls les Celtes ont produit et accumulé ces trésors d'art, qui expriment au mieux leur culture et leur diversité.

Notes

Les renvois dans les notes sont imprimés en caractères italiques gras.

1. Malraux, A. (1950). *Psychologie de l'art,* III: La monnaie de l'absolu, Paris, pp. 202–203.

2. Bianchi Bandinelli, R. (1956). "Organicità e astrazione", Milan, pp. 17–38, Fig. 1–24, PLANCHES II–VII.

Discussion sur la qualité artistique des monnaies gauloises: J.-B. Colbert de Beaulieu, (1948). "La trouvaille de monnaies celtiques de Saint-Jacques de-la-Lande", dans *Revue belge de numismatique,* **94,** pp. 64–71.—Voir mes articles sur L'art des Celtes et la Gaule, dans *Art de France,* IV, 1964, pp. 26–27 "L'art des monnaies gauloises" dans *Comptes rendus Acad. Inscript.* 1972, pp. 633–648.

3. C'est le cas des monnaies des *Volcae Tectosages* du Languedoc, dites "monnaies à la croix": le flan, découpé approximativement au carré, est toujours nettement plus petit que le coin. Voir la note suivante.

4. Sur cette expérience, quelques (1945) lignes dans la *Revue numismatique,* **5**e série, 8, p. LXXI;

exposé par J.-B. Colbert de Beaulieu, "Notules de numismatique celtique III, 7.— Numismatique de l'Aquitaine: la frappe des monnaies à la croix", dans (1954) *Ogam,* **VI,** pp. 126–130, PLANCHE V, Fig. 1–5 en bas.

Le puzzle réalisé par M. Baille est imparfait: la branche verticale de la croix est gauchie, probablement parce qu'il a disposé de pièces de coins légèrement différents, quoique du même type. L'expérience a toutefois le grand intérêt de nous révéler à quel point ces monnaies à la croix étaient incomplètes: seule la partie centrale du coin gravé était utilisée, pour des flans découpés en forme grossièrement quadrangulaire.

5. C'est le coin de droit D2 et le coin de revers D1, couplés sur une même monnaie, de mes planches montrant tous les coins connus du monnayage de Vercingétorix, graphiquement restituées,

dans l'article de Colbert de Beaulieu, J.-B. (1970). "Les monnaies de Vercingétorix, Nouvelles acquisitions" (II), dans *Gallia,* **28,** pp. 1–9, PLANCHE 5 et 6 (sur le dessin du droit, PLANCHE 5, la partie gauche du grènetis avait été portée par erreur: je donne ici le dessin rectifié, Fig. 1).

6. Un grand nombre des monnaies connues des *Parisii* sont reproduites dans l'ouvrage de Colbert de Beaulieu, J.-B. (1970). *Les monnaies gauloises des Parisii,* Paris, Imprimerie nationale, p. 171, Fig. 65, PLANCHE 1.

7. Le dessin de motifs isolés a été commencé mais à des fins d'exégèse mythographique par le regretté Lancelot Lengyel, dans un ouvrage posthume intitulé *Le secret des Celtes* (éditions Robert Morel, Forcalquier, 1969) et dont les illustrations photographiques sont tirées, pour la plupart, de *L'Art gaulois dans les médailles,* du même auteur (Corvina, Montrouge, 1954), dont les planches restent un admirable instrument de travail.

Résumé

Celtic Coins, their Art and Styles: Material offered for a Study.

Celtic coins were not, till lately, often considered as works of art. They were seen as imitations, more or less clumsily done, of Greek coins; and of Roman coins next, but still maladroit. Their imperfections of manufacture greatly discouraged deeper study: for various reasons inherent in their fabric and technique, designs appear on most of them not in full but incomplete.

In the last twenty years, the situation has been retrieved owing to two main causes: in studies of art and in numismatics. On the one hand, the coins have attracted art-historians. The schematic, expressionist character, caricature and even "abstract" art, evinced in their imagery, has gained an appreciation through recalling aspects of modern art today. Numismatists, on the other, led in France by J.-B. Colbert de Beaulieu, can study the coins of Gaul through seriations revealed by die-links (as has long been done with classical coins), on the lines of modern science.

Gaulish coins, from a start at least well back in the IIIrd century, only ceased to be struck towards the end of the Ist B.C. Their range was coeval thus with the main middle and final periods of La Tène art in Gaul: those of the Free and Plastic Styles and of the final style ensuing, which reverts under Roman influence to the character of the Early Style, one of severe regularity and of symmetry. Plastic by nature, as coins, they require an art to suit their size: even more than most of the rest of Celtic works, an art of small scale. Of their models brought from outside Gaul, the chief is the gold Macedonian stater: obverse, a male head, which soon undergoes decomposition, and is recomposed into quite original patterns; reverse, a *biga* (chariot and two-horse team), which reduces soon to one horse, always recognizable in himself. Their development gives the coinages, like the rest of La Tène creations, an art with a unity of style and design throughout their creators' world. Yet within it, like the rest again, they run to styles that are regional: Armorican, Belgic and British, others besides.

Coins that bear their designs complete are ready for immediate study. From the mass that have them incomplete (on flans misplaced, or struck too weakly, or often anyhow too small), one must first pick examples that are struck from the same die. On recognizing these, one can next proceed to reconstitute designs, by a simple graphic method, giving perfectly exact results, in a synthesis of their incomplete appearances. One traces these in succession on to thin transparent sheets, superimposes all the sheets, with their common elements coinciding, and, on a final sheet above them, traces the whole of what they show. If they supplement each other fully enough to combine the elements totally, this final tracing will give the authentic image of the whole design—as the strikers of the coins and the die-engraver himself originally saw it, and as no one else, perhaps, has seen it since. The art-historian of coins using this method, one ought to add, must be furnished by numismatists with thorough documentations, and himself have means to get everything brought—drawings, engravings, photographs, rubbings—to a scale strictly identical throughout.

Material thus assembled can be offered for study as follows: comparison of numerous coin designs, complete, with other La Tène work; analysis for detection of resemblances and differences; inventory of the elements, forms, motifs, displayed on the coins, giving them numbers to identify every component of the repertory; and distinguishing of those that are borrowings from non-Celtic models, those from purely Celtic art, and those that the die-engravers invented.

Examples already studied now include coins of Vercingetorix, of the Parisii, and of peoples in Armorica.

Discussion

Speakers:— Professor Hawkes, Mr Allen, Dr Kruta, Professor Duval.

HAWKES: I am greatly impressed to see the drawings *not* embellished beyond the outlines—those on the dies as we actually see them. It shows an admirable rigour to keep out details actually absent. As for analysing of the elements, giving them numbers, and comparing them—with elements in the non-coin art—these are things that will take some time! The element or sign beneath the head on coins of the Parisii (a *signe*, not a *cygne*) might surely be a boat or ship: we all know the Gallo-Roman boatmen of the Seine, and Caesar had ships in 54 built by the Meldi, of Meaux on the confluent Marne, to descend the Seine for his voyage to Britain. But I will turn from details to dates. When did Celtic coinage commence? This is a matter of silver, I think: Macedonian and Danube-Celtic. Would Allen give an opinion?

ALLEN: There is a hoard found in Hungary including Greek coins that date it, to the end of the IVth century or the very first years of the IIIrd, in which Philip II's Macedonian silver tetradrachms have their earliest Danubian imitations. In Northern Italy, a hoard with a coin from Rome, very near 210, has North Italian Celtic coins, much worn and not the first of their kind, and therefore allows the first to have been of the middle IIIrd century. And I think it was not long after (though some disagree) that Celts in the Languedoc—from the Greeks near them at Rhoda (coins with the cross of a four-petalled rose)—struck their first silver *monnaies à la croix*, as claimed from two hoards in Spain. As these, inland at Valeria and Griente, have Roman coins that are dated, and as the coins *à la croix* are close in design to the Rhoda prototypes—besides being the only ones on record in Spain at all—the dispute is on the hoards' integrity, which allows of possible doubt. Accepting closeness in design to prototypes as meaning closeness also in time, I would think the dating is valid. And accepting it in Bohemia allows the early IInd century as an opening date for Celtic coins there: half a century after North Italy's start, and a century after the Danube's. Yet there is still nothing so firm for first imitations of the gold Philippus. No one has found an early one of these in a context in any way datable. I myself, as an opinion that is only an opinion, would start them in the late IIIrd: within the IIIrd century surely. I would put many more of the imitations in the IInd. But amongst the later ones only, as yet, are there firmly datable contexts.

May I revert to Duval's drawings, now, and his mode of representation? It interests me all the more because of experiments of my own. And of the two planes of the coins' surface, the flat and the relief, I have found it better not to outline the relief, but to darken it. This avoids showing the edge of its plane as a line (which is artificial, because really this is inclined and not abrupt). I should be glad to hear opinions.

KRUTA: Il serait bon d'adopter ici une convention générale. Quand les numismates font des frottis, ils expriment le relief en noir (*they darken the relief when they show it by rubbings*). Mais, en dessin, il me paraît plus logique de le montrer clair (*in drawings, better to leave the relief clear, and darken the ground*). C'est la façon que j'adopte moi-même pour faire mes dessins. Car on peut alors dessiner des détails au trait sur les reliefs, ce qui est impossible avec le procédé inverse. (*One can then draw any details, on the reliefs, in dark line: impossible if one uses the opposite method.*) Il y a une difficulté parfois à interpréter les dessins; une convention simple pourrait le rendre plus facile (*a standard convention could make interpretation easier*).

ALLEN: To darken the ground brings a difficulty too: you have to know the exterior limit of the design. It need not even be circular. An enclosing fillet or border of dots (a *grènetis*) may define it, but the border might be double or triple; one can never be sure what has missed the flan.

DUVAL: One could darken the ground and make it fill a purely conventional area, of a standard size on the page, enclosing whatever relief one has. On this, being white, one can then draw its details in—just as on objects cast in openwork, where the parts to darken are the open ones. One would thus gain a unity of convention.

HAWKES: An *unité de convention* for drawings—rubbings apart—deciding what shall be white and what be darkened, should be agreed and kept by everyone. The question is fundamental.

13

Some Contrasts in Gaulish and British Coins

Derek Allen

London

Mr Allen had passed the proofs of what follows before his untimely death (1975).

Introduction: the key word is Regionalism

The identification of regional styles in La Tène Celtic coins is not a straightforward matter. The very pronounced regionalism of the coins is in the main a reflection of the fact that different regions chose different models to copy. The traditional bond with a prototype, never more than half-forgotten, limited coin designers' freedom of invention, and their ability to reflect contemporary fashions in other art. Within the art of coins, regional and temporal styles are detectable; the links with other art forms current in the same areas and times, are tenuous. In the history of Celtic art as a whole, coins stand apart.

I shall here draw attention to four selected aspects of the coins. The first shows how, in different parts of the Celtic world, coin designers faced with similar problems reached similar solutions. The second, in contrast, takes the most familiar of the models, the gold stater of the Macedonian king Philip II (359–336) copied in the west from the IInd century, and shows how within the basic pattern it supplied—obverse, laureate head of Apollo; reverse, two-horse chariot (with legend)—differences grew up, essentially regional. The third picks up some of the scattered instances where the coin design can be shown to have positive links with other Celtic art forms. The fourth, through applying detailed study to a chosen British example, shows how fallacious style may be as a measure of chronology. Some differences emerge between coins in Gaul and in Britain.

That coins stand apart may be perceived from the minor, almost negligible, role played by coins in our Oxford colloquy till M. Duval gave his address on them. It is true that in Celtic lands (apart perhaps from a few direct copies from the Greek) coins did not yet exist during most of the times discussed. But through what I hope I am allowed to call Middle La Tène times, and on into Later La Tène, coins existed in their millions; altogether, indeed, hundreds of millions. The distinctions which we can draw between Middle La Tène and Later (or II and III or C and D) are in coin art not detectable as such. Despite exceptions, the system of coin art is, much more often than not, self-centred. Its craft was confined within a repetitive and mass-producing industry.

The unity of approach among Celtic coin designers. Figure 1

To show this, I have chosen 10 pairs of Celtic coins, each from a different country, yet each containing similar elements. Treatment of heads, their hair, their wreaths, of the shape of horses' heads, duplication of legs, adoption of a wreath as a sole design, or as background to another—all recur in areas so remote from one another that direct interconnection is excluded. Thus, the conventions of the art, where problems of design were similar, produced results remarkably similar, all within a Celtic idiom. Minor ornaments or symbols, too, recur in different contexts: wheels, crescents, harps, tribrachs, swastikas, pentacles. Some such devices can be standard fill-in ornaments, as in many forms of primitive art; yet the *répertoire*, although not exclusively Celtic, was so widespread among the Celts that it must include specifically Celtic emblems.

The almond-eyed human heads, on innumerable coins, have a certain hardness or dryness of features, common to every region in expressing a "Celtic physiognomy". And over wide areas, too, there are common mythological beasts. One is the man-headed horse, found all over northern Gaul; in Britain, it acquires a sphinx-like form with wings, while in Slovakia it becomes a female centaur with wings for arms. The horse is a beast common to almost all Celtic coins. And besides the numerous boars—to which I return under 3 below—there are the boar-effigy standards, seen on rare Celtiberian coins, as well as much more commonly in Central Gaul, North-western or Armorican Gaul, and Britain. Thus the boar is supra-regional, even if the method of representing him may acquire a regional character. There is a nameless beast also, which appears throughout the Celtic world, embodying horror and ferocity; it is neither lion, wolf, nor boar, but combines the more terrifying features of each.

We may first note, therefore, that within the relatively limited range which coin art can offer there are elements of design and repertory showing a common tradition of forms, throughout the regions where coinage in La Tène civilisation flourished.

The foregoing three paragraphs now represent my spoken words. My 10 pairs of coins, each with reverse beside its obverse, made an array of 40 types altogether. I believe they fulfilled my purpose. A printed page, however, although it certainly could contain them, would do so only on a scale unduly small for appreciating details, so would serve my purpose much less fully than my other plates of coins. The maximum showing that I gave is therefore here reduced to a minimum: setting a coin of Armorican Gaul, in typical bold and imaginative style (reverse having horse above boar), beside one of Britain's extreme reductions of the Philip design Fig. 2 (cf. 3: 6, 12). So I omit my intended no. 12 of Noricum (pp. 271–2, crested helmet).

FIG. 1.

1, Silver stater, Armorican: Coriosolites (Côtes-du-Nord). One version of the style's development. On all of it, see J. B. Colbert de Beaulieu, in *Annales de Bretagne* and listed to 1960 by P. R. Giot, *Brittany*, p. 212. N. V. L. Rybot, Armorican Art, *Soc. Jersiaise* 1952, saw in Jersey six classes.

2. Silver stater, S. British: Durotriges (Dorset), later than 60 B.C. "Philip" design, head to r. but horse now to l., from gold Gallo-Belgic (cf. Fig. 3, no. 5) through British, degraded in succession. Cf. Fig. 3: 6, 12.

Photos. Ashmolean Museum, Oxford. On former no. 12, see text above.

THE VARIETY WITHIN A SINGLE TRADITIONAL TYPE. FIGURE 3.

Notwithstanding what I have said, there are notable regional differences in the development of single models. The easiest type by which to show this is the gold stater of Philip II (Fig. 2). It is possible to detect more than a dozen regional styles within France in the treatment of what is in essence the same design, a beardless head with laurel wreath on the obverse and a two-horse chariot or biga with charioteer on the reverse. It is not possible in the published version of this paper to illustrate as many examples as were shown when it was delivered, but the twelve magnificent photographs on Fig. 3 will indicate the range. Anyone who wishes to go further into this aspect must consult the specialist literature.

An imitative coinage in principle goes through at least two and sometimes three stages. It starts with plain copies, substitutes for the original. In time deviations occur fortuitously in the copying, and may take on a regional flavour, but at this stage are not intended. In the second stage deliberate differences are introduced, so that the imitative coinage acquires a personality of its own, still in the tradition of the original, but self-consciously distinct and identifiable. Often this stage introduces an element of disintegration into the pattern. The third stage consists of the reintegration of the fragments of the pattern into a newly conceived whole. All three stages occurred in the treatment of Philip II's stater in Gaul and Britain.

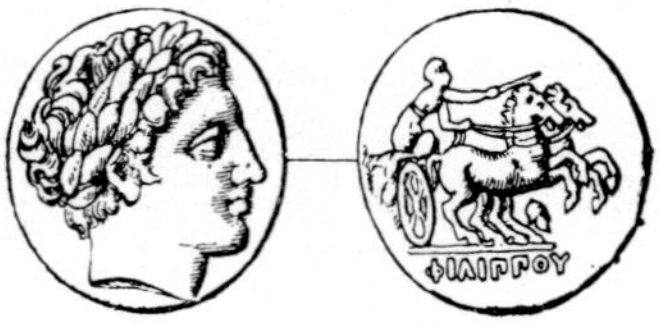

FIG. 2. Gold Stater of Philip II of Macedon
Obverse, laurel-wreathed head of Apollo
Reverse, chariot and two-horse team (*biga*)

With the first stage we are not here much concerned. Some copies, such as one in the British Museum, found at Reims, are barely distinguishable from the originals; others, of as good weight, have acquired individual traits. Thus, on versions of exactly the same coin from Thrace (often treated mistakenly as Helvetian), the charioteer, to make him locally credible, is shown seated, not as he is on the originals, standing[1].

It is in the second stage that regional characteristics first obtrude. On a coin from Picardy (Fig. 3, 1 obverse, 7 reverse), a relatively early one, the face is bearded and the wreath is lost in a profusion of curls, while the charioteer on the reverse, still driving a biga, wears his at feminine length. But we may contrast the head with a later coin, probably originally from the Côte d'Or (Fig. 3, 2), where appreciably more of the original head has survived, or with a reverse of much the same date, but from Caux, where all that survives is the concept of the horse (Fig. 3, 8).

Although regional styles are found throughout "long-haired" Gaul, it is in Armorican Gaul, in and on the borders of Brittany, that the most vigorous and distinctive styles occur. There is only room for a few examples here, two of heads, from Manche and Finistère respectively (Fig. 3, 3–4), and three of human-headed horses, which are particularly characteristic of the region (Fig. 3, 9–11). While the details of each are distinct, it will, I hope, be apparent that there is an element of style in common. This style reached its zenith in the very remarkable coins of the Veneti (Vannes). The human-headed horse, incidentally, is not confined to Armorican Gaul, but occurs in almost the same form amongst the Treviri.

Another regional style which is particularly distinctive is that of Belgic Gaul. This begins with large flat coins of the Ambiani on which the head carries a head-dress of S-shaped locks (Fig. 3, 5). This striking type, obviously immensely popular at the time, was much copied; indeed, the coins of the Parisii, with which M. Duval has dealt, were strongly influenced by this model. But in Belgic Gaul, and later in Britain, where the type too was copied, the pattern disintegrates into separate

FIGURE 3. Celtic coins: Designs derived from the Philip II Gold Stater

All coins of gold, some base, except nos. 6 and 10, which are of base silver. Scales vary, and cannot be given for each individual coin.

1 Half-stater of Ambiani (early: T8380)
2 Stater of type as found in hoard from Tayac: possibly of Aedui
3 Quarter-stater from Unelli (T6963)
4 Stater of Osismii (T6578)
5 Stater of Ambiani (developed: T7878)
6 Stater of Durotriges, Dorset in Britain (M317)
7 Half-stater of Ambiani (early: T8380; reverse of no. 1)
8 Stater perhaps of Caleti (Pays de Caux, Seine-Maritime: T8694)
9 Stater perhaps of Osismii
10 Stater of Unelli (TJ1)
11 Stater of Osismii (T6578; reverse type of no. 4)
12 Stater of Durotriges, Dorset in Britain (M32)

T=H. de la Tour, *Atlas des monnaies gauloises*, Paris 1892.

M=R. P. Mack, *The Coinage of Ancient Britain*, London 1953; 2nd ed. 1964.

Photographs by kindness of Mrs. Marie P. König, Saarbrücken

elements, all deriving from fragments of the original (for British examples see Fig. 3, 6 obverse and 12 reverse, in silver and gold respectively, the Durotriges in Dorset).

The third stage is the reintegration of these *disjecta membra*. This is characteristic of Britain, but the process is not confined to it. I have recently published a remarkable case amongst the Suessiones of Soissons (Aisne), whose coins with the name *Criciru* were first struck about 60 B.C.[2] The designer reinterpreted the detached arms of the charioteer, all of him that had survived disintegration, into a representation of a special type of fibula. It was well enough done to give a new fixed point in the chronology of fibulae.

This circumnavigation of Gaul and Britain could be pursued and a bewildering selection of styles presented, each characteristic of a people or region. An equivalent itinerary could be pursued in the Danube basin, where, however, the model was Philip II's silver tetradrachms. But I do not think it could be said of any of the regions from which coins such as these have come that there is any detectable characteristic common between the style of its coins and of its other La Tène antiquities. It would be pleasing if it were so, but it is not.

Particular links between coins and Celtic religious art Figure 4.

There are nevertheless a few individual correspondences between coins and other objects of Celtic art; though comparatively rare they are not without interest, and, as the examples below show, may sometimes have associations with other manifestations of Celtic religion.

(a) On the neck of the head on coins of the Aulerci Eburovices, of Evreux (1), upside down, is the symbol of a boar (1a). Its form and detail (2) afford comparison with the boar on the celebrated effigy from Euffigneix (Haute-Marne), where it is sideways (3) on the trunk beneath the male head with torc, between the stylized eyes on the trunk's two sides. The boar, like the wheel among the symbols mentioned above (p. 266), frequently recurs amongst the monuments of Celtic religious art[3]. Heads on Armorican coins have boars among the symbols shown in their hair; the head from Callians (Var) has animal emblems on its cheeks.

(b) My second example is pleasing; it has not had wide enough notice.

In the region west of Lyon, home of the Celtic Segusiavi, is found a silver coin (5) with the legend SEGVSIAVS ARVS. It is derived from a Roman denarius dating from after Caesar's conquest (4). The denarius reverse shows Hercules, carrying on his shoulder a miniature trophy on a pole: not a popular symbol in the conquered Gaul of the 40's. So in the Gaulish version a good wooden Celtic god takes its place. It is beautifully engraved, with the features of the torc and mantle clear. Among the Celtic wooden images (6) from the sacred sources of the Seine (barely 150 km off to north) are figures similar in all essential respects[4].

FIG. 4. Coins and figures from Gaul, showing connections with Celtic Religion

1 Coin, gold, head to left; on neck boar-symbol inverted ($\frac{1}{1}$); Aulerci Eburovices, of Evreux (reverse, boar below horse).

1a The same (obverse) turned to show the boar-symbol standing.

2 Enlargement of 1a (5:2), for comparison with boar on 3.

3 Effigy-pillar, sandstone, Euffigneix (Haute-Marne); boar-symbol in relief on front of trunk. H. 30 cm.: Mus. des Antiquités Nats., St.-Germain (inv. 78243).

4 Roman denarius, after conquest of Gaul; reverse, Hercules bearing trophy. ($\frac{4}{3}$)

5 Coin, silver like 4, inscribed SEGVSIAVS ARVS: Segusiavi, Gaul W. of Lyon; design taken from 4 but trophy replaced by Celtic image ($\frac{4}{3}$).

6 Image, wood, Sources-de-la-Seine. H. 74 cm.: Mus. Archéologique, Dijon (inv. 35).

Photos: Ashmolean (1–2), *S. Germain* (3), *Copenhagen* (4), *British* (5) *and Dijon* (6) *Museums*

(c) My third example, pleasing again, is from Noricum (Austria). On a coin from Celtic Noricum, of SVICCA (Fig. 1, no. 12) is a helmeted Celtic spearman; the crest of his helmet is the figure of an animal (which re-appears enlarged on the coin's reverse). The best analogy to this is on the Gundestrup cauldron (Fig. 5): in the scene of the march in arms, a helmet with bird crest is worn by the leading horseman, one with boar crest by the second, and another similar by the man on foot in front of the

FIG. 5. Sketch of a scene in relief on the Gundestrup silver cauldron, showing soldiers, horse and foot, with crested helmets.

carnyx-blowers (whose instruments are famed for their terrific animal mouths).[5] The coin was in the 1970 Celtic Art Exhibition, Edinburgh (Catalogue no. 19); it invites some further study of the helmets.

STYLISTIC VARIATION WITHIN SINGLE TIME AND PLACE FIGURE 6

The stylistic range of a single coin type, in a single king's reign in which he progressively enlarged his realm, has clearly an interest of its own, and it can at the same time demonstrate the pitfalls of too simple a trust in style as a sign of date. My example will be the gold British staters of Cunobelinus. They exist in sufficient numbers to allow a fairly thorough study. The time-range is approximately A.D. 10–40.

I have studied more than 150 coins; I have so far found 67 obverse dies and 77 reverse dies, in 95 combinations. Quarter-staters give 19 or 20 obverses, and 22 reverses, in 22 combinations[6]. It is possible from this work, which continues, to arrange the dies in a single sequence; some parts of it are proven, others highly probable, and I hope that more examples will prove the whole.

(a) The first coins retain traces on the obverse of the traditional British broken-up and re-arranged face pattern, but with the name of the mint inserted in a central panel. The reverse has a pair of horses or *biga*, with chariot suggested by a wheel beneath. This first type has been found exclusively in Essex.

(b) The main series follows, with obverse changed to an ear of barley. Its earliest coins are those where the ear of barley is shown somewhat

FIG. 6. Gold coins of Cunobelinus, minted at Camulodunum (Colchester); types in succession *c.* A.D. 10–40.

a: early, 2 horses (*biga*) to left. b: "linear" horse to right. c: "wild" horse.

d: "wild" horse with added ring ornament. e: "plastic" horse. f: "classical" horse.

Photos: R. L. Wilkins, F.S.A., Oxford. Coins in British Museum. *See pp.* 272–4 schematically, with a strong central stalk. The horse on the reverse shares many *linear* features with the previous (a, the *biga* type). Distribution of finds is wider now, from Essex and Kent to Oxfordshire.

(c) Following the linear form of the type is one in a very different style. The horse on the reverse is essentially monstrous or *wild*. On the coins of this type, the barley on the obverse has no central stalk—transition from the previous form being shown by certain coins that do have it. A ground-line is added and the legend is now longer; there are now more finds from Kent.

(d) At a certain stage in the "wild" series a *ring ornament* is introduced between the horse's belly and the legend. This is the only part of the range where obverse dies are materially outnumbered by reverse dies.

(e) This ring ornament provides a link with the next group, where the "wild" design gives place to a *plastic* version, with less monstrous features, though still far from classical. The ring itself soon disappears and the design becomes simplified. By now the coinage of Cunobelinus was near its full territorial extension. The style is not far removed from that of the coins of his father, Tasciovanus (approximately 15/10 B.C.–A.D. 10).

(f) There is a direct die-link, however, which shows that the plastic form of the type was followed by yet another, now in a purely *classical* vein, usually with horse to the right, occasionally to the left. At this final stage of the coinage distribution includes Suffolk.

This order of styles may be seen as possessing a certain logic, when established in part by the positive proof of die links, and otherwise by close attention to developing features of detail. But if it were studied (as by me 30 years ago) without that guide to the sequence, very different conclusions could result. The "wild" type would be taken as either primitive or decadent, its coins thus as either the first or the last. In fact it comes in the middle, and probably corresponds with a period of prolific output by the mint, when standards went to the winds. The first two groups of coins, preceding it, could well be the work of a single engraver, or his school. But the wild, plastic, and classical styles, ensuing in succession, certainly each represent different "hands". And these hands can equally be detected in the vast output of Cunobelinus's coins in silver and in bronze.

We should remember that the range of time that the five groups cover is probably some 30 years between about A.D. 10 and 40. If this could not be shown (as it can) on historical grounds, would any art-historian think the range of styles probable, or even possible, in that bracket of time? I wonder. There is much else of interest to be learnt from the chain of evidence. For instance, knowing approximately the full number of dies, we may infer the order of magnitude of the amount of gold coins struck. Cunobelinus cannot have issued less than a million gold coins, each weighing c. 5.39 gm, or two-thirds of a Roman *aureus*; in all, they will have amounted to a weight of about 15 000 Roman pounds of the gold used, or nearer 3 000 pounds of fine gold. But this is not the time or place to pursue this aspect. My remarks and illustrations are no more than an introduction to a subject deserving far more penetrating treatment, but they may serve to show its potentialities.

Notes

Cross-references within the notes are indicated by bold italic type

1. The series comprises staters, distaters and tristaters: see *e.g.* R. Forrer (1908), *Keltische Numismatik der Rhein und Donaulande*, fig. 505.

2. *Germania* 50, 1972, 122–132 (Derek F. Allen, "The Fibula of CRICIRV"), with previous literature of which the chief recent work, in *Revue belge de numismatique* 110, 1964, 69–101, is by J.-B. Colbert de Beaulieu and J. M. Desbordes.

3. The literature in French here is larger than I can quote; among its distinguished contributors, headed by J.-B. Colbert de Beaulieu, is now our colleague P.-M. Duval: most lately in his "L'art des monnaies gauloises", *Comptes rendus . . . Acad. des Inscr. et Belles-Lettres, 1972* (Paris 1973), 633–648. The best conspectus of recent work on the subject altogether is in the 2nd edition of R. Forrer's *Keltische Numismatik der Rhein- und Donauländer*, Band II, edited by K. Castelin, Graz 1969. The *Celtes et Gallo-Romains* of J.-J. Hatt (1970: Geneva, and (London) in English as *Celts and Gallo-Romans*) has a chapter on the gods of Gaul which briefly expounds the Euffigneix symbols (English pp. 271, 315), with plates 61–62; front view again of the effigy-pillar, Exhib. Catalogue plate opp. p. 9; text (Piggott), p. 14. For the coin of Svicca see the monograph by R. Göbl (1973) on Norican coins, *Typologie und Chronologie der Keltischen Münzprägung in Noricum*, Wien.

4. R. Martin and Simone Deyts, *Ex-voto de bois . . . du Sanctuaire des Sources de la Seine* (Dijon, Mus. Arch., 1966); English introduction, Martin, R. (1965). *Antiquity* **39,** (Dec.), 247–252.

5. The scene has often been reproduced. Besides Ole Klindt-Jensen's *Gundestrupkedelet* (Copenhagen, Nationalmuseet, 1961), J.-J. Hatt *see **note 3***) here has it as his Plate 55, with brief interpretation (in the English, p. 315).

6. I have allowed the figures to stand as presented at the Colloquy. The numbers have now increased slightly, but the conclusions unaltered. A full publication will appear in a forthcoming volume of *Britannia* (London).

Résumé

Monnaies gauloises et bretonnes : quelques contrastes.

Les monnaies celtiques forment un secteur à part de l'art celtique: leurs aspects régionaux reflètent la différence des modèles copiés dans les diverses régions et les liens traditionnels avec un prototype limitaient la liberté d'invention des artistes. Pourtant, ces monnaies existaient par millions et centaines de millions.

L'unité des sujets, des motifs et de leur traitement est incontestable d'un bout à l'autre du monde celtique. Il en résulte un style monétaire celtique. Un répertoire des motifs le montrerait clairement. Cheval, sanglier, monstres indéterminés, paraissent partout.

Pourtant, il y a des différences régionales dans le traitement des modèles similaires: par exemple, le statère de Philippe II, dans ses versions gauloises (Nord, *Parisii*, *Aedui*, *Treviri*, *Aulerci Cenomani*), thraces, bretonnes. La recomposition du modèle désintégré en une création originale est remarquable chez les *Suessiones* (monnaie de *Criciru*, à la fibule) et chez les Bretons.

Il y a aussi des correspondances entre monnaies et oeuvres d'art celtiques, au moins dans certains cas particuliers: sans doute le sanglier est-il ici un symbole religieux; le guerrier dont le casque porte un sanglier se trouve sur une monnaie du Norique (*Suicca*) comme sur le chaudron de Gundestrup; sur une monnaie des *Segusiavi* imitant un denier, figure, à la place du trophée porté par Hercule, un dieu celtique en bois avec torque et manteau.

Le degré d'évolution stylistique n'est pas forcément un critère chronologique. L'étude de 150 pièces de *Cunobelinus* (vers 10–40 ap. J.-C.), comportant 67 coins de droit et 77 de revers avec 95 accouplements divers, permet un classement chronologique en partie sûr de ces émissions: or, c'est la dernière en date qui manifeste l'image la plus classique et le style le plus primitif apparaît à la période moyenne, non initiale. D'ailleurs, en l'espace de trente ans, aucun historien de l'art n'oserait proposer une évolution stylistique marquée: il s'agit plutôt d'émissions confiées à des graveurs différents, plus ou moins habiles ou "à la mode". Et *Cunobelinus* peut avoir émis un million de pièces d'or.

Discussion

Speakers:— Professors Duval and Jope, Mr Allen, Dr Schwappach, Mrs Hawkes, Professors Hawkes, Duignan, Piggott, Frey and Klindt-Jensen.

DUVAL: Mr Allen, from the many fine coins he has shown, in their regional developments all over Europe, has insisted on the unity in their ornaments and their style. In some of his examples, too, the design is complete on the flan: even if unaware that some are likenesses due to the use of a single die, I should be struck by the resemblances he has pointed to.

JOPE: I have always taken the view that the history of art has something to learn from the study of coins that is absolutely essential.

ALLEN: The forms used ornamentally on Celtic coins, which could be the basis for a classified study—swords, lyres, wheels, cauldrons, etc.—might amount to as many as 50 or 60.

SCHWAPPACH: Many of the coins shown to us by each of the two speakers, Allen and already Duval, make me want to recall how yesterday, on previous Celtic art, we talked of forms in the Early and Waldalgesheim Styles. Then, the latest we reached were forms of the IVth and IIIrd centuries. So we should now, perhaps on the earliest of the coins next ensuing, expect to find some forms with some relation to those styles, such as whirligigs or lyres resembling Waldalgesheim motifs. How far, in the art of the coins, did those previous styles live on? Might I suggest some work be done on this?

DUVAL: In the work being undertaken now, this certainly has to be studied.

MRS HAWKES: Mr Allen showed examples of pattern that runs to convolutions, which remind me of the Northern art of the Migration Age. There, one talks about signs of the hand of individual masters. Can we talk about similar signs among Celtic coins?

ALLEN: Individual hands are, in a sense, reflected in what you have seen. I would add, however, taking the case of the coins of Cunobelinus, that my third or "wild" phase might not reveal them as clearly as the earlier phases, my first and my second.

HAWKES: Individual masters might be an aid in answering Schwappach too. The Merovingian Frankish Dagobert had his royal *orfèvre en chef*, Saint Éloi, the great master goldsmith Eligius, minting his coins and designing other precious objects too. Would a man who presided over the design of Celtic coins be a man who also designed other objects?

ALLEN: I know of no positive evidence. But what is it you imagine? A goldsmith responsible both for making torques (say) and coins? Or a man who made torques and melted others down to make coins?

DUVAL: The ideas need not exclude each other. Evidence should be searched for.

HAWKES: A second question, on estimating the amount of gold used for Cunobelinus's coinage altogether: how do you do it?

ALLEN: By inference from the number of dies used, and the probable life of the average die, to the total number of coins. Roughly, I suggested, about a million minted in all, weighing some 15 000 Roman pounds' weight.

HAWKES: Might his later issues partly use the same gold as earlier ones, called in for melting and minting again?

ALLEN: Quite possibly yes; the standard is constant throughout.

DUIGNAN: May I turn now to chariots? In Celtic Ireland, on the evidence that we have from Christian times, the man who drove a chariot was *seated.* Are there seated charioteers at all on your coins?

ALLEN: The man in the chariot appears seated only in Thrace.

DUIGNAN: Do coins ever show a warrior too, whom the charioteer is driving?[1]

PIGGOTT: And if so, are the chariot and warrior both seated? Presumably the types with chariot, as being derived from Philip's, had the tradition of one standing driver alone, in the classical Greek chariot-racing manner?

ALLEN: The types with chariot are surely all derived from Greek or Roman coins. The only case of a driver accompanied by a warrior is a clear Roman imitation. Some coins have charioteers whose hands they show as *carrying* things, e.g. a ship, a torque or a branch, typical Celtic fantasies. But it would not be safe to infer anything about the driving of the Celtic chariot, from any of these coins, because of their dependence on classical prototypes.

HAWKES: Yet a driver really seated could not, of course, be derived from those. It would mean he was driving something like the old Irish war-chariot.

FREY: The people in chariots sometimes seeming seated, on the coins, are I think not really sitting but are fighting.

HAWKES: I should like to get to the horses. Celtic art, though indeed not all an aniconic and abstract art, is certainly one in which representation of living things, as images, has a tendency to disguise them, even conceal them. But the horse, on the coins, takes the centre of the die; he held this position whether lifelike or disguised. If dismembered thus—*déchiré*—he is still the old horse. And while the Philip type's Apollo head can disintegrate altogether (in spite of Celtic head-veneration) into totally abstract patterns, the non-coin art matches up rather seldom to the coin art's passion for the horse. The big round rump, which the coins so often give him, I do remember as matched on the horse of a painted vase, from the Marne, but it looks like a rarity, or seems so at present. Bétheny is the site; the horse's rump has a flowing tail. And its head has a flowing crest; these do recall the coins; but recall also plant-derived forms in the earlier styles. Flowing features for horses on coins, anyhow, far from being rare, are of course among the art's most vital characters. Enterprise in style was surely expected of coin designers; the horse was a special thing for this, and their work keeps showing it—far outside the range of classical models.

KLINDT-JENSEN: Besides the manner of treatment, we should attend to recurring elements. Whirligigs are foreign to British art except on coins, but not foreign to Gaulish; they even pass into Gallo-Roman.

HAWKES: Gaul could certainly use them apart from coins. There are big ones straggling around the plaque from Châtillon-sur-Indre[2]. And enclosed in rings, with voluted streamers, on the Aylesford bucket, where the style is again Gaulish[3].

FREY: One certainly ought to trace these forms of decorative element, on the coins and in other art.

HAWKES: The site of La Tène itself is important here (see *Additional Note*).

JOPE: Surely we need to remember, too, in the coins, their smallness of size. Forms in the rest of the art could vary in scale. On coins, they could not. The designers must have been very short-sighted men, who worked very closely. I have found it myself in studying coins, if I use the naked eye. It would give them a world of their own, with diminutive forms conceived as large ones.

ALLEN: Contacts within their world they must have had, as I have tried to show—and in Britain, right into the Ist century A.D. I now end the discussion with my thanks.

[1] See David Greene ,"The Chariot as described in Irish Literature", pp. 59–73 (with Fig. 16 by Líam de Paor, p. 65) of *The Iron Age in the Irish Sea Province*, Council for British Archaeology, Research Report 9 (London 1972), on Conference at Cardiff, 3–5 Jan. 1969; and contrast the non-Irish evidences (from excavations, coins, and Hellenistic art) assembled by Ian Stead, *Antiquity* ***39***, 1965 (Dec.), 259–65.

[2] De Lisle du Dreneuc, *Revue arch.* 1917, 321–7, in the grave-group pl. VI, whence *Proc. Prehist. Soc.* 21, 1955, pl. XXVI, 8, with p. 223; La Tène III, within 1st century B.C.

[3] E. T. Leeds, *Celtic Ornament*, Oxford 1933, p. 38 (with fig. 16): imported (unless the work of a Gaul himself brought to Kent), and implied as such in the primary publication by Arthur Evans (1890). *Archaeologia* ***52***, 360, fig. 11 compared with Plate XIII. Of course the burial, "almost certainly" before 10 but after *c.* 30 B.C. (Ann Birchall, (1965) *Proc. Prehist. Soc.* ***31***, 290, "Aylesford Y"), lets the bucket itself be older: perhaps by 30 to 50 years, so in Gaul's La Tène III (cf. note 2).

Additional Note

The Horse on the Painted Vase from Bétheny (Marne)

The Bétheny vase with the big-rumped horse (see opposite) was reproduced by Jacobsthal *ECA* PLATE 217*b* from Déchelette, as here. His text on it (indexed p. 234, as "horse") is on p. 3. The horse *d* that he compares with it (though no big rump, nor foliate crest) is an Italian-Alpine rock-engraving; so also are *a* and *c*, which I leave aside as their figures are human. All three are in the Val Camonica, where this horse and also a further one had by Altheim been ascribed to Archaic Greek (Corinthian) influence. Jacobsthal made this Celtic instead (*Journ. Roman Studies* 28, 1938, 65–9, with other arguments here not so relevant), and briefly there re-stated his case, scorning Altheim (notes 1, 7) and also Brendel (p. 208); in a "Raetian backwater" (*coin rétique arriéré*), this Veneto-Celtic art was IVth century. The intensive work in the Val Camonica now, by E. Anati (*La Civilisation du Val Camonica,* Paris 1960; translation, *Camonica Valley,* New York 1961, where see pp. 148–9: no "backwater", but close to a main trans-Alpine route), makes the influence shown by the horse, if not Greek, then Etruscan; in his summarized chronology for all the Camonica rock-engravings, *La Datazione dell'Arte Preistorica Camuna* (Studi Camuni II, 1963), Anati has dated its style, "Style IV E–F" (pp. 69–72, 83) in any case from the Vth century onwards. The Bétheny vase's horse, thus parted from Jacobsthal's comparison, can be viewed on the lines proposed in the discussion above by Schwappach: as a form of horse connectable with horses on the coins, and also with earlier Celtic art through its foliate-ended crest. This crest, resembling nothing in the art of the Val Camonica, falls in front of the horse as a forelock (long and foliated *toupet*) and behind floats over its back as a mane, a *crinière en spirale*, recurved up at the end in a huge leaf. It is just a form of the sinuous asymmetric swinging plant-scrolls, Plates 276–7 of Jacobsthal's "Grammar" in *ECA*.

Déchelette remarked it at once, and had more to say. It is no. 3 of Fig. 661 in his La Tène *Manuel*; p. 1465 in 1st ed., 1914, and modern reprint; p. 971 in 2nd ed., 1927; he followed L. Demaison (1912) in *Bull. Soc. Antiquaires de France* 279, 362, with the further information (n. 4, from him) that the graves in the Bétheny cemetery were almost all cremations. Unusual for the Champagne (the site is in Marne, very close to Reims), this has at times been overlooked (as by Ann Birchall, *Proc. Prehist. Soc.* **31**, 1965, 259–62); the bad excavation and lack of record are irretrievable, through the destruction, directly afterwards, of Reims Museum in the First World War, so that the full associations of the vase remain unknown. There were coins, however, from the site, assigned to Remi and Catalauni; and a date not far from those, for the vase, may be guessed from Déchelette, in the comparison he made for its horse with those on the *fourreau* (scabbard) from La Tène, no. 5 on his Fig. 463. Like the second horse behind it, which Fig. 661 shows in part—paintings on a second vase, found along with it, were decayed—this horse resembled those in having, *en guise de queue et de crinière, des rinceaux de feuillage repliés en volutes:* . . . the equine mane *est remplacée, ici aussi, par un ornement en S qui se termine en fleuron*. And for this foliating fantasy he cites designers not only of scabbards—like the La Tène one whom he calls here *armurier helvète*—but also of Celtic coins, *les graveurs de beaucoup de monnaies gauloises*.

For dating the renowned Swiss site of La Tène, from the coins that have come from it, Mr Allen gave his grounds just a year before our Colloquy, to the International Celtic Congress at Rennes (July 1971). His discourse and verdict are now published in its Acts, *Études celtiques* (ed. P.-M. Duval 1973) XIII, 2, 477–521: D. F. Allen, "The Coins found at La Tène". The sequence of Celtic coins there, running beside its other material—archaeologically late-Middle La Tène—flows down to a point of break, which comes along with the site's abandonment. That was not later than 60 B.C. nor earlier than 75, and probably within the years 70–65. And the Celtic art of the scabbards and swords, outstanding amongst its relics, has the fullest of all its studies published now by the British Academy (London, November 1972): *The Finds from the site of La Tène, Vol. I, Scabbards and the Swords found in them* (text, catalogue, plates) by J. M. de Navarro. Theirs is the period, ending some dozen years before Caesar, for a start on comparing the non-coin art with the coin art. This is put in hand, indeed, in the book itself. Floriation of animal forms, like very much else in the art of the time, will be found to grow from the earlier. Our separate studies should meet. Jacobsthal also made this start: see *ECA* Index 6. The Bétheny horse is only one more example. Mr Allen now tells me that its numismatic analogies are to be found in the stater of the Mediomatrici T8933 (quarter T8937, cf. 8945); for a split mane, he also compares that of the Treviri T9297 (quarter T9298)). I thank him.

C. Hawkes

14

Summing up of the Colloquy

STUART PIGGOTT
Edinburgh

As MY COLLEAGUES, who are sitting there so happy that they have not got this task themselves will realise, I have an impossible job in front of me. I think I can do no more than to indicate some of the points in the Colloquy which particularly struck me—first of all in a general way, and then in reference to individual papers. If I omit to mention the communication by any one member of the Colloquy it may be not that I did not find it interesting, but that the field was so completely surveyed that I am unable to add any useful comment.

I would like to start with PROFESSOR HAWKES's comments at the beginning, not merely because this was the opening paper, but because in it he spoke in a general way about the background of the Celtic world, in which all the art, whether it be of the larger metal-work, or the coins, or other material, was created. May I take up this point again, with some additions?

One of the questions which we were constantly encountering was the relationships between objects or groups of objects found in different places: the relations between East and West; objects in Gaul, objects in Bohemia. In MISS SANDARS's paper we looked further east still, at the relationships with the ultimately Oriental world as a result of Achaemenid Persian influences on Eastern Europe. I would follow that by saying that the Celtic art we have been studying is essentially an aristocratic phenomenon, and that aristocratic phenomena among societies may not exhibit, if indeed there are any rules in these archaeological and art-historical matters, the same pattern as what I might call by contrast the peasant crafts. When listening to Miss Sandars I thought of this more concisely in the phrase "aristocratic art can be discontinuous, peasant crafts more often continuous". This can be taken in the dual sense of geographical distributions, and also of sequential series of developing styles, or non-developing (if successive) styles. With such aristocratic art we are dealing with a situation in which objects can be transmitted from one point of the European continent to another, without necessarily leaving, so to speak, a trail of little lesser objects at the same time on their way. The art styles with which we have been concerned can be discontinuous also in the sense that a sudden innovation may be introduced, which will alter an apparently evolving sequence. Professor Frey was concerned with this in connection with the question of the beginnings of the "Waldalgesheim style", if we can still so call it. Here is a discontinuity, not a continuity, from the Early Style. When we were looking at various distribution maps we were often seeing discontinuity on the geographical side, again in the same context.

It is worth glancing for a moment at the kind of aristocratic society in which these objects were being made, were being commissioned, and in which the craftsman worked. This world is an aristocratic one, within a stratified society known to us from the classical references to it and from the early vernacular writings of the Celtic peoples themselves. But this is also the world of Homer, and indeed of much of the ancient world at large, which is something that one might profitably remember. Treasuries of more than one kind are very important in such societies, and there can be two main kinds of accumulation of precious metals, and ultimately of coinage when precious metal is expressed in coinage. These can be royal or they can be sacred: treasuries in palaces or treasuries in temples. The boundary line between the two may not always have been an easy one to distinguish in some societies, but as Moses Finley said of royal or princely treasure in Homeric times—*keimélion*, what can be laid away—"the twin uses of treasure were in possessing it and in giving it away, paradoxical as that may appear".[1]

The accumulation is obvious, but what were the circumstances of giving it away? It was largely part of a recognised host-guest relationship in which, when visiting or visited by another of equal rank to oneself, precious objects, usually of metal and of course likely to be of varying styles, were exchanged as gifts. Bohemian potentates would come to the Rhineland and bring Bohemian tribute, and *vice versa*. These treasuries would be variable in content; they would be self-renewing and they would be diverse. They would also of course include an accumulation of objects amassed over a considerable period of time. They would therefore provide a *répertoire* of objects among which craftsmen could see the most varied collection of regional art styles, foreign imports, and old as well as new works of art. If one wants an example of this kind of thing in a recent context, the collections in the Kremlin are a very good example; and in a totally different world, that of traditional West African societies, the presence in the royal treasuries of XIIIth century

Islamic bronzes, and the huge English bronze jug with the royal arms and the badge of Richard II, still in King Prempeh's treasury at Kumasi in 1896[2]. This giving and exchanging of gifts, and the ultimate location of those gifts in places foreign to their origin, is something we should remember; and as for sacred treasuries, we know of these not only throughout the ancient world, but of their specific existence in Celtic society.

Such votive deposits have been discussed on many occasions, but we should note that the famous Toulouse sanctuary-treasure, the *aurum Tolosanum* plundered by the consul Caepio in 106 B.C., was specifically said by Strabo to be unworked and unornamented gold and silver, and so not applicable to our purpose. Caesar also pillaged Gaulish sanctuaries for their offerings, and he describes a particular form of votive deposition after a battle which we will come to later[3]. The temple treasury, with accumulated votive offerings of arms and armour and works of art, was an essential part of ancient Greek life, and the tradition continued in the great church treasuries of the Middle Ages. With this aspect, of the preservation and collection of objects of art and craftsmanship in the ancient Celtic world, in mind, we may turn to the question of how treasure was amassed, if not by gentlemanly exchange.

We must remember the importance of booty and loot obtained on the battlefield. "War in ancient times", wrote Rostovtzeff "was universally regarded as a method not only of settling political questions but also of enriching the victors at the expense of the vanquished". A modern soldier and scholar, in a study of epic warfare, has emphasised the outstanding importance given to stripping the dead and capturing equipment in the Iliad, and uses the technical military phrase "recovery battles" for these episodes—"you wanted to kill the other man, not only to deprive the opposition of his services, but also to secure his arms and his other equipment". The importance of loot and booty has again been discussed in detail in a recent study of ancient Greek warfare[4]. It continued to be important in the Middle Ages and up to recent times: the lower register of the Bayeux Tapestry shows, on the battlefield of Hastings, the dead being stripped of their mail while swords and shields are being systematically collected. In the context of warfare of this kind, and quite apart from Celtic mercenaries serving in Greek or other armies (as we know they did), how much fine metalwork could have been brought back from an alien context and become available for admiration and for, if necessary, inspiration on the part of the Celtic craftsman. A passage in Caesar (BG VI, 17) describes the Gauls collecting the booty from the battlefield and dedicating it as a votive mass-offering *locis consecratis*.

We must of course also take into account the phenomenon familiar to anthropologists, the question of acceptance and rejection of new ideas—and these new ideas can be of any kind, including art motifs—in human societies up to today. Sometimes an idea or a technology may be eagerly taken up by individuals or communities, or alternatively it may not be accepted by the society or craftsman. The people who are like the Waldalgesheim master were those whose quick inventive brains were such that they took up a new idea while others ignored it. I would like to suggest that we might think of this accumulation and interchange of treasures between the ruling houses and so within the aristocratic world, and also the introduction of exotic material as a tangible product of warfare, and a part of the loot which would itself doubtless find its way into princely or priestly treasuries.

So much for the aristocratic context within which so much of our finest Celtic art must lie. But when we come to the coins, we may glimpse another social situation in Celtic society. Nominally tripartite, could this society also possibly have in its later phases seen the rise of something which one might call a merchant class? If so, we might then ask whether such a merchant class might not be associated with the use of coinage, which, however much a royal prerogative and aristocratic privilege to issue, might nevertheless be mainly handled by such merchants. Mr Allen has shown that the potin coinage of England, that very curious, very thin, cast coinage—was cast from moulds which had been prepared by pressing papyrus into clay[5]. This carries the implication that papyrus was used in the first century B.C. south of the Thames estuary where the coin distribution concentrates, and that waste scraps were available from what would normally be writing material. If so, it would surely not have been used for deathless prose or poetry, but by persons keeping accounts, which might again suggest the emergence of this merchant class. The problem has been raised as to how much the coin story—the coin-art story—relates to the general art-story in metalwork. Partly perhaps a question of the short-sighted craftsman, as Professor Jope suggested; but was it also because the die-engravers were working in a somewhat different social context, that their work takes on its peculiar individuality?

Some of these general points are ones that seem to appear again and again in our papers and discussions, initiated by Professor Hawkes's introductory address. The question of trade and its operation is implicit throughout Mrs Champion's paper on coral, where one was dealing with something which was on the fringes of what was certainly thought of as a regular trade in the classical world, and its cessation in Celtic Europe was linked with the competing demands of India: a classic mercantile situation.

With Miss Sandars looking to the East, here were all the factors which I have been mentioning—the warfare and loot, the aristocratic *milieu*, the interchange of presents, and the Duvanlij amphora, which looks very like something that was a royal present. Implicit too is the likelihood of fine objects or stylistic ideas being transmitted from a considerable distance but not necessarily with any other elements of material culture.

Dr Schwappach opened our eyes to the art styles of the more peaceful Celtic world. Some of the pottery he discussed is fine and "upper class", but much of it surely illustrates the peasant continuity of distribution which I was setting against aristocratic discontinuity. The maps of fine metal-work tend to have gaps and discontinuities between finds or groups of finds. But the map of the decorated pottery has continuous distributions from east to west within a peasant continuum, and it is across and through this network of rural relationships that you have the fine objects moving. We must not forget how, in antiquity, craftsmen moved from one place to another. When the Franciscan missions went to Central Asia in the middle of the XIIIth century A.D., William of Rubruck recorded that at the court of Möngke Khan at Karakorum was a master goldsmith from Paris, Guillaume Buchier, who had not only made a wonderful silver fountain in the form of a tree, but church ornaments "sculptured after the French fashion". Here in the remote Mongol court you would have craftsmen with their own particular styles; this Master William of Paris had been captured by the Mongols in Belgrade in 1241 and taken back to practise his skills, while still working in the art styles of earlier XIIIth century France.

With Dr Kruta we came back to this disputed question of whether certain pieces were made in Czechoslovakia or in France, and how this movement came about, bringing us back to the mobile situation with the movement of aristocratic objects and, surely, of craftsmen too.

Professor Frey very nearly, but not quite, introduced us to a master-craftsman face to face. He was a man, if one uses a word taken from English architecture of the early XIXth century, who began working in a "Neo-Grec" manner, taking up afresh the Greek motifs available to him through contacts from the south of the Alps. He, and presumably a small group of those who like him accepted innovations and found excitement in new things, made a break (and not a slow development out of the Early Style) and achieved something new, but still drawing on old sources, old motifs which had been there waiting for the man who could draw new inspiration from them and create an individual style.

Professor Jope's demonstration of the archaic elements in the Witham shield led one to wonder under what circumstances the master who designed this masterpiece could have seen his ultimate models. Here one might reasonably think in terms of accumulations in treasuries where the travelling craftsmen could not only see men and cities, but also foreign craftsmanship. The development of the Wandsworth boss takes up the beginning of the story of the peculiarly British insular style within which Dr Savory was able to show the relationships between our shield series, with all their curious individuality, and the continental ones. We came on a recurrent theme, the subtle alterations in art styles as they suffer a sea change in crossing that stormy English Channel, which seems to have induced an aesthetic dislocation, so that something novel emerged out of the delights of France half-remembered.

This insular story was carried on by PROFESSOR DUIGNAN's demonstration that the major decorative panels of the Turoe stone are derivative from British insular art in a late phase, even if the concept of a stone monument and the "meandroid" band of ornament look back to Armorica.

PROFESSOR KLINDT-JENSEN took us back part of the way along which Miss Sandars had so adventurously led us earlier on, to that East European area, where fine metal-work in silver had a long history. One wonders whether the later popularity of silver-work in the Celtic West was not partly motivated by this tradition. The distribution map of phalerae and related objects shows an axis, so to speak, with one end at the Black Sea and the other in Jutland. This "axis" had been established certainly from the beginnings of metal-working, and becomes a recurrent distribution pattern. It starts off with the first imported copper objects about 3 000 B.C. which come into the northern Neolithic; these are of Romanian and Transylvanian types. It goes on, as Werner and others have shown, well into the second millennium B.C.[6], and here we see this going on right up to this last phase of prehistory and indeed continuing after the Roman conquest, in Migration-Period times.

And finally we come to our fascinating discussion this afternoon about the coins. There is numismatics, but surely also there is the Higher Numismatics, which is the exalted field of study with which such people as PROFESSOR DUVAL and MR ALLEN are concerned. This is unattainable to the rest of us who are trying to work on Celtic art as a whole, or at most it is something of which we can only touch the very fringes. This new approach is something that is only just beginning, and this is why it was so fascinating and exciting to find that in every part of the Colloquy we were agreed we had come to a beginning and not an end. This should be a most important new stage in interpretation, and should advance our knowledge, not only of coin-art but of the art history of the Celts in more obvious and larger objects than the coins.

We have seen a brilliantly planned series of papers, all relating one to another, all interlocking, and each of them, I think, contributing something to the other. Nothing can be more satisfactory at a colloquy, and the gratitude of all of us here is due to PROFESSORS HAWKES and DUVAL, the organisers, and of course the Maison Française and M. LEQUILLER for making it possible to have this highly successful conference under such pleasant auspices.

Notes

1. M. I. Finley, *The World of Odysseus*, Cambridge, 1956, p. 65.

2. T. Shaw, "The Analysis of West African bronzes", *Ibadan* XXVIII, 1970 80–89; *Brit. Mus. Guide to Mediaeval Antiquities* . . . , 1924, 241; *London Mus., Medieval Cat.*, 1940, 199.

3. Cf. C. Fox, *Llyn Cerrig Bach*, 1946, 69–70; Suetonius, *Julius* LIV; Caesar *BG* VI, 17.

4. General Sir John Hackett, "Reflections upon Epic Warfare", *Proc. Classical Assoc.* LXVIII, 1971, 13–32 (Presidential Address); W. Kendrick Pritchett, *Ancient Greek Military Practices, Part 1* (Univ. California Class. Studies VII, 1971) quoting Rostovtzeff.

5. D. F. Allen, "British Potin Coins: A Review", in *The Iron Age and its Hill-Forts* (eds. D. Hill and M. Jesson), Southampton Univ. Monogr. I, 1971, 127–154.

6. J. Werner, "Mykenä-Siebenbürgen-Skandinavien", *Atti 1º Cong. Internaz. Preist. e Protost. Mediterranea 1950,* Florence 1952, 293–308; E. Lomborg, 'Donauländische Kulturbeziehungen der frühen nordischen Bronzezeit", *Acta Arch.* XXX, Copenhagen 1959, 51–146.

15

Résumé du Colloque

STUART PIGGOTT

COMME MES COLLÈGUES qui siègent ici à côté de moi, si heureux de ne pas devoir assumer eux-mêmes cette tâche, vont s'en rendre compte, j'ai devant moi un travail impossible à accomplir. Je ne puis faire plus qu'indiquer quelques-uns des points qui m'ont particulièrement frappé dans ce Colloque: tout d'abord, d'une façon générale, puis en me référant aux exposés particuliers. Si j'omets de citer telle ou telle communication, ce n'est pas par manque d'intérêt pour elle, mais parce que le sujet y a été si complètement traité que je me sens incapable d'y ajouter le moindre commentaire utile.

Dans son "ouverture", le PROFESSEUR HAWKES a parlé d'une façon générale de l'arrière-plan du monde celtique, où l'art tout entier, qu'il soit orfèvrerie, monnayage ou autre, a été créé. Permettez-moi d'y ajouter quelque chose. L'une des questions que nous avons rencontrées constamment concerne les relations entre des objets ou groupes d'objets trouvés dans des endroits différents: rapports entre l'Est et l'Ouest, entre la Gaule et la Bohême. MISS SANDARS nous a entraînés encore plus loin vers l'Est, en nous montrant, dans les relations avec le monde oriental le plus éloigné, un résultat des influences de la Perse achéménide sur l'Europe de l'Est. J'ajouterais que l'art celtique que nous venons d'étudier est essentiellement un phénomène aristocratique, qui ne peut manifester—si toutefois il existe des règles en matière d'archéologie et d'histoire de l'art—les mêmes caractères que ce que je pourrais appeler par contraste les artisanats paysans. J'écoutais Miss Sandars exprimer cette idée de façon plus concise: "l'art aristocratique peut être discontinu, l'artisanat rustique est plus souvent continu", ce qui peut être pris dans le sens géographique mais aussi par rapport aux séries de styles évolutifs ou non évolutifs (s'ils se succèdent). Avec cet art aristocratique nous avons à faire à une situation dans laquelle les objets peuvent être transmis d'un point du continent européen à un autre sans laisser nécessairement derrière soi, pour ainsi dire, une trace de petits objets moins nombreux, au même moment, sur leur route. Les styles dont nous avons traité peuvent aussi être discontinus en ce sens qu'une innovation soudaine peut y être introduite, qui dérange une séquence en apparente évolution. Le PROFESSEUR FREY a eu à faire avec ce phénomène à propos du problème que posent les débuts du Style de Waldalgesheim, si nous pouvons encore l'appeler ainsi. Il y a là une discontinuité, non pas une continuité, avec le Premier style. En considérant les diverses cartes de répartition, nous avons souvent observé la discontinuité du point de vue géographique, de nouveau dans le même contexte.

Il vaut la peine de jeter un coup d'oeil sur la nature de la société aristocratique dans laquelle ces objets ont été fabriqués, transmis et dans laquelle les artisans ont travaillé. C'est un monde aristocratique, dans une société stratifiée connue de nous par des témoignages classiques et par les premiers écrits des peuples celtiques eux-mêmes. C'est aussi le monde d'Homère et en grande partie de tout l'ancien monde: il sera utile de ne pas l'oublier. Des trésors de toute espèce sont très importants dans de telles sociétés et il peut y avoir deux sortes principales d'accumulation de métaux précieux, et finalement de monnaies quand le métal précieux est employé pour la frappe des monnaies. Ces trésors peuvent être royaux ou sacrés: trésors de palais, trésors de temples. La limite entre les deux peut n'être pas toujours facile à distinguer dans certaines sociétés, mais comme Moses Finley l'a dit du trésor royal ou princier à l'époque homérique—*keimélion*, ce qu'on peut mettre de côté—"les deux façons d'employer un trésor étaient de le garder et de le disperser, aussi paradoxal que cela paraisse"[1].

L'accumulation est évidente, mais quelles étaient les circonstances de la dispersion? C'était, dans une grande mesure, les liens avec des hôtes reconnus qui entraînaient l'échange de présents à l'occasion de visites réciproques entre personnages de même rang: objets précieux, habituellement de métal, et généralement, comme il est naturel, de styles divers. Les potentats de Bohême venaient en Rhénanie et apportaient un tribut de chez eux, et *vice versa*. Le contenu de ces trésors était variable; ils pouvaient se répéter et se diversifier. Ils pouvaient aussi, naturellement, comprendre une accumulation d'objets amassés pendant une très longue période. Dans ce cas, ils composaient un répertoire d'objets parmi lesquels les artisans trouvaient la collection la plus variée de styles régionaux, d'importations étrangères et d'oeuvres d'art anciennes ou récentes. Un exemple moderne de ce fait est fourni par les collections du Kremlin ou, dans un monde tout différent, celui des sociétés traditionnelles de l'Ouest africain, par la présence dans les trésors royaux de bronzes islamiques du XIIIe siècle et par le grand récipient de bronze anglais aux armes royales et à l'écusson de Richard II, conservé encore en 1896 dans le trésor du roi Prempeh à Kumasi[2]. Ces dons et échanges de présents, et le dépôt final de ces objets dans des lieux étrangers à leur origine, doivent être présents à la mémoire; quant aux trésors sacrés, nous les connaissons non seulement dans tout le monde ancien, mais particulièrement dans la société celtique.

De tels dépôts votifs ont été étudiés en maintes occasions mais nous devons noter que le fameux trésor sacré de Toulouse, l'*aurum Tolosanum* pillé par le consul Caepio en 106 av. J.-C., était composé—Strabon le dit textuellement—d'or et d'argent non travaillé et non orné: il ne concerne donc pas notre propos. César aussi a pillé les sanctuaires gaulois et s'est emparé de leurs offrandes et il décrit une forme particulière de dépôt votif fait après une bataille, dont nous reparlerons[3]. Le trésor de temple, avec des offrandes votives accumulées d'armes, d'armures et d'oeuvres d'art, jouait un rôle essentiel dans la vie des Grecs et la tradition continua dans les grands trésors d'église médiévaux. En gardant à l'esprit cet aspect de préservation et collection d'oeuvres d'artistes et d'artisans dans le monde celtique ancien, nous pouvons aborder la question de la formation des trésors autrement que par échanges de courtoisie.

Rappelons-nous l'importance du butin ramassé sur le champ de bataille. "La guerre dans l'antiquité", a écrit Rostovtzeff, "était considérée universellement comme un moyen non seulement de régler des questions politiques mais aussi d'enrichir les vainqueurs aux dépens des vaincus". Un érudit et soldat moderne, dans une étude sur la guerre dans l'épopée, a mis en valeur l'importance exceptionnelle donnée au détroussage des morts et à la capture des équipements dans l'Iliade; il emploie l'expression de technique militaire "combats de récupération" pour ces épisodes—"on voulait tuer l'adversaire non seulement pour priver l'ennemi de ses services mais aussi pour s'approprier ses armes et son équipement". L'importance attachée au butin a été de nouveau discutée en détail dans une étude récente sur la guerre chez les Grecs[4]. Elle a continué d'exister au Moyen-Age et jusqu'aux temps modernes: le registre inférieur de la Tapisserie de Bayeux montre, sur le champ de bataille de Hastings, les morts dépouillés de leur cotte de mailles et le ramassage systématique des épées et des boucliers.

Dans le contexte de moeurs militaires de cette nature, et sans tenir compte des mercenaires celtiques servant, comme on sait, dans les armées grecques et autres, combien de belles pièces de métal ont pu être rapportées d'une région étrangère pour devenir objets d'admiration et, si besoin était, d'inspiration de la part des artisans celtiques! Un passage de César (B.G. VI, 17) montre les Gaulois amassant le butin fait sur le champ de bataille et le dédiant, comme une offrande massive, *locis consecratis*.

Nous devons naturellement aussi tenir compte d'un phénomène

familier aux anthropologues, la question de l'acceptation et du rejet des idées nouvelles—et ces nouvelles idées peuvent être de toutes sortes, y compris les motifs d'art—dans les sociétés humaines de tous les temps. Quelquefois une idée ou une technique peut être avidement adoptée par des individus ou des communautés, ou alternativement elle peut ne pas être acceptée par la classe des artisans. Les hommes dans le genre du maître de Waldalgesheim étaient de ceux dont l'esprit vif et inventif était capable de saisir une idée nouvelle alors même que d'autres l'ignoraient. Je suggère que nous réfléchissions à cette accumulation et à ces échanges réciproques de trésors entre maisons régnantes et donc dans le monde aristocratique, et aussi à l'introduction d'un matériel exotique comme le produit tangible de la guerre et comme une partie du matériel pillé qui prenait sans aucun doute le chemin des trésors princiers ou sacrés.

Voilà pour le cadre aristocratique dans lequel se situent tant de nos plus belles oeuvres d'art celtique. En abordant les monnaies, nous entrevoyons un autre aspect de la société chez les Celtes. En principe tripartite, cette société pouvait-elle aussi avoir vu dans ses dernières phases l'essor de ce qu'on pourrait appeler une classe marchande? Si oui, nous pourrions nous demander si une telle classe marchande ne pourrait pas être mise en relation avec l'emploi de la monnaie; certes, la frappe des monnaies était une prérogative royale ou un privilège aristocratique, mais elles pouvaient néanmoins être maniées principalement par les marchands. Mr Allen nous a montré que le monnayage de potin d'Angleterre, ce monnayage moulé très curieux, très fin, était sorti de moules préparés en pressant du papyrus dans de l'argile[5]. Ceci suppose l'emploi de papyrus au Ier siècle av. J.-C. au sud de l'estuaire de la Tamise, où la répartition des monnaies est concentrée, et implique que les déchets de papyrus venaient de ce qui devait être normalement le matériel d'écriture. S'il en est ainsi, il n'était sûrement pas employé pour immortaliser la prose ou la poésie, mais pour tenir des comptes, ce qui peut de nouveau suggérer l'ascension de cette classe marchande. On s'est demandé si l'histoire de l'art monétaire avait un rapport avec l'histoire de l'art du métal en général. C'est peut-être en partie parce que nous avons ici à faire avec des artisans à courte vue, comme le Professeur Jope l'a suggéré; mais si les oeuvres des graveurs de coins revêtaient une individualité aussi particulière, n'était-ce pas aussi parce qu'ils travaillaient dans un contexte social différent?

Certains de ces problèmes généraux sont de ceux qui semblent revenir à plusieurs reprises dans nos communications et nos discussions, inaugurées par l'introduction du Professeur Hawkes. La question du commerce et de son fonctionnement est implicitement présente tout au long de l'exposé de Mrs Champion sur le corail, qui traite de quelque chose qui était sur la frange de ce qui était certainement conçu comme un commerce régulier dans le monde classique: l'arrêt de ce commerce dans l'Europe celtique est lié aux demandes compétitives de l'Inde—situation économique classique.

Miss Sandars regarde vers l'Orient : là se retrouvent tous les éléments que j'ai mentionnés, la guerre et le butin, le pillage, le milieu aristocratique, l'échange des présents, et l'amphore de Duvanlij qui a bien l'air d'être une manière de cadeau royal. Là aussi, on retrouve implicitement la probabilité d'un transfert des beaux objets ou des idées stylistiques à une distance considérable, mais non pas nécessairement avec d'autres éléments de culture matériels.

Le Dr Schwappach nous a ouvert les yeux sur les styles artistiques d'un monde celtique plus paisible. Certaines poteries étudiées par lui sont belles et de "classe supérieure", mais la plus grande partie illustre par sa répartition la continuité paysanne que j'ai opposée à la discontinuité aristocratique. Les cartes des beaux objets de métal montrent des lacunes et des discontinuités entre les trouvailles ou les groupes de trouvailles. Mais la carte de la poterie ornée montre des répartitions continues de l'Est à l'Ouest dans un *continuum* paysan et c'est à travers ce réseau des relations rurales que se déplacent les beaux objets. Nous ne devons pas oublier la façon dont, dans l'Antiquité, les artisans se déplaçaient d'un endroit à l'autre. Quand les missions franciscaines atteignirent l'Asie centrale au milieu du XIIIème siècle, William de Rubruck rapporte qu'à la cour de Möngke Khan, à Karakorum, il y avait un maître orfèvre de Paris, Guillaume Buchier, qui avait fait non seulement une merveilleuse fontaine d'argent en forme d'arbre mais encore des ornements d'église "sculptés à la manière française". Là, dans la lointaine cour mongole, étaient des artisans avec leurs propres styles particuliers; Maître Guillaume de Paris avait été fait prisonnier par les Mongols à Belgrade en 1241 et emmené pour exercer ses talents, tout en continuant à travailler dans le style français du XIIIème siècle.

Le Dr Kruta nous a ramenés à la question controversée de l'origine, (Bohême ou Gaule ?) de certaines pièces et des modalités de ces transferts, et au problème de cette situation fluctuante, de ce mouvement des objets aristocratiques et sûrement aussi des artisans eux-mêmes.

Le Professeur Frey nous a mis face à face, ou peu s'en faut, avec un maître artisan. C'était un homme qui commença de travailler, pour employer un mot emprunté à l'architecture anglaise du début du XIXème siècle, dans le style "néo-grec", rafraîchissant les motifs grecs qu'il pouvait connaître par des contacts transalpins avec l'Italie du nord. Cet artisan, et probablement un petit groupe de ceux qui, comme lui, acceptaient les nouveautés et les trouvaient stimulantes, accomplirent une rupture (et non pas un lent développement à partir du Premier style) et réalisèrent quelque chose de nouveau mais en dessinant toujours d'après des motifs anciens qui avaient attendu là l'homme capable d'en tirer une inspiration nouvelle et de créer un style original.

Le Professeur Jope, en nous montrant les éléments archaïques du bouclier de Wandsworth, nous a amenés à nous demander dans quelles circonstances le maître qui a dessiné ce chef-d'oeuvre a pu voir ses derniers modèles. Ici l'on peut raisonnablement penser en termes d'accumulation dans les trésors de ces cours où les artisans ambulants pouvaient voir non seulement des hommes et des villes mais aussi des objets d'art étrangers. Le développement du bouclier de Wandsworth inaugure l'histoire du style insulaire proprement breton à propos duquel le Dr Savory a pu montrer les rapports entre nos séries de boucliers, avec toute leur curieuse originalité, et les séries continentales. Puis vint un thème qui revient souvent, les subtiles altérations des styles artistiques dus au passage du tempêtueux *Channel*, qui semble avoir provoqué une dislocation esthétique, si bien qu'il est sorti quelque chose de nouveau des délices de la France encore à moitié présents dans les mémoires.

L'étude de cette question insulaire a été poussée plus loin par la démonstration du Professeur Duignan : les grands panneaux décoratifs de la pierre de Turoe s'inspirent de l'art insulaire breton dans une phase tardive, même si la conception d'un monument de pierre et la bande décorative "méandroïde" nous invitent à regarder vers l'Armorique.

Le Professeur Klindt-Jensen nous a remis sur la voie des aventures que Miss Sandars nous avait fait emprunter, vers cet Orient européen où le beau travail de l'argent a une longue histoire. On se demande si la popularité ultérieure de l'argent ouvragé dans l'Occident celtique n'a pas été en partie causé par cette tradition. La carte de répartition des phalères et objets apparentés montre un axe, si l'on peut dire, ayant une extrémité sur le Mer Noire et l'autre au Jutland. Cet "axe" a été établi certainement dès les débuts du travail du métal et réapparaît périodiquement. Il naît avec les premiers objets de cuivre importés vers 3 000 av. J.-C., qui arrivent dans le Nord néolithique : ils sont de types roumain et transylvanien. Cela continue, comme Werner et d'autres l'ont montré, jusqu'en plein IIème millénaire av. J.-C.,[6] et là nous voyons cela se poursuivre jusqu'à la dernière phase de la préhistoire et même après la conquête romaine, dans la période des Migrations.

Et finalement nous arrivons à cette discussion si intéressante sur les monnaies. Il y a la numismatique, mais sûrement il y a aussi la numismatique supérieure, ce domaine de hautes études qui est l'affaire d'hommes comme le Professeur Duval et Mr Allen. Elle est inaccessible à ceux qui, comme nous, essaient de travailler sur l'art celtique comme un tout ; tout au plus, c'est quelque chose dont nous pouvons seulement effleurer le pourtour. Cette nouvelle approche en est à ses débuts, et c'est pourquoi il était si stimulant de découvrir que, dans chaque secteur de ce Colloque, nous reconnaissons que nous sommes à un commencement et non à une fin. Cette constatation devrait être une nouvelle étape très importante dans l'interprétation et faire progresser nos connaissances, non seulement de l'art des monnaies, mais de l'histoire de l'art celtique, à propos d'objets plus grands que les monnaies.

Nous avons écouté une série d'exposés brillament programmés, tous reliés entre eux, et chacun d'eux, je pense, apportant quelque chose aux autres. Rien ne peut être plus satisfaisant dans un colloque, et notre gratitude à tous est due aux PROFESSEURS HAWKES et DUVAL, les organisateurs, ainsi que, naturellement, à la Maison Française et à M. LEQUILLER qui a rendu possible cette conférence hautement réussie sous d'aussi agréables auspices.

Notes

1. M. Finley dans son étude odysséenne *The World of Odysseus* (Cambridge 1956), 65.

2. Sur ces bronzes et celui de Kumasi, voir Th. Shaw dans *Ibadan* **28,** 1970, 80–9; *London Mus. Medieval Catalogue* (1940), 199; *Brit. Mus. Guide to Mediaeval Antiquities* (1924), 241.

3. A comparer: C. Fox, *Llyn Cerrig Bach* (Cardiff 1946), 69–70 (dépôt votif); Suetonius, *Julius* LIV; César, *Bell. Gall.* VI. 17.

4. Pour la guerre homérique, voir *Proceedings of the Classical Association* 68, 1971, 13–32, discours présidentiel du général Sir John Hackett; le butin chez les Grecs, W. Kendrick Pritchett, *Ancient Greek Military Practices, part I* (Univ. California Classical Studies 7, 1971), où est cité Rostovtzeff.

5. "British Potin Coins: a Review", étude de D. Allen dans *The Iron Age and its Hill Forts* (mélanges Wheeler, edd. M. Jesson et D. Hill, Southampton Univ. Monographs I, 1971), 127–54.

6. J. Werner, "Mykenä—Siebenbürgen—Skandinavien", dans *Atti I. Congresso Internaz. di Preistoria e Protostoria Mediterranea 1950*, (Florence 1952), 293–308; E. Lomborg, "Donauländische Kulturbeziehungen der frühen nordischen Bronzezeit", dans *Acta Archaeologica* 30, Copenhague 1959, 51–146.

Index

This is in three parts, *A* NAMES, *B* OBJECTS, *C* SUBJECTS. *A* or *B* or *C* are therefore used for cross-referencing, from an item in any one of the parts to an item in another.

In every item, the numbers in **bold** type (*caractères gras*) are the numbers of the book's chapters, **1** to **15**, each comprising author's text and notes, Résumé, Discussion and Additional note if any. The page-reference numbers are thus referred to their relevant chapter.

Any numbers in *italic* are those of pages with an illustration. Notes are referenced only where exceeding the simply bibliographical.

The reference may be aided by an explanatory word or phrase. Where it applies to more numbers than one, they are linked by &. Otherwise all are separated by simple comma (*virgule*); further punctuation is kept to a minimum.

In *A* the names are of peoples, or of persons—with initial(s) where modern—or else are geographical: r.=river, mts=mountains, I(s)=islands. *Italic* is used for French (or German), or for ancient names not adopted into English: *Aedui*, *Caere* (but Anatolia, Caesar).

In *B* the objects are material, things or their forms. Where subjects also are connoted, there is a reference to *C*. French equivalents are given where judged most likely to be helpful.

In *C* the subjects are general, or are specifically archaeological, or convey descriptively features appearing in art.

Especially for these features, authors have varied in their use of terms. I have brought nearly all of them in, but still have tried to further the purpose, in English and partly also in French, of a standardized vocabulary. As my colleague Duval has reminded us here, the art of the Celts now demands one.

C.H.

Index A: Names

Index B: Objects

Index C: Subjects